SQA

Official

SQA

Past Papers

WITH ANSWERS

Higher
History

2012–2014

HODDER
GIBSON
AN HACHETTE UK COMPANY

Hodder Gibson is grateful to the copyright holders, as credited on the final page of the book, for permission to use their material. Every effort has been made to trace the copyright holders and to obtain their permission for the use of copyright material. Hodder Gibson will be happy to receive information allowing us to rectify any error or omission in future editions.

Hachette UK's policy is to use papers that are natural, renewable and recyclable products and made from wood grown in sustainable forests. The logging and manufacturing processes are expected to conform to the environmental regulations of the country of origin.

Orders: please contact Bookpoint Ltd, 130 Park Drive, Abingdon, Oxon OX14 4SE. Telephone: (44) 01235 827720. Fax: (44) 01235 400454.

Lines are open 9.00–5.00, Monday to Saturday, with a 24-hour message answering service. Visit our website at www.hoddereducation.co.uk. Hodder Gibson can be contacted direct on: Tel: 0141 848 1609; Fax: 0141 889 6315; email: hoddergibson@hodder.co.uk

This collection first published in 2014 by

Hodder Gibson, an imprint of Hodder Education,

An Hachette UK Company

2a Christie Street

Paisley PA1 1NB

iBrightRED
PUBLISHING

Hodder Gibson is grateful to Bright Red Publishing Ltd for collaborative work in preparation of this book and all SQA Past Paper, National 5 and Higher for CfE Model Paper titles 2014.

Typeset by PDQ Digital Media Solutions Ltd, Bungay, Suffolk NR35 1BY

Printed in the UK

A catalogue record for this title is available from the British Library

ISBN 978-1-4718-3683-1

3 2 1

2015 2014

Introduction

Study Skills – what you need to know to pass exams!

Pause for thought

Many students might skip quickly through a page like this. After all, we all know how to revise. Do you really though?

Think about this:

"IF YOU ALWAYS DO WHAT YOU ALWAYS DO, YOU WILL ALWAYS GET WHAT YOU HAVE ALWAYS GOT."

Do you like the grades you get? Do you want to do better? If you get full marks in your assessment, then that's great! Change nothing! This section is just to help you get that little bit better than you already are.

There are two main parts to the advice on offer here. The first part highlights fairly obvious things but which are also very important. The second part makes suggestions about revision that you might not have thought about but which WILL help you.

Part 1

DOH! It's so obvious but …

Start revising in good time

Don't leave it until the last minute – this will make you panic.

Make a revision timetable that sets out work time AND play time.

Sleep and eat!

Obvious really, and very helpful. Avoid arguments or stressful things too – even games that wind you up. You need to be fit, awake and focused!

Know your place!

Make sure you know exactly **WHEN and WHERE** your exams are.

Know your enemy!

Make sure you know what to expect in the exam.

How is the paper structured?

How much time is there for each question?

What types of question are involved?

Which topics seem to come up time and time again?

Which topics are your strongest and which are your weakest?

Are all topics compulsory or are there choices?

Learn by DOING!

There is no substitute for past papers and practice papers – they are simply essential! Tackling this collection of papers and answers is exactly the right thing to be doing as your exams approach.

Part 2

People learn in different ways. Some like low light, some bright. Some like early morning, some like evening / night. Some prefer warm, some prefer cold. But everyone uses their BRAIN and the brain works when it is active. Passive learning – sitting gazing at notes – is the most INEFFICIENT way to learn anything. Below you will find tips and ideas for making your revision more effective and maybe even more enjoyable. What follows gets your brain active, and active learning works!

Activity 1 – Stop and review

Step 1

When you have done no more than 5 minutes of revision reading STOP!

Step 2

Write a heading in your own words which sums up the topic you have been revising.

Step 3

Write a summary of what you have revised in no more than two sentences. Don't fool yourself by saying, "I know it, but I cannot put it into words". That just means you don't know it well enough. If you cannot write your summary, revise that section again, knowing that you must write a summary at the end of it. Many of you will have notebooks full of blue/black ink writing. Many of the pages will not be especially attractive or memorable so try to liven them up a bit with colour as you are reviewing and rewriting. **This is a great memory aid, and memory is the most important thing.**

Activity 2 — Use technology!

Why should everything be written down? Have you thought about "mental" maps, diagrams, cartoons and colour to help you learn? And rather than write down notes, why not record your revision material?

What about having a text message revision session with friends? Keep in touch with them to find out how and what they are revising and share ideas and questions.

Why not make a video diary where you tell the camera what you are doing, what you think you have learned and what you still have to do? No one has to see or hear it, but the process of having to organise your thoughts in a formal way to explain something is a very important learning practice.

Be sure to make use of electronic files. You could begin to summarise your class notes. Your typing might be slow, but it will get faster and the typed notes will be easier to read than the scribbles in your class notes. Try to add different fonts and colours to make your work stand out. You can easily Google relevant pictures, cartoons and diagrams which you can copy and paste to make your work more attractive and **MEMORABLE**.

Activity 3 – This is it. Do this and you will know lots!

Step 1

In this task you must be very honest with yourself! Find the SQA syllabus for your subject (www.sqa.org.uk). Look at how it is broken down into main topics called MANDATORY knowledge. That means stuff you MUST know.

Step 2

BEFORE you do ANY revision on this topic, write a list of everything that you already know about the subject. It might be quite a long list but you only need to write it once. It shows you all the information that is already in your long-term memory so you know what parts you do not need to revise!

Step 3

Pick a chapter or section from your book or revision notes. Choose a fairly large section or a whole chapter to get the most out of this activity.

With a buddy, use Skype, Facetime, Twitter or any other communication you have, to play the game "If this is the answer, what is the question?". For example, if you are revising Geography and the answer you provide is "meander", your buddy would have to make up a question like "What is the word that describes a feature of a river where it flows slowly and bends often from side to side?".

Make up 10 "answers" based on the content of the chapter or section you are using. Give this to your buddy to solve while you solve theirs.

Step 4

Construct a wordsearch of at least 10 X 10 squares. You can make it as big as you like but keep it realistic. Work together with a group of friends. Many apps allow you to make wordsearch puzzles online. The words and phrases can go in any direction and phrases can be split. Your puzzle must only contain facts linked to the topic you are revising. Your task is to find 10 bits of information to hide in your puzzle, but you must not repeat information that you used in Step 3. DO NOT show where the words are. Fill up empty squares with random letters. Remember to keep a note of where your answers are hidden but do not show your friends. When you have a complete puzzle, exchange it with a friend to solve each other's puzzle.

Step 5

Now make up 10 questions (not "answers" this time) based on the same chapter used in the previous two tasks. Again, you must find NEW information that you have not yet used. Now it's getting hard to find that new information! Again, give your questions to a friend to answer.

Step 6

As you have been doing the puzzles, your brain has been actively searching for new information. Now write a NEW LIST that contains only the new information you have discovered when doing the puzzles. Your new list is the one to look at repeatedly for short bursts over the next few days. Try to remember more and more of it without looking at it. After a few days, you should be able to add words from your second list to your first list as you increase the information in your long-term memory.

FINALLY! Be inspired...

Make a list of different revision ideas and beside each one write **THINGS I HAVE** tried, **THINGS I WILL** try and **THINGS I MIGHT** try. Don't be scared of trying something new.

And remember – "FAIL TO PREPARE AND PREPARE TO FAIL!"

Higher History

The course

The Higher qualification in History gives you the opportunity to study the subject across a variety of time periods and places. You will be given an understanding of one important part of Scottish history, as well as British history, European history and World history. You will gain skills in the understanding of key historical areas and be able to structure writing, support arguments with knowledge, analyse presented information and draw conclusions based on presented and recalled information. You will also learn how to research and present your findings.

How the course is graded

The final grade you get for Higher History depends on three things:

- The internal assessments you do in school or college (the "NABs") – these don't count towards the final grade, but you must have passed them before you can achieve a final grade.

- Your Extended Essay – this is an independent piece of research on an essay question that you have agreed with your teacher/lecturer. You will complete the essay in a two hour supervised write-up. The essay is submitted in April for marking by SQA and counts for 30% of your overall grade.

- The two exams you sit in May – that's what this book is all about!

The exam

The Paper 1 exam is 1 hour 20 minutes long and there are 40 marks available in total. This represents 40% of your overall grade. In the Paper 1 exam you have to complete two essays. Each essay is worth 20 marks. One of these essays is from a period of British history and one is from a period of European or World history. You will have a choice of three essays from each period you study. You will need to answer **one** of these essays from **each** period.

The Paper 2 exam is 1 hour 25 minutes long and there are 30 marks available in total. This represents 30% of your overall grade. The Paper 2 exam is about a period of Scottish history. You will have a choice from **five** periods of Scottish history. The exam paper is based around a variety of primary and secondary sources – you will have to answer four questions about these sources. One question tests your ability to evaluate a source, one question tests your ability to compare two sources, and two questions test your ability to contextualise the presented source information.

The SQA gives detailed advice on the course content and assessment in the arrangements document on its website: http://www.sqa.org.uk/sqa/files/nq/HistoryHigher.pdf

Paper 1: Essays

Essay writing is a useful skill to master. You have to show the ability to **structure** your answer correctly, **use relevant knowledge** in your answer and **comment on** and **analyse** this information in order to answer the question effectively.

Structure

There are **four** structure marks available in an essay, which assess the quality of the introduction and conclusion. Each of these is given a mark out of four and the total is then averaged to give a final mark out of four. So it's always worth including these in your essay!

The introduction

Your introduction should place your essay in context. This means that you show knowledge of events that surround the topic of your essay. Describing what went before or after the event can be an effective way of doing this. You are showing that you understand the broader topic that the question has identified.

You also need to give a line of argument – this will depend upon the question asked. The easiest way to do this is to use the words of the question directly in the argument. So, if a question asks, *'How important were the reports of Booth and Rowntree in causing the Liberal reforms of 1906–14?'*, a relevant line of argument might be, *'the reports of Booth and Rowntree were important in causing the Liberal reforms of 1906–14, but they were not the only reason for those reforms.'* This is a basic line of argument.

You will also need to identify areas or factors that you are going to explore in the main body of your essay. These can be shown in a list or, more effectively, treated separately. This shows that you understand the topic and are telling the marker what you are going to discuss.

A good introduction is well worth taking time over. It shows the direction that the essay is going to take and will help settle you and give you confidence before you develop the main part of the essay.

The conclusion

Your conclusion must be based on the information you have mentioned in the main part of the essay. Do not introduce new information in the conclusion.

In the conclusion you should summarise the arguments that you have made in the main part of your essay. This should balance the arguments for and against what the question is asking. You then need to come to an overall judgement in terms of the question. The last sentence must refer back to the specific question asked, as well as provide a response to that question, if you are to get a good mark.

Knowledge

There are **six** marks given for the use of accurate and relevant knowledge in the main part of the essay. Reading the question carefully is important here as this helps to prevent your answer being irrelevant – irrelevant information is not awarded any marks. Good essays will contain more than six points of accurate and relevant knowledge.

Argument

There are **ten** marks given for the way in which you use the knowledge to answer the question posed. This is half of the total marks for an essay question so is very important to get right. At a basic level most people can comment on the information that they have used. This means that they say, for example, that a factor is important, but give little further development. Better answers explore the factor in more depth – they analyse the information and explore arguments for and against the factor's importance. Answers that analyse the information and answer the question posed achieve high marks. In other words, it is vitally important to read the question carefully and ensure that you answer it.

Organisation

It is important to organise your information effectively. This will depend on the question you are answering. Information can be organised in themes that assess a trend in history, or as factors that lead to a development or event in history.

The biggest problem with essay writing is when people write descriptive essays or remember an essay they did well in class and try to copy it. You must react to the wording of the question asked. The quality of comment and analysis is what makes a good essay. If this is carefully linked to the question posed then the mark will be good.

It is very important to keep an eye on time in Paper 1. You are given forty minutes per essay. You are expected to do a lot in forty minutes. It is far better to write two essays of the same length rather than one long essay and one short essay. Two consistent essays will always score more marks than one good and one poor essay.

Paper 2

Paper 2 of your Higher History exam is based entirely on source analysis. The exam paper will be divided into five special topics and you will have to answer one special topic section. Make sure you select the correct special topic in the exam.

You must answer all of the questions set on the special topic you have studied.

You must do three things to succeed.

1. You must do what you are asked to do with each question.

2. You must refer to information in the presented source[s].

3. You must also include your own relevant recalled information when asked to do so.

You get a mark for each specific point you make. For the evaluation and contextualisation questions, a point means a piece of information from the presented source OR from relevant recalled information *that has been used in the correct way* when answering the question. For the comparison question, a point means that an individual point of similarity or difference has been identified and is then illustrated or explained using the content of the source.

There are no marks for just copying out sections of the presented source or sources. If you use relevant information, but do not comment on it effectively or make a correct comparison, you may only get one overall mark for listing.

With this paper it is important to keep an eye on your time. You will need to build in reading time and thinking time before you start to write. It is also important to look at the number of marks that are on offer. The 'How useful' question and 'comparison' question are each out of five marks. Both contextualise questions are out of ten marks. Therefore you should spend more time on the Contextualise answers as they are worth more marks!

The 'How useful' question

This question asks you to evaluate a source. It will ask you *'How useful is Source X in explaining/ illustrating a historical event/development.'* You are given instructions to comment on the source's **origin**, **purpose**, **content** and relevant information, or **recall information**, that has not been mentioned in the presented source.

The biggest problem with this sort of question is when people do not read the question carefully. As a result, the source is simply described when what the marker is looking for is some link with the 'usefulness' of the source in answering the question. So the trick is to identify information that is relevant to the answer and then comment on it. You need to do both things to be sure of the mark.

The 'Comparison' question

This question will ask you to compare two sources. It will ask you, *'To what extent do Sources X and Y agree about an event/issue, etc'*. You are given instructions to comment on the sources **overall** and then **in detail**.

The biggest problem with this sort of question is that people give 'ghost' comparisons. You will get NO MARKS for 'ghost' comparisons. In other words, no marks will be awarded for writing *'Source B says ... but Source C makes no mention of this.'* The two sources will contain four different points that agree or disagree with each other. You have to identify the area they agree or disagree about and then illustrate this difference by selecting relevant phrases from the sources that show this. The overall comparison refers to the general areas of agreement and disagreement that are identified. You do not need specific detail from the sources to make an overall comparison, but you do need to identify these general areas.

The 'Contextualise' question

This question asks you to contextualise a source. It asks *'how fully or how far does Source X explain/ illustrate a historical event/development'*. The question tests your knowledge on one specific issue or sub-issue that is relevant to the course. You can find all the issues and sub-issues in the Specimen Question Paper on the SQA syllabus website at the following address: http://www.sqa.org.uk/sqa/ files_ccc/History%20Higher%20Specimen%20 2011.pdf

Put simply, the 'how fully' question will ask you about 25% of the course content. The 'how far' question will ask you about 8% of the course content. Therefore the 'how far' question is much harder than the 'how fully' question, because it requires more detailed knowledge.

The biggest problem with this sort of question is, again, that people do not read the question carefully. If you do not read the question carefully, then there is a danger of writing irrelevant information in your answer. This will not be credited. The second problem is when people simply describe the information without commenting on it. As with the evaluation question, you need to identify relevant information then link it to the question with relevant comment.

No individual source will tell you the whole story. The presented source will contain four points that are relevant to the question asked. You need to identify these and comment on them in terms of the question asked. You then need to identify relevant information that is not in the source and explain that these areas provide a more complete picture. You will need at least six relevant points of recalled information if you want to get full marks.

Good luck!

History is an interesting and rewarding subject to study. It teaches useful skills such as how to structure extended writing and how to be critical of presented evidence. In the exam, think before you put pen to paper. You will have worked hard to get to this stage. Don't Panic! Keep calm, answer the questions and do the best that you can. GOOD LUCK!

HIGHER

2012

[BLANK PAGE]

X259/12/01

| NATIONAL QUALIFICATIONS 2012 | FRIDAY, 25 MAY 9.00 AM – 10.20 AM | HISTORY HIGHER Paper 1 |

Candidates should answer **two** questions, **one** from Historical Study: British History and **one** from Historical Study: European and World History.

All questions are worth 20 marks.

Marks may be deducted for bad spelling and bad punctuation, and for writing that is difficult to read.

[BLANK PAGE]

HISTORICAL STUDY: BRITISH HISTORY

Answer ONE question. Each question is worth 20 marks.

Church, State and Feudal Society

1. To what extent was the contribution of the Church to society in medieval Scotland and England confined to religion?

2. How successful were David I of Scotland and Henry II of England's attempts to increase royal authority?

3. How important was the growth of towns in causing the decline of feudal society?

The Century of Revolutions 1603–1702

4. How effective was Charles I's rule in Scotland between 1625 and 1642?

5. How important were religious issues in causing the Revolution of 1688 to 1689?

6. "Financial reform was the most significant change brought about by the Revolution Settlement." How valid is this view?

The Atlantic Slave Trade

7. To what extent was the slave trade the major factor in the development of the British economy in the eighteenth century?

8. "The slave trade was too important to the British economy to allow it to be abolished." How valid is this view?

9. How significant was the campaign organised by the Anti-Slavery Society in bringing about the abolition of the slave trade?

Britain 1851–1951

10. "Britain was still far from being a democratic country by 1928." How valid is this view?

11. To what extent did the Liberal reforms of 1906 to 1914 make a significant improvement to the lives of the British people?

12. "The Labour Government of 1945 to 1951 met the needs of the people 'from the cradle to the grave'." How valid is this view?

[Turn over

Britain and Ireland 1900–1985

13. How far did World War One change political attitudes towards British rule in Ireland?

14. How important were economic issues in contributing to the developing crisis in Northern Ireland up to 1968?

15. How important were the religious and communal differences between both communities in preventing peace in Ireland between 1968 and 1985?

HISTORICAL STUDY: EUROPEAN AND WORLD

Answer ONE question. Each question is worth 20 marks.

The Crusades, 1071–1204

16. How important were religious factors in the decision of Europeans to go on crusade?

17. "While Richard was a greater military leader, Saladin was a better diplomat." How valid is this view?

18. How far had the crusading ideal declined by the Fourth Crusade in 1204?

The American Revolution 1763–1787

19. How important was the rejection of the Olive Branch petition in the colonists' declaration of independence in 1776?

20. How important was the colonists' advantage of fighting on home ground in their eventual victory in the American Revolution?

21. "The American Constitution of 1787 was an answer to the problems highlighted by the experience of British rule." How accurate is this view?

The French Revolution, to 1799

22. To what extent did revolution break out in France in 1789 as a result of the economic crisis of 1788 to 1789?

23. To what extent did the increasing intervention of the army in politics bring about Napoleon's coup of 1799, which created the Consulate?

24. "The Bourgeoisie gained most from the French Revolution." How valid is this view?

Germany 1815–1939

25. How strong was nationalism in Germany by 1850?

26. To what extent were the weaknesses of the Weimar Republic the major reason for the rise of the Nazi Party between 1919 and 1933?

27. "Through their economic policies the Nazis gave the people what they wanted." How valid is this as a reason for the Nazis maintaining power between 1933 and 1939?

[Turn over

Italy 1815–1939

28. How successful were supporters of Italian nationalism up to 1850?

29. How accurate is it to argue that the appeal of fascism was the main reason why Mussolini came to power in Italy by 1925?

30. How important was the use of fear and intimidation in maintaining Fascist control over Italy between 1922 and 1939?

Russia 1881–1921

31. How important was working-class discontent in causing the 1905 revolution in Russia?

32. To what extent did the Bolsheviks gain power due to the weaknesses of the Provisional Government?

33. How important was the use of terror by the Reds in allowing them to win the Civil War?

USA 1918–1968

34. How far can it be argued that the activities of the Ku Klux Klan was the most important obstacle to the achievement of Civil Rights for black people up to 1941?

35. How important was the emergence of effective black leaders in the growing demand for Civil Rights between 1945 and 1968?

36. To what extent did the Civil Rights campaigns of the 1950s and 1960s result in significant improvements in the lives of black Americans?

Appeasement and the Road to War, to 1939

37. To what extent did fascist powers use diplomacy to achieve their aims?

38. "A reasonable settlement under the circumstances." How valid is this view of the Munich agreement of 1938?

39. To what extent did the occupation of Czechoslovakia in March 1939 lead to the outbreak of World War Two six months later?

The Cold War 1945–1989

40. How effectively did the Soviet Union control Eastern Europe up to 1961?

41. To what extent were the Superpowers' attempts to manage the Cold War between 1962 and 1985 prompted by the economic cost of the arms race?

42. How important was the role of Gorbachev in ending the Cold War?

[END OF QUESTION PAPER]

[BLANK PAGE]

X259/12/02

NATIONAL
QUALIFICATIONS
2012

FRIDAY, 25 MAY
10.40 AM – 12.05 PM

HISTORY
HIGHER
Paper 2

Answer questions on only **one** Special Topic.

Take particular care to show clearly the Special Topic chosen. On the **front** of the answer book, **in the top right-hand corner**, write the number of the Special Topic.

You are expected to use background knowledge appropriately in answering source-based questions.

Marks may be deducted for bad spelling and bad punctuation, and for writing that is difficult to read.

Some sources have been adapted.

SPECIAL TOPIC 1: THE WARS OF INDEPENDENCE, 1286–1328

Study the sources below and answer the questions which follow.

Source A: from the Treaty of Birgham (1290).

Having considered the peace and tranquillity of both kingdoms and in doing so mutual friendship should continue between our peoples for all time, we have granted in the name of our lord (Edward I) that the rights and liberties and customs of Scotland shall be wholly preserved. We promise that the kingdom of Scotland shall remain separate and divided from the kingdom of England by rightful boundaries and borders as has been observed up to now and that it shall be free and independent.

We grant that no tenant-in-chief of the king of Scotland shall be forced to go outside the kingdom to do homage or fealty or to pay relief for his lands. No parliament shall be held outwith the kingdom and borders of Scotland on matters concerning that kingdom or its borders or the position of those that live in the kingdom. No one of the kingdom of Scotland shall be held to answer outwith that kingdom for any agreement entered into, or for any crime committed, or in any other cause contrary to the laws and customs of that kingdom.

Source B: from GWS Barrow, *Robert Bruce* (1988).

The whole course of the negotiations which culminated in the marriage agreement, called the Treaty of Birgham, shows the guardians above all anxious to do nothing that might impair the "rights" or the integrity of Scotland.

The Treaty of Birgham was the high-watermark of the endeavour by the Guardians and the community. The treaty envisaged two feudal kingdoms, England and Scotland ruled separately though in harmony by a king and queen. The Scottish kingdom was to remain, as the Scots had demanded, free and without subjugation. Elections to the clergy in Scotland were to be free of external interference and tenants-in-chief of the Scots Crown need do homage for their lands in Scotland only, persons in Scotland who had been accused of a crime or sued at law should not have to answer in a court outside their country.

The treaty has been praised as a document of wise statesmanship and patriotism, but it was also something else. It was essentially a cautious, protective document.

Source C: from the Chronicle of Walter of Guisborough, 1296.

All that day and the next our king was expecting the burgesses of Berwick to come to his peace but they would not accept the peace which he offered. Twenty-four English warships attacked Berwick but were driven back. When these things were told to our king who was still in the field where everyone could see the smoke rising high from the ships, the king ordered them to sound the bugles and enter the city. When the city was taken they killed more than 8,000 of the enemy. On the same day the men of strength who were in the castle garrison surrendered. The king kept their captain Lord William Douglas until the end of the war. He allowed two hundred men who were with him to go free carrying their arms having first taken an oath from them that they would never lift a hand against him or the kingdom of the English.

Source D: from A.F. Murison, *Sir William Wallace* (2000).

The remnants of the Scots army drew from Falkirk towards the north, burning the town and castle of Stirling as they passed. So far Edward pursued them. Having repaired the castle and garrisoned it with Northumbrians, he is said to have harried St Andrews and St Johnston. He then passed through Selkirk Forrest to the west where he found that Bruce had burned Ayr Castle and retired to Carrick, but Edward could not pursue for lack of food. Continuing his journey through Annandale, Edward took and burned Loch Maben castle. At Carlisle he held a parliament and distributed lands in Scotland to his officers.

Shortly after their retreat from Falkirk, perhaps at Scots Water, or at a meeting in St Johnston, Wallace is said to have resigned voluntarily the office of Guardian of Scotland. The Scots writers at the time stated that this step was necessary because of the impossibility of maintaining the independence of his country in co-operation with the jealous nobles.

Source E: from Richard Oram, *The Kings and Queens of Scotland* (2006).

Robert was quick to capitalise on Bannockburn. Not only was he able to recover his queen and daughter from captivity in exchange for English prisoners, but also at parliament in November he overcame his remaining Scottish opponents and took their lands in Scotland. This gave him extensive resources with which to reward his supporters and subjects in order to secure their loyalty. Robert also intensified his attacks on northern England both in search for cash and to force Edward II to recognise Bruce's kingship of a free Scotland. The bleeding of northern England in 1314–1315 really did little to pressure Edward II.

By 1323 Bruce attempted to secure peace for war-weary Scotland, even negotiating a peace not with Edward II but his lieutenants in northern England. Yet faced with the English King's refusal to give up Scotland, Robert had to settle for a long uneasy truce in 1323. Robert did not withdraw from politics, but worked hard to ensure a relatively stable inheritance for his son. A new mutual defence agreed with France in 1326 was part of this, but a full peace, between England and an independent Scotland, was still his ultimate goal.

[*END OF SOURCES FOR THE WARS OF INDEPENDENCE, 1286–1328*]

SPECIAL TOPIC 1: THE WARS OF INDEPENDENCE, 1286–1328

Marks

Answer *all* of the following questions.

1. To what extent do **Sources A** and **B** agree about the Scots' attempts to protect their independence after the death of Alexander III?
   Compare the sources overall and in detail.   **5**

2. How useful is **Source C** as evidence of the subjugation of the Scots by Edward I in 1296?
   In reaching a conclusion you should refer to:
   • *the origin and possible purpose of the source;*
   • *the content of the source;*
   • *recalled knowledge.*   **5**

3. How far does **Source D** show the changing military balance between Scotland and England, 1298–1301?
   Use the source and recalled knowledge.   **10**

4. How fully does **Source E** explain the reasons for the ultimate success of Bruce in maintaining Scotland's independence?
   Use the source and recalled knowledge.   **10**

                                                                                                           (30)

[*END OF QUESTIONS ON THE WARS OF INDEPENDENCE, 1286–1328*]

SPECIAL TOPIC 2: THE AGE OF REFORMATION, 1542–1603

Study the sources below and answer the questions which follow.

Source A: from *The Treaty of Edinburgh*, 1560.

At Edinburgh on 6 July 1560 the following terms are agreed between France and England. All military forces of each party shall withdraw from the realm of Scotland, and all warlike operations in England, Ireland and Wales shall entirely cease. And since the realms of England and Ireland belong by right to Queen Elizabeth, no other is allowed to call, write, name or have himself called, written or named king or queen of England or Ireland. Nor is anyone to use the signs and arms of those kingdoms. It is therefore agreed that the most Christian King Francis and Queen Mary shall abstain from using or carrying the said title or arms of the kingdom of England or Ireland. And King Francis and Queen Mary will fulfil all those things which were granted by their representatives to the nobility and people of Scotland provided that the nobility and people of Scotland fulfil and observe what was contained in those conventions and articles.

Source B: from Rosalind K. Marshall, *John Knox* (2000).

Mary of Guise died shortly after midnight on 11 June 1560. Elizabeth I had already sent William Cecil to Newcastle to negotiate with French envoys and he now moved to Edinburgh. A truce was arranged between England and France and the Treaty of Edinburgh was signed on 6 July. The principal clause stated that all foreign soldiers were to withdraw from Scotland. Francis II and Mary, Queen of Scots, would henceforth abstain from displaying the English arms with those of Scotland. Since the Scots had spontaneously and freely professed and acknowledged their obedience and loyalty towards their most Christian king and queen, Francis and Mary would fulfil all their obligations in the treaty. Everything relating to religion would be referred to the Scots Parliament, and after the treaty had been signed John Knox held a great service of thanksgiving in St Giles.

Source C: from Sir James Melville, *The Murder of Riccio*, 9 March 1566.

David Riccio obtained the position of secretary to Mary, and got her Majesty's attention, which caused him to be so envied and hated that some of the nobility would ignore him. I told him that it was thought that most of the business of the country passed through his hands, and advised him, when the nobility were present, to give them their place. However, the King, Darnley, probably gave his consent too easily to the slaughter of seigneur Riccio, which the Lords of Morton, Ruthven, Lindsay and others had devised, so that they could be masters of the court and hold the parliament. When the murderers entered, seigneur Riccio clutched the Queen and cried for mercy; but George Douglas drew out the King's dagger and struck him with it. He gave screams and cries and was roughly removed from the Queen, who could not get him safe, neither by threat or entreaty. He was forcibly dragged out of the room and slain and her Majesty was kept captive.

Source D: from Jenny Wormald ed., *Scotland: A History*, (2005).

The King's tolerance of Catholic earls had long been resented by the Kirk. When local feuding between the Catholic Earl of Huntly and the Protestant Earl of Moray led to the latter's murder, the incident was used by the Kirk to gain concessions in the Golden Act. Yet despite the Golden Act, James never conceded the principle of royal supremacy over the Kirk. He would make increasingly successful efforts to tighten royal control over the general assembly and re-establish the authority of bishops. Following the crisis years of the 1590s, James published his works on kingship, reflecting on the necessity of obedience to his divinely ordained authority and on the challenges of managing an unruly Kirk and powerful nobility. These suggest a monarch deeply frustrated by his subjects' lack of respect for the crown's authority, and show his determination to civilise his kingdom by bringing Scotland's remote localities under more direct royal control.

Source E: from Ian B. Cowan, *The Scottish Reformation* (1982).

The way the partnership between Kirk and society worked in post-Reformation Scotland was very different from the pre-Reformation era. The most striking aspect of this new relationship was a new religious fervour demonstrated by an unwavering support for Presbyterian beliefs. In some respects the role of the church in society had been greatly reduced because secular forces undertook duties that had previously been the preserve of the Catholic Church. The right of a congregation to choose its own minister was asserted in the Second Book of Discipline. The place of music in the services of the Kirk and in the life of the people was to suffer as a result of the Reformation. The character of the Kirk was established in the immediate post-Reformation era when political and economic circumstances forced the victorious reformers to adopt a compassionate attitude towards the representatives of the old faith. In this respect the Scottish Reformation was to produce little of the intolerance that characterised the Reformation in England and on the continent.

[END OF SOURCES FOR THE AGE OF REFORMATION, 1542–1603]

SPECIAL TOPIC 2: THE AGE OF REFORMATION, 1542–1603

Marks

Answer *all* of the following questions.

1. To what extent do **Sources A** and **B** agree about the changes brought in by the Treaty of Edinburgh in 1560?
   Compare the sources overall and in detail.   **5**

2. How useful is **Source C** in explaining Mary's difficulties in ruling Scotland?
   In reaching a conclusion you should refer to:
   * *the origin and possible purpose of the source;*
   * *the content of the source;*
   * *recalled knowledge.*   **5**

3. How far does **Source D** illustrate the efforts of James VI to control the Kirk?
   Use the source and recalled knowledge.   **10**

4. How fully does **Source E** explain the impact of the Reformation on Scotland?
   Use the source and recalled knowledge.   **10**

   (30)

[END OF QUESTIONS ON THE AGE OF REFORMATION, 1542–1603]

SPECIAL TOPIC 3: THE TREATY OF UNION, 1689–1740

Study the sources below and answer the questions which follow.

Source A: from Christopher A. Whatley, *The Scots and the Union* (2006).

In the 1690s Scotland was tipped over the edge of an economic abyss that was to have profound political consequences for the nation's history. Factors included a series of harvest failures and the effects of England's war with Scotland's ally France, particularly the damaging loss of French trade. The erection of protective tariffs by countries overseas blocked the export of certain Scottish goods. Finally, there was the disaster of Darien, Scotland's ambitious scheme to establish a colony in South America. As it happened, the outcome—eventually—was incorporating union with England, but the decade of crisis might equally have produced a very different result.

Source B: from Daniel Defoe, *History of the Union* (1709).

Since the Union of the Crowns in 1603, and in a hundred years of joint monarchy with England, the Scots had been very sensitive to the sinking economic condition of their nation. Also, they were aware of the visible damage both to trade and to the wealth of the inhabitants of the country. This was plainly owing to the loss of Scottish ministers' presence at Court in London, the disadvantages of tariffs and the influence the English had over their kings. It was just as plain that one way for the Scots to restore themselves was in terms of incorporating union and alliance with England. There would be advantages for Scottish commerce of free access to English and empire markets. Without incorporating union, the Scottish economy would remain unstable. It was either union, or a return back to their separate self-existing state.

Source C: is from a petition from Stirling Town Council to the Scottish Parliament, 18 November 1706.

We have considered the great affair of Union of Scotland and England as contained in the articles of the treaty. We desire true and continued peace and friendship with our neighbours in England. However, we judge it our duty to the nation and parliament, with all due respect to parliament, to state that this treaty will prove ruinous to our manufacturing industry, since the new freedom of trade will never balance the new insupportable burden of taxation. The treaty will deprive us, and the rest of the royal burghs in this nation, of our fundamental right of being represented in the legislative power. Thus, an ancient nation, so long and gloriously defended by patriots, will be suppressed as our dear parliament is extinguished and we are brought under a burden which we will never be able to bear, with fatal consequences which we tremble to think about.

Source D: is from Douglas Watt, *The Price of Scotland: Darien, Union and the Wealth of Nations* (2007).

It was anticipated that there would be little opposition to the treaty in the English Parliament, so it made sense to secure its passage in Scotland first. The Scottish Parliament opened on 3 October in a tense Edinburgh. The tactics of the opposition were to disrupt and delay proceedings and hope for a popular uprising against the treaty. Riots rocked Edinburgh and Glasgow in November and December. Anti-union petitions flooded into parliament. However, the opposition was divided and poorly led by the unpredictable Duke of Hamilton. He may have been bribed by the Court party. At a crucial point, when there were plans to withdraw from parliament, he called off with the excuse of toothache and then, on his return to parliament, he refused to participate in the walkout. An armed rising by Cameronians and Jacobites turned into a fiasco as its leaders backed down when they were paid off by Queensberry. This attempt proved that the political opposition to union were not willing to engage in violence to support the continued existence of the Scottish Parliament.

Source E: is from Paul Henderson Scott, *The Union of 1707* (2006).

One irony of the Union is that it did not in the end extinguish Scotland as a nation; it retained its own distinctive identity, attitudes and ideas, and its traditions were so strong that they were not easily eradicated. The consequences of the Treaty in this respect were not as harmful as they might have been, although it did exert a strong Anglicising influence. Nevertheless, the guarantees to the Scottish legal system in the Treaty and to the Church in the Act of Security for the Kirk had more influence on Scotland than the distant British Parliament. English and Scottish historians have concluded that the continuation of the Scottish systems of education and local government were a significant achievement of Union.

[*END OF SOURCES FOR THE TREATY OF UNION, 1689–1740*]

SPECIAL TOPIC 3: THE TREATY OF UNION, 1689–1740

Marks

Answer *all* of the following questions.

1. To what extent do **Sources A** and **B** agree about worsening relations between Scotland and England between 1690 and 1705?
   Compare the sources overall and in detail. **5**

2. How useful is **Source C** as evidence of attitudes towards the union in Scotland?
   In reaching a conclusion you should refer to:
   • *the origin and possible purpose of the source;*
   • *the content of the source;*
   • *recalled knowledge.* **5**

3. How far does **Source D** explain the passage of the Treaty of Union through the Scottish Parliament?
   Use the source and recalled knowledge. **10**

4. How fully does **Source E** explain the effects of Union up to 1740?
   Use the source and recalled knowledge. **10**

   (30)

[*END OF QUESTIONS ON THE TREATY OF UNION, 1689–1740*]

SPECIAL TOPIC 4: MIGRATION AND EMPIRE, 1830–1939

Study the sources below and answer the questions which follow.

Source A: from the Quarterly Journal of Agriculture 1832–1834.

I have not the slightest hesitation in declaring, that it appears to me as plain as the sun at noonday, that a farmer in Scotland, occupying a farm that does not pay him, distressed as he must be, struggling from morning to night with mental anxiety and worry pressing upon his mind and yet after all quite unable to support his family or better their circumstances—I say that a farmer continuing to remain in Scotland even when unemployed while so much land lies in Canada to occupy, acts the part of an insane person. In a short time there will be no cheap land to be procured about these parts. The best way for my brothers to lay out their money here in Canada is in buying land which is every year rising in value.

Source B: from the *Scotsman*, 20 February 1923, "Emigration boom in the Hebrides".

Great interest is being taken in the scheme of the Ontario government to emigrate young men and women between 18 and 23 to Canada. The Ontario agent finds that he could treble the number he is authorised to enlist owing no doubt to the depressed state of trade in Lewis, the lack of employment generally and the inability of the farmers to satisfy the hunger of the families. Immediately on landing, employment will be found for farmers and the women can find employment in domestic work. The pay is good as experienced men can at the very start earn £5 to £6 per month. The men also have the prospect of becoming owners of their own farms once again.

Source C: adapted from *New Arrivals* by Tony Jaconelli in *Our Glasgow Story*.

On New Year's day 1921, I trailed along holding on to my younger brother, Michael. Our father, Domenico, carried Biagio. My oldest brother, Giacomo, brought up the rear. We had left our warm village in Italy to join Domenico's brother in some place called Scotland. School was a nightmare for me but Giacomo, a name that was quickly shortened to Jack, revelled in school life. He was a quick learner and always able to take care of himself. A few times I found myself surrounded by classmates chanting at me because I was a foreigner. Jack scattered them and they stopped bothering me completely. Our family moved house a few times in an effort to improve our lot. Domenico took a job in the largely Italian trade of terrazzo tile workers and most of my brothers followed him into the trade. Meanwhile my grasp of the Glasgow dialect improved daily. Within a couple of years I lost all trace of my mother tongue and developed a strong, guttural Glasgow accent. In no time at all I was a complete Glaswegian.

Source D: from Ian Donnachie, *Success in the "Lucky" Country* (1988).

There were many fields of Scottish achievement in Australia. Scots were early and successful pioneers in sheep farming and the wool trade, which became big business, centred in places such as Melbourne and Adelaide. Scots also invested heavily in mining, at first in coal and later in copper, silver and gold. The Gold Rush of the 1850s brought to Australia a considerable number of Scottish miners, many of whom stayed after the initial gold fever died down and prospered. Shipping and trade were other areas of enterprise in which Scots excelled. Two later shipping firms were both fiercely Scottish, McIllwraith McEachan and Burns Philp. The profits of Burns Philp were built on the northern Queensland sugar boom of the 1880s in which Scots played a large part in creating the profitable business. Politics and government was another sphere in which the Scots made a sustained contribution to Australian life.

Source E: from ed. T.M. Devine, *Irish Immigrants and Scottish Society in the Nineteenth and Twentieth Centuries* (1991).

The immigration of the Irish into Scotland forms one of the most significant themes of modern Scottish history. The movement of the Irish changed the population balance of several lowland towns but especially Glasgow, Greenock, Dundee, Paisley and Airdrie, among others. Scotland's industrialisation was made easier because employers had access to a huge reservoir of Irish labour which was not only cheap but, was ready and willing to move anywhere and do anything to find work. The huge construction schemes of the nineteenth-century cities and the roads, railways, canals, docks and harbours that supported Scotland's industrial revolution depended ultimately on this vast labour supply. To local Scots, the Irish arrivals seemed to be overwhelmingly poor, diseased, mainly Catholic and recognisably alien. In short, the Irish were seen as a dangerous threat to the Scottish way of life. The Irish presence is also vital to an understanding of Scottish culture as the Catholic Irish and their descendants have played such an influential role in the evolution and shaping of Scottish society ranging from literature to music and on to football.

[*END OF SOURCES FOR MIGRATION AND EMPIRE, 1830–1939*]

SPECIAL TOPIC 4: MIGRATION AND EMPIRE, 1830–1939

Answer *all* of the following questions.

Marks

1. To what extent do **Sources A** and **B** agree about the reasons for Scottish migration to Canada?
   Compare the sources overall and in detail.

   5

2. How useful is **Source C** as evidence of the assimilation of immigrants into Scottish society?
   In reaching a conclusion you should refer to:
   * *the origin and possible purpose of the source;*
   * *the content of the source;*
   * *recalled knowledge.*

   5

3. How far does **Source D** show the contribution of Scots to the economic growth and development of the Empire?
   Use the source and recalled knowledge.

   10

4. How fully does **Source E** explain the effects of migration and Empire on Scottish society?
   Use the source and recalled knowledge.

   10

   (30)

[*END OF QUESTIONS ON MIGRATION AND EMPIRE, 1830–1939*]

SPECIAL TOPIC 5: THE IMPACT OF THE GREAT WAR, 1914–1928

Study the sources below and answer the questions which follow.

Source A: by John Jackson, *Private 12768: Memoir of a Tommy* (2004) writing about the Battle of Loos.

The situation at Hill 70 was serious. A third time the order was given to attack that awful hillside, but the enemy with his reserves at hand, were too many for us and again we fell back, truly we were holding to the motto of the regiment "A Cameron never can yield". We numbered at this stage less than 100 and for all we knew might be all that was left of 6th Cameron Highlanders. As the evening drew on we made a fourth and final attempt to win and hold the ridge. This time we meant to do or die. To the sound of the pipes and led by our brave old colonel, bareheaded and with no other weapon than his walking stick, we made for the top of Hill 70 through murderous rifle and machine gun fire, while shells crashed all around us. We made the top but now we were desperate for the promised reinforcements but no help could we see.

Source B: by Philip Gibbs, official British wartime correspondent on the Western Front for the *Daily Chronicle*, writing about the Battle of Loos.

By seven-forty the two assaulting brigades of the 15th Division had left the trenches and were in the open. Shriller than the scream of shells above them was the skirl of pipes, going with them. The orders of the Scottish troops, which I saw, were to go "all out," and to press onto Hill 70, with the absolute assurance that all the ground they gained would be held behind them by supporting troops. With the promise of reinforcements to follow, they trudged on to Hill 70. For a time there was a kind of Bank Holiday crowd on Hill 70. The German machine gunners, knowing that the redoubt on the crest was still held by their men, initially dared not fire. Then the quiet of Hill 70 was broken by the beginning of a new bombardment from German guns. "Dig in," said the officers. "We must hold on at all costs until the reinforcements come up." None came and they were forced to withdraw.

Source C: from *The Glasgow Herald,* 29th October 1915.

The first attempt to put into force the eviction notices which have been issued against Glasgow tenants who are participating in the "Rent Strikes" was made yesterday afternoon in Merryland Street, Govan. The householder is a woman who has not been making her rent payments. As has been the custom since the beginning of the movement against increased rents, a demonstration of the "strikers" was held at the time when the eviction notice became operative. While Mrs Barbour of the Glasgow Women's Housing Association was addressing those who had assembled, two sheriff officers arrived and endeavoured to gain admission to the house. As soon as it was known that it was proposed to evict the tenant the demonstrators determined to resist. Most of them were women, and they attacked the officers and their assistants with peasmeal, flour, and whiting. A woman was arrested on a charge of assaulting one of the officers.

Source D: from Clive H. Lee *The Scottish Economy and the First World War* (Scotland and the Great War edited by C.M.M. MacDonald and E.W. McFarland 1999).

Many of the changes caused by the war were temporary such as the readjustment of agricultural production to improve self-sufficiency and the boom in the jute industry. When normal trade was resumed in the 1920s, the massively weakened position of British manufacturers in export markets became apparent. As a consequence of the war, Scottish and British industry lost its international competitiveness. The war certainly shifted the balance of international trade against Scottish shipbuilders by increasing world-wide capacity which hit the industry after the war. Also, Scottish textile manufacturers were never able to regain the Asian markets, especially India, as the war allowed competitors to move in. But the war also demonstrated the fragility of the Scottish heavy industry base and the growing need for imported raw materials.

Source E: from W. Hamish Fraser, *Scottish Popular Politics From Radicalism to Labour* (2000).

The war years also showed that support for Scottish Home Rule had not really declined. The policy of the Scottish Trade Union Congress was to call on the Parliamentary Labour Party to support "the enactment of a Scottish Home Rule Bill". The same spirit of nationalism forced Arthur Henderson and the Labour leadership in London, much against their better judgement, to allow a separate Scottish Council of Labour with a considerable amount of self-government. At the same time, the war undermined even further the organisation of Scottish Liberalism, but also much of its moral authority. The more radical elements were disenchanted by Lloyd George's political tactics and by his aggressive determination to accept nothing less than unconditional surrender. Liberalism was thrown into disarray while the ILP was able to emerge as the natural successor to advanced liberal radicalism.

[END OF SOURCES FOR THE IMPACT OF THE GREAT WAR, 1914–1928]

SPECIAL TOPIC 5: THE IMPACT OF THE GREAT WAR, 1914–1928

Marks

Answer *all* of the following questions.

1. To what extent do **Sources A** and **B** agree about the experience of Scots on the Western Front?
    Compare the sources overall and in detail.   **5**

2. How useful is **Source C** as evidence of the impact of the war on Scottish women?
    In reaching a conclusion you should refer to:
    *   *the origin and possible purpose of the source;*
    *   *the content of the source;*
    *   *recalled knowledge.*   **5**

3. How far does **Source D** illustrate the economic difficulties faced by Scotland after 1918?
    Use the source and recalled knowledge.   **10**

4. How fully does **Source E** describe the impact of the war on political developments in Scotland?
    Use the source and recalled knowledge.   **10**

                                                                                                  (30)

[END OF QUESTIONS ON THE IMPACT OF THE GREAT WAR, 1914–1928]

[END OF QUESTION PAPER]

[BLANK PAGE]

HIGHER

2013

[BLANK PAGE]

X259/12/01

NATIONAL
QUALIFICATIONS
2013

TUESDAY, 14 MAY
9.00 AM – 10.20 AM

HISTORY
HIGHER
Paper 1

Candidates should answer **two** questions, **one** from Historical Study: British History and **one** from Historical Study: European and World History.

All questions are worth 20 marks.

[BLANK PAGE]

HISTORICAL STUDY: BRITISH HISTORY

Answer ONE question. Each question is worth 20 marks.

Church, State and Feudal Society

1. To what extent was the secular church more important than the regular church in the Middle Ages?

2. "The desire to develop "Law and Order" was the main factor in the development of centralised monarchy." How valid is this view on the reigns of David I and Henry II?

3. How important were changing social attitudes in causing the decline of feudal society?

The Century of Revolutions 1603–1702

4. "The policies of Charles I led to problems ruling Scotland." How valid is this view?

5. How important was the role of the Army in the failure to find an alternative form of government between 1649 and 1658?

6. How successfully did the Revolution Settlement of 1688–1702 address the key issues between Crown and Parliament?

The Atlantic Slave Trade

7. How important was the slave trade in the development of the British economy in the eighteenth century?

8. "African societies were to benefit from their involvement in the slave trade." How valid is this view?

9. To what extent was the decline in the economic importance of slavery the main reason for the abolition of the slave trade?

Britain 1851–1951

10. How accurate is it to describe Britain as a fully democratic country by 1918?

11. To what extent did the Liberal Government of 1906–1914 introduce social reform due to the social surveys of Booth and Rowntree?

12. "The social reforms of the Labour Government of 1945–1951 failed to deal effectively with the needs of the people." How valid is this view?

Britain and Ireland 1900–1985

13. "The decline of the Nationalist Party was the most significant impact of World War One on Ireland." How valid is this view?

14. How important were divisions in the Republican Movement in causing the outbreak of the Irish Civil War?

15. "The British government policy of Direct Rule was the main obstacle to peace in Northern Ireland between 1968 and 1985." How accurate is this statement?

HISTORICAL STUDY: EUROPEAN AND WORLD

Answer ONE question. Each question is worth 20 marks.

The Crusades 1071–1204

16. To what extent was peer pressure the main reason for going on Crusade?

17. How important were divisions amongst the Crusaders in bringing about the fall of Jerusalem in 1187?

18. "By the Fourth Crusade in 1204 the Crusading Ideal was dead." How valid is this view?

The American Revolution 1763–1787

19. "Disputes over taxation was the main reason for the outbreak of the American colonists' revolt against British rule in 1776." How valid is this view?

20. "French intervention changed the whole nature of the American War of Independence." How valid is this view?

21. To what extent did the American Constitution successfully address the issues raised by the experience of rule by Britain?

The French Revolution, to 1799

22. How important was the role of the bourgeoisie in the collapse of royal authority in France by 1789?

23. How important was the threat of counter-revolution as a cause of the Terror between 1792 and 1795?

24. To what extent did the peasants gain most from the French Revolution by 1799?

Germany 1815–1939

25. "By 1850 political nationalism had made little progress in Germany." How valid is this view?

26. How important was the attitude of foreign states in the achievement of German unification by 1871?

27. "Propaganda was crucial to the maintenance of power by the Nazis." How accurate is this view?

Italy 1815–1939

28. To what extent was the idea of nationalism well established in Italy in the years before 1850?

29. To what extent was the unification of Italy by 1870 the result of foreign intervention?

30. How important was the use of propaganda in maintaining Fascist power in Italy between 1922 and 1939?

Russia 1881–1921

31. To what extent was Bloody Sunday responsible for the 1905 Revolution in Russia?

32. To what extent did working class discontent cause the outbreak of the February Revolution in 1917?

33. "The role of Trotsky was the main reason why the Reds won the Civil War." How valid is this statement?

USA 1918–1968

34. To what extent were divisions within the black community the main obstacle to achieving civil rights before 1941?

35. How effective was the New Deal in solving America's problems in the 1930s?

36. How far did the Civil Rights Movement meet the needs of black Americans, up to 1968?

Appeasement and the Road to War, to 1939

37. To what extent did Fascist governments use military threat and force in pursuing their foreign policies from 1933?

38. "British foreign policy was a complete failure in containing the spread of Fascist aggression up to March 1938." How valid is this view?

39. To what extent was the outbreak of war in September 1939 brought about by the failure of British diplomacy and relations with the Soviet Union?

The Cold War 1945–1989

40. "The Soviet Union effectively controlled Eastern Europe in the years up to 1961." How accurate is this statement?

41. To what extent were the difficulties faced by the US military the reason why America lost the war in Vietnam?

42. "The economic weakness of the Soviet Union led to the end of the Cold War." How valid is this view?

[END OF QUESTION PAPER]

[BLANK PAGE]

X259/12/02

NATIONAL
QUALIFICATIONS
2013

TUESDAY, 14 MAY
10.40 AM – 12.05 PM

HISTORY
HIGHER
Paper 2

Answer questions on only **one** Special Topic.

Take particular care to show clearly the Special Topic chosen. On the **front** of the answer book, **in the top right-hand corner**, write the number of the Special Topic.

You are expected to use background knowledge appropriately in answering source-based questions.

Some sources have been adapted.

SPECIAL TOPIC 1: THE WARS OF INDEPENDENCE, 1286–1328

Study the sources below and answer the questions which follow.

Source A: from Alan Young, *Robert the Bruce's Rivals: The Comyns, 1212–1314* (1997).

Behind the legal arguments, there were clearly intense political manoeuvrings. The Comyn family used all their power and influence as the dominant political group to support the candidature of their relative, John Balliol. Balliol's success would both maintain and even increase Comyn power. This must be set beside the ambitions of the Bruce family who were determined to stake their claim to power and were prepared to take advantage of every opportunity that came along in order to turn this claim into reality. Even before the Maid's death in September 1290 Bruce had tried to increase his territorial power in the north. In the winter of 1290–1291, Bruce had also presented himself as the rightful heir. During the "Great Cause" he put forward a case that he was the recognised successor of Alexander II.

Source B: from *The Chronicle of John of Fordun*, 1350.

In March 1296, the King of England, being strongly stirred up, marched in person, with a large force, on Scotland. Upon the town of Berwick, sparing neither sex nor age, the aforesaid King of England, put to the sword some 7500 souls. On 27 April, in the same year, was fought the battle of Dunbar, where Patrick of Graham and many Scottish nobles fell wounded in defeat, while a great many other knights fled to Dunbar Castle. However, up to 70 of them, including William, Earl of Ross, were betrayed by the warden of the castle and handed over to the King of England, like sheep offered to the slaughter. In this, Balliol's war, all the supporters of Bruce's party were generally considered traitors to their King and country.

Source C: from Michael Penman, *The Scottish Civil War* (2002).

King John must have feared the danger from within his borders from disappointed Scottish nobles who preferred to side with the English King, this of course included the Bruces. For Edward in early 1296 the campaign to Scotland was carried out from the outset by using the full force of England's experienced army. On 30 March his large army made a swift example of the town of Berwick, slaughtering over 7000 inhabitants. When a small Scottish force attempted to relieve the besieged castle of Dunbar, King John was absent. In the ensuing battle at Dunbar on 27 April the Scots were defeated resoundingly by a small English force led by Surrey. Edward then progressed north unhindered. The Scots leaders soon lost all stomach for the fight.

Source D: from *The Chronicle of Walter of Guisborough*, around 1300.

Meanwhile two friars were sent to the army of the Scots, to that robber William Wallace, to see if they wanted to embrace the peace which the English offered. Wallace replied, "Tell your men that we have not come for peace but are ready for the fight, to vindicate ourselves and to free our kingdom." There was not a more suitable place to put the English into the hands of the Scots. When the Scots saw that they could win, they came down from the hill. Sending men with pikes, they seized the end of the bridge so that no Englishman could cross or return. Among the English nobles cut down by the Scottish pikemen there fell Lord Hugh de Cressingham. The Scots hated him and cut his hide into little bits for he was a bonny man and pretty fat, and they called him not the King "treasurer" but his "treacherer".

Source E: The anonymous author of the *Vita Edwardi Secundi* on the reign of Edward II, around 1326.

O day of vengeance and disaster, day of utter loss and shame, evil and accursed day, people will ask why we gave in to the Scots, when for the last twenty years we have always had the better of them. Thus our men, who came in pride, returned in shame. The proud arrogance of our men made the Scots rejoice in victory at Bannockburn, under the assured leadership of Robert Bruce.

On Sunday, approaching Stirling Castle, a certain knight, Sir Henry de Bohun pursued the Scots. For he had in mind that if he found Robert Bruce there he would either kill him or carry him off captive. But Robert opposed him and struck him on the head with an axe that he carried in his hand. When the next day came it was abundantly clear that the Scots were prepared for the conflict with a great force of experienced armed men. Meanwhile Robert Bruce marshalled his force, about forty thousand men he brought with him, and split them into three divisions. They had axes at their sides and carried lances in their hands. They advanced like a thick-set hedge, and such a schiltron could not be easily broken.

[END OF SOURCES FOR THE WARS OF INDEPENDENCE, 1286–1328]

SPECIAL TOPIC 1: THE WARS OF INDEPENDENCE, 1286–1328

Marks

Answer *all* of the following questions.

1. How fully does **Source A** illustrate the succession problem in Scotland, 1286–1296?
   Use the source and recalled knowledge.   **10**

2. To what extent do **Sources B** and **C** agree about the subjugation of Scotland by Edward I?
   Compare the sources overall and in detail.   **5**

3. How useful is **Source D** as evidence of the growth of Scottish resistance to King Edward, 1296–1297?
   In reaching a conclusion you should refer to:
   * *the origin and possible purpose of the source;*
   * *the content of the source;*
   * *recalled knowledge.*   **5**

4. How far does **Source E** show Robert Bruce's abilities as a military leader?
   Use the source and recalled knowledge.   **10**

(30)

[END OF QUESTIONS ON THE WARS OF INDEPENDENCE, 1286–1328]

SPECIAL TOPIC 2: THE AGE OF REFORMATION, 1542–1603

Study the sources below and answer the questions which follow.

Source A: from Alec Ryrie, *The Age of Reformation: 1485–1603* (2009).

In December 1557 the Protestant nobles of the Lords of the Congregation sent Mary of Guise a set of ambitious but not impossible requests. They asked to be allowed to host Protestant sermons on their estates and they also wanted prayers in the vernacular to be used in parish churches. She gave the petitioners what they felt was a fair hearing, and promised to lay the question before the parliament. A settlement seemed possible. However, Knox had returned to Scotland and on 11th May had preached an inflammatory sermon at Perth which triggered a full-scale riot. Guise regarded this as an act of rebellion and the Protestant Lords mobilised to defend themselves. More or less by accident, a religious rebellion had broken out. Guise's mishandling of the situation in 1559 eventually united most of the political nation against her.

Source B: from a letter from Mary Queen of Scots to the Archbishop of Glasgow, 11 February 1567.

The matter is horrible and so strange. This last night 9th February, a little after two hours after midnight, the house in which the King was lodged was in an instant blown in the air, whilst he was lying sleeping in his bed, with such force, that of the whole lodging there is nothing remaining. It must have been done by force of gunpowder and appears to have been a mine. It is not yet known who carried out this deed and in what manner. At any rate whoever has taken this wicked enterprise in hand, we believe it was intended for us as well as for the King; for we lay the most part of the last week in the same lodging, and were there attended by the lords that were in town that same night at midnight. It was only by chance that we did not stay the night, by reason of some masque in the abbey (of Holyrood); but we believe it was not a chance, but that God put it in our head.

Source C: from Alison Weir, *Mary, Queen of Scots, and the Murder of Lord Darnley* (2008).

In the aftermath of Darnley's death there was much speculation as to who was implicated in the murder and how exactly it was carried out. During the two years after his murder, two people were formally accused of it. These two people were the Earl of Bothwell and the Queen herself. While the Protestant Lords disliked Darnley, they may have seen the murder as an opportunity to rid themselves of another person who posed a threat, namely Bothwell. The Lords of the Council concluded that the Old Provost's Lodging and the Prebendaries' Chamber had been blown into the air by the force of the powder. However, the whole matter remains a mystery. Why would Bothwell or anyone else choose to kill Darnley using gunpowder, instead of poison or suffocation? In addition, from about 4pm until Mary returned to Holyrood around midnight, Bothwell was in attendance on her, and conspicuously dressed in a masquing costume. It is very unlikely that, bent on murder, he made himself so visible by walking in his rich attire up and down the Canongate.

Source D: from *The Second Book of Discipline* (1578).

It is proper for kings and princes to be called lords over their subjects, whom they govern civilly. However, it is proper for Christ alone to be called Lord and Master in the spiritual government of the Kirk. All others who hold positions in the Kirk should not become powerful, and should not be called lords, for they are ministers and servants. Sometimes these men are called pastors, because they feed their congregation; sometimes *episcopi* or bishops, because they watch over their flock; sometimes ministers, by reason of their service and office; and sometimes they are called elders, because they take care of the spiritual government, which ought to be most dear unto them. It is Christ's proper office to command and rule in his Kirk, through his Spirit and word, by the ministry of men.

Source E: from Jenny Wormald, *Court, Kirk and Community: Scotland 1470–1625* (1981).

The new church was a complete break with the immediate past. In its distaste for hierarchy the principle of equality was followed as much as possible. In human terms, the Kirk's sense of urgency could be cruel. Any former Catholic reconciled to the Kirk was required to throw out all religious objects, rosaries, crucifixes and images of saints. The things that brought a sense of comfort and well-being, at least to some, were hard to jettison. Equally harsh, was the abolition of Christmas and Easter reflecting the obsessive fear of Catholic custom. However, in 1598 it redressed the balance by declaring Monday to be the day of rest for all servants. To the modern mind, there is something deeply unattractive about the crusading zeal of the new church. The abolition of saints' days and respect for the Sabbath is understandable, but the changes were harsh on a working population.

[END OF SOURCES FOR THE AGE OF REFORMATION, 1542–1603]

SPECIAL TOPIC 2: THE AGE OF REFORMATION, 1542–1603

Marks

Answer *all* of the following questions.

1. How fully does **Source A** explain the reasons for the Reformation of 1560?
   Use the source and recalled knowledge. **10**

2. To what extent do **Sources B** and **C** agree about the events which brought Mary's marriage to Darnley to an end?
   Compare the content overall and in detail. **5**

3. How useful is **Source D** as evidence of the efforts of the Kirk to maintain its independence?
   In reaching a conclusion you should refer to:
   • *the origin and possible purpose of the source;*
   • *the content of the source;*
   • *recalled knowledge.* **5**

4. How far does **Source E** explain the cultural impact of the Reformation on Scotland to 1603?
   Use the source and recalled knowledge. **10**

   (30)

[END OF QUESTIONS ON THE AGE OF REFORMATION, 1542–1603]

SPECIAL TOPIC 3: THE TREATY OF UNION, 1689–1740

Study the sources below and answer the questions which follow.

Source A: from a speech by Andrew Fletcher in the Scottish Parliament, 1703.

Since the Union of the Crowns, government ministers of England have ruined us by extending great lands and pensions to Scotsmen of the royal court to make them willing instruments of the English. The principal offices in the Scottish government are given to such men whom English ministers know will be submissive to their intentions. We appear to the rest of the world more like a conquered province than a free and independent people. It can be proved that the English court has bribed Scots so that they are now masters of us at our own cost. This is the cause of our poverty, misery and dependence upon England. We have been so long poor, miserable and dependent that we have neither the heart nor the courage to free ourselves.

Source B: from Paul Henderson Scott, *The Union of 1707* (2006).

As the terms of the treaty became known in November, there was an impressive reaction from all over the country, with a flood of Addresses to parliament from shires, Royal Burghs and parishes and all social classes. All of those Addresses were strongly opposed to the union and there was none in favour. This was a remarkable and unprecedented event which should be celebrated as a milestone in political history. There had been no previous instance of such a unanimous, peaceful and rational expression of the views of the people on an important political issue. It showed the strength of national feeling and widespread literacy and awareness of the issues in the union debate. The Addresses protested against the union as "contrary to the honour and independence of the Kingdom". This is especially remarkable at a time when democracy did not exist in any state and when it was widely held that people who were not landowners or Members of Parliament had no right to express views on matters of government policy.

Source C: from Christopher A. Whatley, *The Scots and the Union* (2006).

Ninety-plus Addresses against the union streamed into parliament over a period of just over eight weeks from the beginning of November. The similarity of much of the language in most of the Addresses suggests they were the result of a campaign by the Country party. Yet what is striking is that the very act of signing the Addresses indicates that the signatories had common concerns. The Addresses spoke in defence of Scotland's honour and independent sovereignty, as embodied in its parliament and the "fundamental laws and constitution of this kingdom". The Addresses reveal not only how widespread public opposition to union was but also much about its nature. Signatures were made on behalf of the illiterate, so we cannot be sure that those represented in the Addresses were fully aware of what was being said about the union on their behalf.

Source D: English agent, Daniel Defoe, reporting on the Treaty debates in the Scottish Parliament, 30 December 1706.

The surprise offer of the Equivalent compensation provided for shareholders of the Company had various effects on Scots people. The Darien investment was a dead weight upon many who had wanted their money returned. The money had been long spent, and generally speaking investors had abandoned themselves to despair and thought it to be lost forever. So entirely had they given up hope of reimbursement, that they would be willing to sell their stock at one tenth of its value once the union was concluded. However, after all this, to find that the whole amount would be returned with interest was a happy surprise to a great many, and took the edge off the opposition which some Scots would otherwise have expressed towards union. In particular, those in the Squadrone Volante will now be persuaded to vote in favour of union.

Source E: is from Murray G. H. Pittock, *Jacobitism* (1998).

By 1715, many patriotic Scots found themselves with nowhere to go other than the Jacobite cause if they wished to free Scotland from English domination. In support of this, James promised to "restore the Scottish Kingdom to its ancient, free and independent state". Opposition to the union was the single most important issue in Scottish domestic politics in 1715 and this opposition was strongly Jacobite. It was widely felt that the union had been a mistake: Scotland was dominated by English priorities as much as before 1707; Scotland was heavily taxed, with worse to come. Support for Jacobitism was the main means of expressing discontent in Scotland at that time. This can be seen as 16 of the 45 Scottish MPs were committed Jacobites, and the areas they represented provided a plentiful supply of troops in 1715.

[END OF SOURCES FOR THE TREATY OF UNION, 1689–1740]

SPECIAL TOPIC 3: THE TREATY OF UNION, 1689–1740

Answer *all* of the following questions.

Marks

1. How fully does **Source A** explain the reasons for worsening relations with England after 1690?
   Use the source and recalled knowledge.   **10**

2. To what extent do **Sources B** and **C** agree about attitudes towards union in Scotland?
   Compare the sources overall and in detail.   **5**

3. How useful is **Source D** as evidence of the passage of the Union through the Scottish parliament?
   In reaching a conclusion you should refer to:
   - *the origin and possible purpose of the source;*
   - *the content of the source;*
   - *recalled knowledge.*   **5**

4. How far does **Source E** explain the causes of the Jacobite Rising of 1715?
   Use the source and recalled knowledge.   **10**

                                                                                     (30)

[END OF QUESTIONS ON THE TREATY OF UNION, 1689–1740]

SPECIAL TOPIC 4: MIGRATION AND EMPIRE, 1830–1939

Study the sources below and answer the questions which follow.

Source A: from James Hunter, *Glencoe and the Indians* (1996).

Incessant rain had made it impossible for the population of the west coast to harvest the peat on which they depended for domestic fuel. In this extremity the poor people were, in some places, forced to burn their huts and cottages. They met and drew lots to decide which house was to be destroyed and afterwards in the same manner they decided which of their number was to maintain the poor family deprived of their home. In such situations, the crofts to which the mass of Highlanders had been driven as a result of earlier clearances had long since proved incapable of providing adequately for their occupants. Crofting families survived on a diet consisting largely of potatoes. When that crop failed, as it did regularly, hunger became a severe problem. Landlords, practically none of whom now felt any responsibility for the Highlander's fate, simply organised more evictions in order to create still more sheep farms. People thus deprived of their crofts had little alternative but to go elsewhere. Hundreds, even thousands, of evicted families consequently left each year for Canada.

Source B: from *The Ayr Advertiser*, 1849.

The Irish have been driven by the increasing poverty in their own country to emigrate to Scotland. By their hard work railways have been formed and new and important sources of wealth opened up. However, the Irish, during the past ten years, have absolutely inundated this country. They have also swallowed up our rapidly increasing Poor Rates, have directed charity away from its proper channels, and have filled our jails. By their greatest numbers they have lessened wages or totally deprived thousands of the working people of Scotland of that employment which legitimately belonged to them. Lastly, there can be no doubt that their contact with the Scotch has not been for the benefit morally or intellectually of the latter. Let us redouble our efforts not to keep Scotland for the Scotch, for that is impossible; but to keep Scotland—Scotch!

Source C: adapted from evidence about the poor in Edinburgh contained in the "Report on the State of the Irish Poor in Great Britain", 1836.

We are of the opinion that evils said to arise from Irish immigration have been considerably magnified. However, the wave of Irish immigration that washes over us each year should be restricted and this principally because the Catholic Irish who invade us are of a class which interferes materially with the wants and needs of the labouring poor, particularly in their dependence on adequate funds within the Poor Rates. In general, our own poor are far superior to the newcomers in point of sober and moral habits. We have no doubt that the work of this parish could be done, and the harvest got in, without the competition from Irish labourers whose presence forces down the wages to be earned from this work.

Source D: written by David Laing to his sister in Scotland, 19 February, 1873. Laing emigrated from Edinburgh and settled in Canada after he left the army.

Dear Sister, I have read your letter 20 times over since I received it. I am prospering in life now but I am so lonely. My health has not been so good since I arrived on these shores as part of our army all those years ago, but still I must work. The boys are all grown up men and are working on the same railway I do. I was promoted on the first of April, am foreman of a gang of 20 men receiving all the stores and material. We have 86 locomotive engines to keep in repair and 400 miles of rails to keep in good repair so that the produce of this land can reach the ports and then across the world. Our foremen are nearly all Scots and many of the working men also. I fear that without these men there would be no railway, no prosperity and no trade in this part of the world.

Source E: from Tom Devine, *The Scottish Nation 1700–2000* (2000).

The Italians in Scotland quickly became committed to the catering trade and brought new consumer delights to working class areas of Scotland. "Pokey hats" (ice cream cones) were always popular and fish suppers became the original fast food of the common man. Those chip shops and ice cream cafés also stayed open late into the evening, long after their Scottish competitors had closed for the night. They were a huge attraction for young people who wanted somewhere to meet away from the family home. These cafés attracted support from temperance groups who saw the ice cream parlours as a real and attractive alternative to the alcoholic temptations of the public house. The Italian community did not attract much hostility from native Scots because most Italians worked in family run businesses, kept close ties with their homeland and hoped to return there some day. Marriages were often kept within the Italian family network consequently there was limited assimilation or integration with native Scots.

[*END OF SOURCES FOR MIGRATION AND EMPIRE, 1830–1939*]

SPECIAL TOPIC 4: MIGRATION AND EMPIRE, 1830–1939

Marks

Answer *all* of the following questions.

1. How fully does **Source A** explain the reasons for the migration of Scots?
   Use the source and recalled knowledge.   **10**

2. To what extent do **Sources B** and **C** agree about the experience of Irish immigrants in Scotland?
   Compare the sources overall and in detail.   **5**

3. How useful is **Source D** as evidence of the impact of the contribution of Scots to the economic growth and development of the Empire?
   In reaching a conclusion you should refer to:
   • *the origin and possible purpose of the source;*
   • *the content of the source;*
   • *recalled knowledge.*   **5**

4. How far does **Source E** illustrate the social and cultural impact of immigrants on Scotland?
   Use the source and recalled knowledge.   **10**

    (30)

[*END OF QUESTIONS ON MIGRATION AND EMPIRE, 1830–1939*]

SPECIAL TOPIC 5: THE IMPACT OF THE GREAT WAR, 1914–1928

Study the sources below and answer the questions which follow.

Source A: A diary entry from *Private Moir of the Queen's Own Cameron Highlanders:*
Loos, September 29, 1915.

We were relieved on Sunday morning, after holding our own against the Germans repeated counter-attacks, but we were not out an hour when the lot that came in lost one of the trenches that we had taken. On Monday we had another charge and got the trench back before coming out of the trenches yesterday with about 70 or 80 of us surviving, out of the 1100 originals, "the pride of Scotland".

Sir John French came along just as we were leaving our old billets and he gave us a few words of praise. He told us he was proud to meet us, and congratulated us on our fine work. He told us we had done what Camerons liked to do, and what they always did; he never knew the Camerons to fail in anything they had ever put their hands to, and we, it seemed, were no exception to the rule. That was why he chose Camerons for his bodyguard.

Source B: from William Kenefick, *War Resisters and Anti-Conscription in Scotland:
an Independent Labour Party Perspective* (1999).

Scots responded in great numbers to the call to arms at the outbreak of war in 1914 and by December 1914, 25% of the male labour force of western Scotland had signed up. However it was being reported throughout the press from as early as October that the numbers enlisting were falling slightly. It seemed, according to the editors of *Forward* that "the Cannon fodder was rather backward in coming forward". There was a serious side to this issue as even a slight fall in recruitment meant that the topic of conscription was raised. If matters had been left to the Scottish press the decision to introduce compulsory military service would have been a foregone conclusion. The *Glasgow Herald* reported in December 1914 that if voluntarism did not work then conscription was the only alternative. The *Daily Record* ran similar articles promoting support for conscription. Despite the National Registration Act, recruitment levels fell to around 80,000 per month by January 1916 and conscription became a reality.

Source C: from Trevor Royle, *The Flowers of the Forest* (2007).

Within a day of the declaration of war, the recruiting office in Edinburgh's Cockburn Street was doing brisk business and, by the end of August 20,000 recruits had been processed. In Glasgow six thousand men enlisted over the very first weekend of war and from across Scotland came news of equally high figures. However, the number of volunteers began to fall off in 1915. There were increasing concerns that compulsory military service would be introduced and anti-conscription rallies had been held in Glasgow since the end of 1915, one meeting being addressed by committed anti-war protestors Sylvia Pankhurst and John MacLean. The National Registration Act of July 1915 required all persons to register for possible service which helped to maintain the Liberals' belief in the voluntary principle as most Scottish Liberal MPs were opposed to conscription. The national registration scheme however proved to be cumbersome and unworkable and recruitment continued to fall and, though long resisted, compulsory service became inevitable resulting in the Military Services Act of 1916.

Source D: from *Following the Fishing* accounts of Annie and James Watt who worked with the herring fishing fleets 1914–1920.

All the years that we worked, up till the end of the First World War, the price we got for a barrel of herring was 4 pence, this money was vital for many families. Thousands of barrels were shipped to Germany, Poland and Russia. Things were never as good with the herring after the war. The price went up to six pence for a time then they took it down to three pence. Costs had risen and the men couldn't pay for the gear, the fuel and the wage. Things were that bad that they couldn't pay us for gutting the herring so we went on strike.

One curer we worked for went broke. That was David Buchan. He was one of the richest curers in Peterhead. He'd a big house and everything, but he lost the lot. He'd plenty of money owed to him, but it was all in Germany or in Russia!

Source E: from Ewen A. Cameron, *Impaled Upon a Thistle: Scotland Since 1880* (2010).

Broad movements in Scottish political culture favoured the Unionists. Both the *Glasgow Herald* and the *Scotsman* were Unionist and many local newspapers had also abandoned Liberalism. The Unionists even considered giving financial support to local newspapers to bolster the party's message. More important was the shift to the political right by the Presbyterian church leadership in the 1920s. This is clear in attitudes towards the first Labour Government, the General Strike and the expression of racist views towards Scotland's Irish community. The enfranchisement of women has also been seen as favourable to the Conservatives. The women enfranchised in 1918 were older, over thirty, and reasonably well off. Conservatives paid a great deal of attention to wooing this group and were much more fearful of the equal franchise of 1928 with its inclusion of younger, unmarried women in the electorate.

[*END OF SOURCES FOR THE IMPACT OF THE GREAT WAR, 1914–1928*]

SPECIAL TOPIC 5: THE IMPACT OF THE GREAT WAR, 1914–1928

Marks

Answer *all* of the following questions.

1. How fully does **Source A** describe the involvement of Scots on the Western Front?
   Use the source and recalled knowledge.   **10**

2. To what extent do **Sources B** and **C** agree about recruitment and conscription in Scotland?
   Compare the content overall and in detail.   **5**

3. How useful is **Source D** as evidence of the economic difficulties faced by Scotland after 1918?
   In reaching a conclusion you should refer to:
   • *the origin and possible purpose of the source;*
   • *the content of the source;*
   • *recalled knowledge.*   **5**

4. How far does **Source E** explain the strength of support for unionism in Scotland?
   Use the source and recalled knowledge.   **10**

                                                                              (30)

[*END OF QUESTIONS ON THE IMPACT OF THE GREAT WAR, 1914–1928*]

[*END OF QUESTION PAPER*]

[BLANK PAGE]

HIGHER

2014

[BLANK PAGE]

X259/12/01

NATIONAL
QUALIFICATIONS
2014

WEDNESDAY, 7 MAY
1.00 PM – 2.20 PM

HISTORY
HIGHER
Paper 1

Candidates should answer **two** questions, **one** from Historical Study: British History and **one** from Historical Study: European and World History.

All questions are worth 20 marks.

[BLANK PAGE]

HISTORICAL STUDY: BRITISH HISTORY

Answer ONE question. Each question is worth 20 marks.

Church, State and Feudal Society

1. "The landed class was the most important feature of feudal society." How valid is this view?

2. To what extent had the power of the Church declined by the end of the fourteenth century?

3. How important was the need to develop the economy in David I's and Henry II's attempts to centralise royal power in Scotland and England?

The Century of Revolutions 1603–1702

4. How significant were economic issues in the growing challenge to the authority of James I in England?

5. How important were political issues as a cause of the English Civil War?

6. "Cromwell's dominance was the main reason for the failure to find an alternative form of government, 1649-1658." How valid is this view?

The Atlantic Slave Trade

7. How significant were religious factors in the development of the slave trade?

8. "Financial considerations were the most important factor in the treatment of slaves." How valid is this view?

9. To what extent did the slave trade have a major impact on West African society?

Britain 1851–1951

10. "Britain became more democratic between 1851 and 1928 due to the effects of industrialisation and urbanisation." How valid is this view?

11. How significant was the militant Suffragette campaign in helping women achieve the vote?

12. How important were fears over national security as a reason why the Liberal Government introduced social welfare reforms, 1906–1914?

Britain and Ireland 1900–1985

13. How important were the Unionist and Nationalist responses to the Home Rule Bill for the growth of tension in Ireland up to 1914?

14. How significant were IRA tactics and policies as an obstacle to peace, up to the Anglo-Irish Treaty, 1918–1921?

15. "The role played by de Valera meant that the Irish Civil War was inevitable." How valid is this view?

HISTORICAL STUDY: EUROPEAN AND WORLD

Answer ONE question. Each question is worth 20 marks.

The Crusades, 1071–1204

16. How important was the threat to the Byzantine Empire as a reason for the calling of the First Crusade?

17. To what extent was the success of the First Crusade due to Muslim misunderstanding of the Crusaders' intentions?

18. "The lack of resources of the Christian states explains the fall of Jerusalem in 1187." How valid is this view?

The American Revolution 1763–1787

19. How important was the role of George III in the development of threats to the British position in North America by 1763?

20. "The views of the Earl of Chatham represented British people's opinion on the conflict with America." How valid is this view?

21. To what extent was the American War of Independence global in nature?

The French Revolution, to 1799

22. To what extent was corruption the main threat to the security of the Ancien Régime before 1789?

23. How important was the outbreak of war in 1792 in bringing about the end of the constitutional monarchy in France?

24. "The role of Robespierre was the key factor leading to the Terror." How valid is this view?

Germany 1815–1939

25. How important was the Zollverein in the growth of German nationalism between 1815 and 1850?

26. "The German princes were the most important obstacle to German unification before 1850." How valid is this view?

27. To what extent was Prussian military strength the main reason for German unification being achieved by 1871?

Italy 1815–1939

28. How important was resentment of Austria in the growth of Italian nationalism before 1850?

29. To what extent were divisions among the nationalists the main obstacle to Italian unification between 1815 and 1850?

30. How important was the role of Cavour in the creation of a united Italy by 1870?

Russia 1881–1921

31. "The authority of the Tsarist state was never seriously challenged in the years before 1905." How valid is this view?

32. How successful was the Tsar in strengthening his authority between 1905 and 1914?

33. How important was the impact of the First World War in bringing about the February Revolution, 1917?

USA 1918–1968

34. How important was fear of revolution as a reason for changing attitudes towards immigration in the 1920s?

35. To what extent was the saturation of the US market to blame for the economic crisis of 1929–1933?

36. How successful was the New Deal in dealing with America's problems in the 1930s?

Appeasement and the Road to War, to 1939

37. To what extent did the weakness of the League of Nations encourage the aggressive nature of Fascist foreign policies in the 1930s?

38. How important were changing attitudes to the Paris Peace Settlement as a reason for the British policy of appeasement between 1936 and 1938?

39. How successful was Britain in containing Fascist aggression between 1935 and March 1938?

The Cold War 1945–1989

40. How important was the crisis over Korea in the emergence of the Cold War up to 1955?

41. How significant were domestic pressures on Kennedy in explaining the Cuban Crisis of 1962?

42. "Changing public opinion in the USA was the main reason why America lost the Vietnam War." How valid is this view?

[END OF QUESTION PAPER]

[BLANK PAGE]

X259/12/02

NATIONAL
QUALIFICATIONS
2014

WEDNESDAY, 7 MAY
2.40 PM – 4.05 PM

HISTORY
HIGHER
Paper 2

Answer questions on only **one** Special Topic.

Take particular care to show clearly the Special Topic chosen. On the **front** of the answer book, **in the top right-hand corner**, write the number of the Special Topic.

You are expected to use background knowledge appropriately in answering source-based questions.

Some sources have been adapted.

SPECIAL TOPIC 1: THE WARS OF INDEPENDENCE, 1286–1328

Study the sources below and answer the questions which follow.

Source A: from Amanda Beam, *The Balliol Dynasty, 1210–1364* (2008).

In April 1291, various 'barons and ladies of the Northern counties' were summoned to meet Edward I at Norham on 3rd June, 'with horses and arms', including Edmund, the King's brother, John de Warenne, John Balliol, Robert Bruce, Gilbert de Umfraville, John Comyn of Buchan and Alexander de Balliol. This meeting signified the opening of the judicial process leading up to the Great Cause. The Scots initially refused to cross the border into Norham, instead remaining just across the water at Upsetlington, in an attempt to prove to Edward that they would not accept his authority. On 10th May, Roger Brabazon, one of Edward's justices, addressed the Scots gathered at Norham. At this meeting, the Bishop of Glasgow, Robert Wishart, made a strong protest, provoking Edward's threat that if denied, he would direct the English Army at Norham against the Scots. Yet, the claimants eventually accepted the English King as overlord, out of fear of war against them as well as the general assumption that it was necessary to resolve their problems.

Source B: *The Chronicle of Lanercost*, the work of the canons of Lanercost Priory, 1272–1346.

In 1295, as the story goes, the Scots were unsuccessful in making John defy Edward, so they chose instead to replace his authority as King with a council of twelve peers. The Scots craftily sent envoys to the King of France to conspire against their lord, King Edward of England. The envoys took with them advisers, endeavouring to bring about war with England. After the report had reached the ears of my lord the King of England, he was very angry, and he commanded to the King of Scotland, to attend his parliament in accordance with his legal obligation both for the kingdom of Scotland and for lands owned by him within the English realm. But King John utterly refused to attend, and, which was worse, began assembling a large army to withstand the King of England. Hearing of this the King of England sent an expedition against the Scottish King, invading at Berwick.

Source C: Lubeck Letter, 1297, Wallace and Murray issued this letter, informing European trading partners that Scottish ports were open for business once again.

Andrew Murray and William Wallace, leaders of the army of resistance in the Kingdom of Scotland, and the community of the same kingdom send greetings and wishes of sincere friendship. The message is intended for their worthy and beloved friends the mayors and citizens of Lubeck and Hamburg, greeting and increase always of sincere friendship. Trustworthy merchants of the said Kingdom of Scotland that you by your own goodwill are giving advice, help and favour, in our struggle against the English, in all causes and business concerning trade with Scotland. We are grateful to you and give thanks. Therefore, in return we ask that it be made known among your merchants that they will now have secure and safe access to all ports of Scotland. The kingdom of Scotland, thanks be to God, has been recovered from the power of the English by force of arms. Written at Haddington, on the 11th day of October, in the year of grace, one thousand two hundred and ninety seven. The letter is written in the name of Lord John, illustrious King of Scotland, by agreement of the community of the realm, in whom we fight for.

Source D: from Ronald McNair Scott, *Robert the Bruce, King of Scots* (1993).

Robert Bruce had no wish to prolong the war. He saw his victory, above all, as an opportunity for reconciliation and peace: with the Scottish nobles who had fought against him, with the English whom he had defeated. Soon after Bannockburn many Scottish barons and knights who had served under the two Edwards offered to him their allegiance and were received into his peace. In November 1314 Bruce with increased confidence, convened a Parliament at Cambuskenneth. The Parliament adjudged that all Scottish landowners who had failed to offer allegiance by that date should be disinherited. His sole aim was that those who wished to regain their Scottish lands must do homage to him alone. They could no longer be feudatories in two countries and serve two kings. They must choose their nationality once and for all.

Source E: from Raymond Campbell Paterson, *For the Lion, A History of the Scottish Wars of Independence, 1296–1357* (1996).

Few battles in history are truly decisive, and Bannockburn was no exception. The war was nowhere near an end, the military campaign would continue, despite Bruce's hopes for peace. However, in the November, after the battle, Bruce was ready to take the next step. The Scots Parliament met at Cambuskenneth Abbey. The Parliament passed sentence that all who held land in Scotland, but continued to fight against the King, would lose their lands. Landowners could no longer have divided political loyalties: they had to choose one side or the other. The new class of the "disinherited" were men on the English side, usually with Comyn and Balliol associations, who refused to accept the new realities; men in other words, who wished to remain loyal to the King of England but continue to hold estates and titles in Scotland.

[END OF SOURCES FOR THE WARS OF INDEPENDENCE, 1286–1328]

SPECIAL TOPIC 1: THE WARS OF INDEPENDENCE, 1286–1328

Marks

Answer *all* of the following questions.

1. How far does **Source A** explain Edward's resolution of the Great Cause?
   Use the source and recalled knowledge. **10**

2. How useful is **Source B** as evidence of John Balliol's difficulties in ruling Scotland 1292–1296?
   In reaching a conclusion you should refer to:
   * *the origin and possible purpose of the source;*
   * *the content of the source;*
   * *recalled knowledge.* **5**

3. How fully does **Source C** illustrate Scottish resistance to Edward I, 1296–1305?
   Use the source and recalled knowledge. **10**

4. To what extent do **Sources D** and **E** agree about the ambitions of Robert the Bruce?
   Compare the sources overall and in detail. **5**

   (30)

[END OF QUESTIONS ON THE WARS OF INDEPENDENCE, 1286–1328]

SPECIAL TOPIC 2: THE AGE OF REFORMATION, 1542–1603

Study the sources below and answer the questions which follow.

Source A: from Michael Lynch, *Scotland, A New History*, (1992).

The pre-Reformation Church was a patchwork of existing faults and new initiatives. The health of the religious orders—monks, canons and friars—tended to vary from one order to another and from one religious house to another. The monasteries were criticised as being out of touch with the needs of sixteenth century society. Arguably monasteries survived only as property owning businesses and played hardly any part in the Reformation. If there was a monastic crisis, it was one of economics rather than one of religion. All were faced with the same economic pressures—such as huge tax demands—which forced them to rent out monastic property to help them survive. The sixteenth century search for reform established a cycle of poverty from which there was little escape. To increase their income, parish priests resorted to pluralism or imposed unpopular charges on their parishioners.

Source B: from *The Memoirs of the Earl of Bothwell*, January, 1568.

Having repeatedly denied involvement in the death of Lord Darnley, I found my enemies to be so strong that I gathered an army. At Carberry Hill those enemies, the Confederate Lords, made out that they had been sent to offer the Queen genuine loyalty and safe-conduct which she foolishly believed. She trusted that this promise would be honoured by the two armies and asked me to return to Dunbar with my army, where she would shortly come to find me. I left her there, leaning on the faith and promise which the Lords had given her in word and in letters. Yet, it seems their intention was unjustly to challenge the authority and power of the Queen and take over her Realm. She was then taken to Edinburgh Castle. The following day they moved her to another castle located on a small island named Lochleven, to make sure that she would not be able to warn me or receive word from me, and also for fear that I would attempt to release her from that castle.

Source C: from Ralph A. Houlbrooke (ed.), *James VI and I: Ideas, Authority and Government*, (2006).

Although James had a Protestant education, the Kirk remained suspicious of the king. James's ideas about church and state did not improve the situation: his firm belief that kings should have control over the church led to a powerful struggle which was present under the surface throughout his reign erupting into open conflict at regular intervals. To make matters worse, James tended to openly favour Catholic noblemen. Although for James himself this may have been a matter of personal loyalty rather than religion, the Kirk and the Presbyterian faction amongst the nobility saw things differently. However, by the late 1580s the relationship with the Kirk improved. Following the publication of his religious ideas in 1588 and 1589, there was a brief period of harmony between himself and his Protestant subjects. At the General Assembly of June 1590 he even described the Scottish Presbyterian Church as the "sincerest Kirk in the world".

Source D: from J McCallum, *Reforming the Scottish Parish*, (2010).

The year 1560 is one of the most famous milestones in Scottish history, because things could begin to change. However, the parish churches which emerged from the Reformation achieved much of what had been aimed for in the early 1560s in preaching, worship, ministry and discipline. Protestant ministers appointed to parishes were well educated, enjoyed career stability and were only rarely disciplined for any moral failings. Ministers and elders imposed a strict programme of discipline for minor offences such as drunkenness and there was surprisingly little hostility to this. Evidence suggests that people accepted the need for this disciplinary system even though they were not always so content when they were the ones to have offended. There are also signs of a strong religious culture, and the role of psalm, prayer and in some cases poetry and song were important in spreading Protestant doctrines and values.

Source E: from Archbishop John Spottiswoode, *The History of the Church of Scotland*, (circa 1600).

In the Reformed church, ministers must be educated and godly and appointed following election, examination and admission. If a minister does not look after his congregation he should be punished. The Church of God cannot exist without discipline. For faults such as drunkenness, fighting and common swearing, the offender must be called before the minister, elders and deacons and admit to his sin. Individuals who accept discipline must appear before the whole church to repent, before being received again into the society of the church. Every year individuals must stand before their minister and elders to give confession to their faith, rehearse the Commandments of the Law with the Lord's Prayer and declare their understanding in those things. All persons should be encouraged to learn the Psalms and when the Psalms are sung, they may be the more able with common heart and voice to praise God.

[END OF SOURCES FOR THE AGE OF REFORMATION, 1542–1603]

SPECIAL TOPIC 2: THE AGE OF REFORMATION, 1542–1603

Marks

Answer *all* of the following questions.

1. How far does **Source A** explain the weakness of the Catholic Church in Scotland?
   Use the source and recalled knowledge.   **10**

2. How useful is **Source B** in explaining the contribution Mary, Queen of Scots made to the loss of her throne?
   In reaching a conclusion you should refer to:
   * *the origin and possible purpose of the source;*
   * *the content of the source;*
   * *recalled knowledge.*   **5**

3. How fully does **Source C** explain the relationship between monarch and Kirk in the reign of James VI?
   Use the source and recalled knowledge.   **10**

4. To what extent do **Sources D** and **E** agree about the impact of the Reformation?
   Compare the sources overall and in detail.   **5**

    (30)

[END OF QUESTIONS ON THE AGE OF REFORMATION, 1542–1603]

SPECIAL TOPIC 3: THE TREATY OF UNION, 1689–1740

Study the sources below and answer the questions which follow.

Source A: from J. D. Mackie, *A History of Scotland* (1977).

In 1701 the English parliament passed the Act of Settlement which stated that, if Anne died with no heirs, the succession would pass to the house of Hanover. Members of the Scottish parliament passed two acts in 1703 which did not improve the relations between the two countries. The Act anent Peace and War stated that no successor of Queen Anne should declare a war involving Scotland without consulting the Scottish parliament. The Act of Security stated that the Scottish parliament would name Anne's successor, who would not be the person named by the English parliament unless under conditions which guaranteed Scottish freedom of government, trade and religion. In 1705 the English parliament passed the Alien Act which threatened that, unless Scotland accepted the Hanoverian succession, Scots would be treated as aliens in England, which would severely harm Scottish trade. The task of the Scottish government was not easy, as the Court party was opposed by the Country party and the Jacobites.

Source B: from the Address of Dunbar Town Council to the Scottish parliament, 18th November 1706.

The shipmasters, fishermen and inhabitants of Dunbar cannot emphasise enough the damaging effect of the Treaty of Union and its present Articles in their current form. Since the treaty will disallow foreigners from owning British ships, it will ruin and destroy this town's trade with the Dutch and other overseas merchants who part-own virtually all of our ships. In addition, the proposal for the tax on salt in Scotland to rise as high as it is in England will bring an end to the salt-manufacturing industry upon which so many people in this and other coastal districts depend. Misery will be inflicted on our burgh, not to mention the loss of commerce, as well as prejudice towards the fishing trade of the whole nation. We calculate that the treaty will pass through parliament, in which case we desire that our interests are secured.

Source C: from the Act of Security for the Kirk, 1706.

Her Majesty Queen Anne, with the advice and consent of the parliament of Scotland, hereby establishes and confirms the true Protestant religion for Scotland, and hereafter the monarch shall defend the security of the Kirk. The worship and government of this Protestant Kirk shall continue without any alteration in all future generations. More especially, Her Majesty approves and forever confirms the settlement of Presbyterian church government in Scotland. It is now established by law that all professors, masters and office bearers of the universities of St. Andrews, Glasgow, Aberdeen and Edinburgh should be members of the Church of Scotland. Masters in the colleges and schools in this kingdom shall be members of the Church of Scotland. Her Majesty, with advice and consent, hereby confirms the act of the first parliament of King William and Queen Mary in the year of 1690 confirming the Presbyterian church government.

Source D: from A. MacInnes, *Union and Empire* (2007).

The immediate reaction to union in Scotland was far from favourable, with growing resentment at breaches in the spirit of the treaty and delays in paying the Equivalent. Increased duties and an attempt to impose the malt tax led to an effort by Scottish MPs to reverse the union in 1713, and their proposal was hotly debated in parliament. However the union survived and endured, as Scottish landowners and merchants realised that Empire presented them with a golden opportunity for personal advancement and learned the ways of enterprise. Association with England's military force allowed for continuing prosperity and free access to the largest commercial market then on offer. Overseas trade opened up opportunities for Scots through colonies.

Source E: from T. M. Devine, *Scotland and the Union* (2008).

Undeniably, as a result of union, Scotland was faced with an increased tax burden after 1707, most notoriously in 1711 with the salt and linen taxes. Customs records show increasing amounts of cases of intimidation and violent assaults on customs officers. Nevertheless, the possibilities of union were fundamental, presenting the Scottish landed elites with a golden opportunity. The benefit of English naval protection for trade with America was obvious. Employment of Scots in colonial trade became a crucial lifeline. In the decades after union, streams of eager Caledonians from impoverished backgrounds poured into British colonies at every point from Canada to Bengal. Career openings were greater than before and Scots were very keen to exploit them.

[END OF SOURCES FOR THE TREATY OF UNION, 1689–1740]

SPECIAL TOPIC 3: THE TREATY OF UNION, 1689–1740

Marks

Answer *all* of the following questions.

1. How far does **Source A** explain the relationship between the Scottish Parliament and England?
   Use the source and recalled knowledge.   **10**

2. How useful is **Source B** as evidence of attitudes towards union in Scotland?
   In reaching a conclusion you should refer to:
   • *the origin and possible purpose of the source;*
   • *the content of the source;*
   • *recalled knowledge.*   **5**

3. How fully does **Source C** explain the reasons for the passing of the Treaty of Union?
   Use the source and recalled knowledge.   **10**

4. To what extent do **Sources D** and **E** agree about the economic effects of Union up to 1740?
   Compare the sources overall and in detail.   **5**

                                                                                                                   (30)

[END OF QUESTIONS ON THE TREATY OF UNION, 1689–1740]

SPECIAL TOPIC 4: MIGRATION AND EMPIRE, 1830–1939

Study the sources below and answer the questions which follow.

Source A: from Old Statistical Account (Banffshire, Moray and Nairnshire) 1840.

Some individuals from these parts went to North America, a few of whom returned and settled at home bringing bad news of the country which their imaginings had favoured to be the fairy land of wealth. Since that time those who would have gone to America, had the prospects been favourable, have preferred a home migration to the southern parts of Scotland. They preferred Glasgow and Paisley where the textile mills cry out for more workers. From this part of the north there is and always has been a constant pressure through lack of land and money. That pressure was lessened by the employment given in lowland farms during the harvest. From other places, those people made homeless by the arrival of sheep or from farming changes that need less folk to work have become adventurers reaching for wealth in the British capital, the East and West Indies and other parts of the Empire.

Source B: from the Scottish Jewish Archives Centre. Testimony given by Alec Bernstein, a first-generation Scot born to an immigrant family.

I was born in Ayr on 24th June 1911 and in Ayr at that time there were about nine Jewish families in all. My father's full name was Philip Bernstein; he came from Skood in Russia. My mother came from Weidz in Russia near Vilna. They must have come here at the turn of the century. When I went to school I was the only Jewish kid in class, in fact I was the only Jewish kid in the school. And at that time, during the Great War, I was knocked around a lot. The kids used to crowd around me, pinch my lunch from me and shout "You German Jew, you German Jew" (even though I was of Russian descent). As a result my life was miserable there. It made me a very timid child. My full name is Isaac. When I was 14, I went to work in a warehouse and the Jewish manager there said "That's some name you've got. We'll call you Alec from now on". So since I was 14 I've been called Alec.

Source C: from Owen Dudley Edwards, *North America, The Scottish Contribution* (1984).

To think of Canada as Greater Scotland makes little sense in terms of the population—Scots accounted for less than 1/6 of the population in 1871—but it would be hard to find another country where the imprint of the immigrant Scot has been so firmly established on an entire country. Scots dominated Canadian politics. Sir John MacDonald, Glasgow born, was the father of the Canadian Confederation and the first Prime Minister. Scots were also important in the development of journalism with the influential Toronto Globe newspaper founded and ruled by Scotsman George Brown. The Scottish hold on the Canadian imagination is reinforced by the high number of figures of Scottish origin who became legends of the Great Western expansion. The names of Sir Alexander Mackenzie and Simon Fraser are remembered in the Mackenzie and Fraser rivers. Finally, the symbolic achievement in the conquest of the west was achieved when Donald Smith, one of the founders of the Canadian Pacific Railway, completed the railway in a ceremony at Eagle Pass in 1875. The spot was thereafter known as Craigellachie, in memory of where Smith was born in Scotland.

Source D from Christopher Whatley, *Jam, Jute and Journalism* (1984).

For a time Dundee could boast the title Juteopolis, the jute capital of the world, exporting to the world and especially the Empire. World demand for the linen and jute textiles made in Dundee rose sharply in the 19th century. As world trade with the Empire expanded so did demand for jute sacks for corn, wool, fertilisers and other bulk goods. By the 1860s the Camperdown factory at Lochee was the world's largest jute factory. These were great days for the city's jute and linen barons such as the Baxter Brothers and the Gilroys. They made great fortunes from the growing trade, some of which were devoted to the construction of big mansions on the outskirts of the city in West Ferry and Broughty Ferry. Their money was also used to purchase great country estates further away from Dundee. Although jute imports peaked in 1902 the profit levels of the 1860s were never matched. Competition was growing from Indian jute mills. The First World War brought a temporary boom to Dundee's jute mills but after the war the advantages of Empire trade that had made Dundee boom now deserted the town.

Source E: from Simon Wood, *Migration and Empire 1830–1939* (2011).

Dundee developed a way of turning jute fibre from Bengal into a useable cloth. As a result a handful of families made huge profits exporting jute sacking to the Empire. The display of their wealth and confidence can be seen in the growth of elegant suburbs such as at Broughty Ferry near Dundee. Money from the Empire also helped some landed families who were struggling in Scotland's rural economy. For example, money from the Indian textile trade was used by Alisdair Forbes to purchase and improve country estates in the Strathdon area. However, once the Empire developed its own industries, they became serious competitors for Scottish producers. The First World War saw a boom in Scottish industry. Dundee's jute mills worked hard producing sand bags as well as tent material. However, even by 1914 Bengal jute mills were making huge profits. Prices for jute fell after the war and employment levels in the jute industry in Scotland fell between 1929 and 1939.

[*END OF SOURCES FOR MIGRATION AND EMPIRE, 1830–1939*]

SPECIAL TOPIC 4: MIGRATION AND EMPIRE, 1830–1939

Marks

Answer *all* of the following questions.

1. How far does **Source A** show the reasons for internal migration within Scotland?
    Use the source and recalled knowledge.   **10**

2. How useful is **Source B** as evidence of relations between native Scots and immigrants?
    In reaching a conclusion you should refer to:
    *   *the origin and possible purpose of the source;*
    *   *the content of the source;*
    *   *recalled knowledge.*   **5**

3. How fully does **Source C** illustrate the impact of Scots emigrants upon the Empire?
    Use the source and recalled knowledge.   **10**

4. To what extent do **Sources D** and **E** agree about the impact of the Empire on Scotland?
    Compare the sources overall and in detail.   **5**

                                                                                            (30)

[*END OF QUESTIONS ON MIGRATION AND EMPIRE, 1830–1939*]

SPECIAL TOPIC 5: THE IMPACT OF THE GREAT WAR, 1914–1928

Study the sources below and answer the questions which follow.

Source A: from a letter sent by Sir Douglas Haig, Earl of Bemersyde, in 1922 which was read at the memorial to the 16th (Service) Battalion Royal Scots.

To all ranks of the Army I commanded, I owe a debt which I can never sufficiently acknowledge. Yet, as a Scotsman, I need to honour the huge contribution made by Scots in the war. I have a special sympathy for those who mourn our countless thousands of Scottish dead. I am grateful for this opportunity to express my thanks to the officers and men of the gallant battalion that Sir George McCrae so loyally helped to raise in 1914. As the commander of our Army in its first great offensive battle (the Somme), I can pay a special tribute to this Scottish regiment, which on 1st July 1916 suffered such heavy loss and served its country so well. The thought that Scotsmen served our country truly and well offers some consolation for the loss of our comrades and friends.

Source B: from an article in *The Daily Telegraph*, 1916 written by the journalist Rebecca West about the Gretna munitions workers.

The 250 girls work a twelve-hour shift before returning to the barracks where they live two miles away. The girls who take up this work sacrifice almost as much as men who enlist and have to be ready to face an emergency, for example only two days ago an explosion of air with chemicals ignited the cordite. Two huts were gutted, and one girl lost a hand. Surely, never before can women have lived lives so completely similar to that of the regular army. They face more danger every day than any soldier on home defence has seen since the beginning of the war. It is because of this army of cheerful and disciplined workers that this cordite factory has been able to increase its output since the beginning of the war by something over 1500 per cent; the country owes them a great debt.

Source C: from T.M. Devine, C.H. Lee and G.C. Peden, *The Transformation of Scotland* (*The Economy since 1700*), (2005).

The Scottish economy was devastated by four years of war; overseas trade had been disrupted and was very slow to recover. Those who returned from war faced many difficulties. Employment prospects in agriculture, fishing and the heavy industries were poor with unemployment levels growing during the 1920s. The Land Settlement (Scotland) Act in 1919 produced more funds for land settlement but the shortage of available land in the Highlands and Islands remained a problem and land raids continued. So with high unemployment, low wages and a shortage of available land to farm, thousands of Scots made the decision to emigrate to build a new life in the colonies. They were helped in making their decision as the Overseas Settlement Committee, set up in 1921 with government support, provided assistance to people wanting to emigrate and granted free passage to ex-servicemen and women until the end of December 1922.

Source D: from "*The Strike Bulletin*", February 1st 1919.

The strikers were being addressed by the Strike Committee until their leaders returned from meeting the Lord Provost. The strike leaders were kept waiting in the City Chambers and the police were ordered to draw their batons and forcibly disperse the crowd waiting in George Square. On hearing the sounds of conflict the strike leaders rushed out to help restore order with Willie Gallacher (of the Clyde Workers' Committee) urging the crowd to disperse peacefully. But, instead of listening, the police made an attack on them and Davie Kirkwood (of the Clyde Workers' Committee) was thrown to the ground. The outrage looks like a prearranged affair with the attack on the strikers being deliberately planned and ordered. The government, afraid to do their own dirty work, employed the police to do it for them. This was sheer brutality by the police and January 31st 1919 will be known in Glasgow as Bloody Friday.

Source E from William Ferguson *"Scotland 1689 to the Present"* (1968).

The violence was touched off by the outnumbered and understandably nervous police who charged with batons raised to try to clear the tramlines. It continued with blows landing indiscriminately on both strikers and curious bystanders. Gallacher's horrified reaction was to try to get the crowd to disperse. Kirkwood was trying to pacify the crowd when he was beaten to the ground by police truncheons. He was later able to provide photographic evidence of this and was found not guilty while William Gallacher and Emanuel Shinwell were each sentenced to five months imprisonment for "incitement to riot". However, the "riot" in George Square was not planned; the situation was simply misread and violence erupted, but not because of a revolutionary plot. Thousands of people had been brought together through fears of unemployment and high prices but the government, plagued by fears of communism, seems to have taken the possibility of revolution seriously.

[*END OF SOURCES FOR THE IMPACT OF THE GREAT WAR, 1914–1928*]

SPECIAL TOPIC 5: THE IMPACT OF THE GREAT WAR, 1914–1928

Marks

Answer *all* of the following questions.

1. How far does **Source A** explain the contribution of Scots to the military effort on the Western Front?
    Use the source and recalled knowledge.   **10**

2. How useful is **Source B** as evidence of the impact of the war on Scottish women?
    In reaching a conclusion you should refer to:
    *   *the origin and possible purpose of the source;*
    *   *the content of the source;*
    *   *recalled knowledge.*   **5**

3. How fully does **Source C** describe the impact of the war on the Scottish economy between 1914 and 1928?
    Use the source and recalled knowledge.   **10**

4. To what extent do **Sources D** and **E** agree about the events of "Red Clydeside" in 1919?
    Compare the content overall and in detail.   **5**

                                                                                                                (30)

[*END OF QUESTIONS ON THE IMPACT OF THE GREAT WAR, 1914–1928*]

[*END OF QUESTION PAPER*]

[BLANK PAGE]

HIGHER HISTORY PAPER 1
2012

1. Each question is marked out of 20.

2. In Paper 1 candidates will be rewarded according to:

   (a) **Knowledge and Understanding – 6 marks are allocated for** the relevant knowledge they use to address the question. Marks will be awarded for each accurate, full point they make; these points may be further developed, as in the following example, relating to the effectiveness of the Liberal Reforms:

   Old age pensions *(0 marks for stating this)* **were given to all people over 70** *(1 mark)*; **married couples received 7/6 and single people 5s** *(a second mark for knowledge)*. **This provision was not enough to live on, but old people were able to help pay their families if they lived with them** *(no further mark for knowledge, but an argument which would receive credit under the category Argument and Evaluation).*

   (b) **Argument/Evaluation – 10 marks are allocated for** the quality of thought revealed in their answers by the arguments and evaluation demonstrated. This should be taken as including the extent to which the candidate:

   - gives an answer which is relevant to the question and relates explicitly to the question's terms;
   - argues a case;
   - makes the various distinctions required by the question;
   - responds to all the elements in the question, and to any isolated factor in particular;
   - explains, analyses, debates and assesses rather than simply describes or narrates;
   - answers with clarity and fluency and in language appropriate to historical writing at this level.

   (c) **Structure – 4 marks are allocated for** the appropriateness of the introduction and conclusion, according to the degree to which the response

   - establishes the context of the question, line of argument and the relevant factors to be considered in the introduction
   - responds to the question in the form of a balanced conclusion based on the evidence and arguments deployed.

3. The following descriptions provide additional guidance on the marks awarded to essays displaying various characteristics. Many essays will exhibit some, but not all, of the features listed; others will be stronger in one area than another.

KNOWLEDGE – Up to 6 marks can be awarded
These are for substantive points and points further developed which are relevant and accurate.

STRUCTURE – Up to 4 marks can be awarded if:
The introduction clearly sets the issue in its wider context, indicates relevant factors and demonstrates a solid line of argument.
The conclusion is balanced, summarising the arguments and coming to an overall judgement directly related to the question.

ARGUMENT – Up to 10 marks can be awarded if:
The evidence is integrated into a sustained analysis.
The argument is sustained and balanced, with some awareness of alternative interpretations and/or historical debate.

Historical Study: British History

Church, State and Feudal Society

1. The candidate assesses the extent to which the contribution of the Church to society in medieval Scotland and England was confined to religion, using evidence and arguments such as:

Religious Role
- The medieval church offered the people the hope of salvation. The Church promised that in the afterlife things would improve, assuming that your soul was pure and free of sin This offered a certain amount of social control but offered comfort and stability, providing answers to difficult questions
- Church services such as christenings, marriages and burials were an important part of everyday life. The Church also celebrated holy days
- Religion offered a certain amount of understanding about the world. The existence of God helped to explain not only how the world worked but in a society without the benefit of science, the unexplained could often be frightening
- The importance of saints, relics and pilgrimages not only reinforced the power of God, but pilgrimage especially provided a way of opening new horizons and helping expand medieval Europe and trade
- Monasteries provided hope for a greater salvation through a life of prayer and devotion.

Social Role
- The Church often provided alms to the poor, offering the only real poor relief available
- The Church provided basic education for lay people, notably sons and daughters of nobility. The Church, particularly the monasteries, helped develop architecture, art and music. Universities provided degrees in theology, medicine and arts
- Church hospitals provided free medical care, especially for lepers
- The Church provided a social centre for rural and urban life; games and music were common after Sunday services.

Economic Role
- Monasteries made significant contributions to the economic development of the 12th century
- They helped to cultivate many barren areas of England and Scotland
- Some monasteries helped to fund and maintain important trades, such as the wool trade in Scotland.

Political Role
- The Church legitimised monarchs
- The papacy was a European power, able to influence other monarchs through the threat of excommunication and interdict
- Monarchs required the help of the clerics to run the government, count taxes and write laws
- In England the church was part of the feudal structure, able to raise armies to defend their lands, as the Bishop of Durham did at the Battle of the Standard in 1138.

2. The candidate assesses how successful David I of Scotland and Henry II of England's attempts to increase royal authority were, using evidence and arguments such as:

Development of royal authority
- Henry II faced a kingdom in turmoil after the civil war
- Bands of mercenaries roamed through the countryside, until Henry dismissed them
- English Barons had seized land, castles and taxes that they were not entitled to
- Henry successfully reformed criminal and civil law in England, through the Assizes of Clarendon (1166) and Northampton (1176). However, his attempt to reform ecclesiastical law was less successful
- David I was faced with several rebellions, the first in 1130, only six years after his inauguration
- New Scottish barons were given the rights to hold their own courts within their fiefs. This was an obvious extension of the king's law, rather than reliance on the traditional Celtic courts led by Brechons, experts in the law. Eventually these Celtic courts died out and were replaced with sheriff courts
- The gradual acceptance of the king's law led the way to the decrease of importance of the Mormaers and the acceptance of central control.

Development of the royal government
- David created a small but loyal group that had specific roles to aid him in the running of his household and the kingdom. Sheriffs replaced thanes in the remote areas of the kingdom. They offered direct royal contact for those away from the traditional seat of power
- Henry ordered an investigation into his sheriffs in 1170. Many were dismissed and replaced with Henry's loyal followers.

Development of the royal military forces
- The new feudal forces brought to David by his introduction of feudalism offered a significant advantage when dealing with the Celtic Mormaers. Traditionally it was the Mormaers who controlled the summoning of the Common army of Scotland. Now David had an independent force loyal to him. However, this force often did not work well with the other elements of the Scottish forces, as seen at the disastrous Battle of the Standard
- Henry's introduction of scutage allowed him to get around the problem of 40 days' knight service. He successfully restored order in England by dismantling illegally built castles and removing the barons' private armies of Flemish knights.

Development of the economy
- David introduced numerous monasteries, which helped to develop the wool trade, eg Melrose Abbey, and cultivate barren land. David granted charters to over 15 towns. Trade was encouraged with Germany, Scandinavia and France. David introduced the first Scottish coins to help promote trade
- Henry II established the exchequer under Nigel of Ely to rein in sheriffs who failed to pay taxes and ensure scutage (shield tax) and other forms of aid and direct taxes were paid on time.

Introduction of feudal landholding
- During his time in England, David became an admirer of the feudal landholding system. He introduced a form of military feudalism into areas of Scotland, notably the southwest, Lothian and the northeast. Noble families were given grants of land. In return they offered David their support, both politically and militarily.

Development of the Church
- Started by David's mother Margaret, the introduction of the Roman Church at the expense of the Celtic one offered a significant boon to the development of royal authority. As the Church preached the divine grace of the king, it was hard to justify any rebellions against him
- Henry famously ran into trouble in his attempts to establish more authority over the church in his dispute with Thomas Becket.

3. The candidate evaluates the extent to which the growth of towns led to the decline of feudal society, using evidence and arguments such as:

The growth of towns
- Townsmen had different rights than those living in the countryside
- Many had the rights to hold their own courts, and these were seen as free from feudal interference
- Towns could buy a charter, granting Burgh status, allowing them to freely trade with overseas merchants. Burgesses could buy and sell their holdings
- A villein who lived in the town for a year and a day would become a freeman
- The development led to creation of a sort of middle class gentry in the fifteenth century, the mediocre or middling sort.

Other factors

Gradual decline in the old feudal manor economy
- With markets for their goods fluctuating considerably, many nobles came to understand their weak economic position. For some it was better to let their peasants become tenants who rented their land than to continue as their feudal protector
- Without the need for a feudal lord and protector, there was little need for serfs or villeins. It was easier to hire laborers, and relying on fixed rates of income from rents or salaries became more common.

Changing social attitudes
- Peasants who could afford to purchase or rent extra land could propel themselves upwards on the social ladder
- The de la Poles family in Hull rose from traders to become royal bankers, and the Pastson family rose out of serfdom to become country gentry
- Social commentators like Peter Idley complained that it had become impossible to tell the difference from "knave and Knight", because they dressed alike.

Growth of trade/mercantilism
- It has been argued that the feudal structure and serfdom hampered entrepreneurial merchants in England and Scotland. Many found the freedom of burgh life allowed them to develop trade without the burden of labour services or restrictions in movement
- Others discovered that sheep were a far more profitable resource than peasants could ever be, leading to development of mercantile skills
- Development of an affluent merchant class.

Black Death
- The decline in the population meant that the survivors, particularly of the lower classes, could demand and often received better wages for their labour. Wage levels in England roughly doubled. Indeed, the shortage of laborers is often seen as causing the decline of serfdom in Western Europe
- Parliament in England attempted to halt this decline by passing the "Statute of Laborers" in 1351, but it wasn't very effective and was mostly ignored

- Landowners for the first time needed to negotiate for their serfs' services, leading to higher wages and better living conditions for those that survived
- The Black Death led to the old feudal relationship between lord and serf disappearing.

Peasants' Revolt

- In England, the attempts of the Statute of Laborers in 1351 to force peasants back into serfdom were widely and strongly resisted. The extent of the revolt and the impressive way in which it was organised shows that the old feudal consensus had broken down
- The Peasants' Revolt was a reaction to the attempts to force peasants to return to the old ideas of labour services.

The Century of Revolutions 1603 – 1702

4. The candidate assesses the effectiveness of Charles I's rule in Scotland between 1625 and 1642, using evidence and arguments such as:

Political policy

- Charles I's policies which took power and land from Scottish nobles
- King did not visit Scotland until 1633 when he was crowned there
- Appointed bishops rather than nobles to Scottish Privy Council
- John Spottiswoode appointed Chancellor, first non-secular official in this position since Reformation
- Charles I gave increasing power to bishops, undermining status of Scottish nobility
- Stuart notion of Divine Right of Kings was brought to an end by Scots opposition to Charles I's attempts to impose his will on Scottish people.

Religious policy

- Charles I introduced William Laud, the Archbishop of Canterbury, to Scotland in 1633
- Laud proceeded to oversee Anglican practice in Scottish churches
- Many resented influence of Laud
- King approved of unification of churches without consulting Privy Council
- 1635 Book of Canons declared that monarch had authority over Church of Scotland and introduced new Service Book, a Scottish bishops' variation of English Prayer Book
- 23 July 1637 English Prayer Book was read at St Giles Cathedral by Dean, John Hanna, who subsequently had a stool thrown at him by a serving woman, Jenny Geddes
- In chaos that ensued, Bishop of Edinburgh was shouted down by crowd in support of Geddes
- Across Scotland people declared opposition to Service Book, placing Charles I's Privy Council in difficult position, caught between king and his rivals.

The Covenanters

- Covenanting movement challenged Charles I over religious policies and was active politically
- Covenanters wanted to preserve Presbyterianism in Scotland
- National Covenant was signed in 1638
- Covenant designed to promote a church free from monarchical meddling
- Charles I failed to suppress Covenanters, contributing to outbreak of War of the 3 Kingdoms
- During war, English Parliament's treaty of alliance with Scottish Covenanters – the Solemn League and Covenant of 1643 – was key feature of positive change in fortunes of king's enemies.

1st Bishops' War

- 1st Bishops' War took place in 1639
- Charles I could not raise enough money to fight war effectively, was forced to agree to truce in June as part of Pacification of Berwick
- As well as conceding military failure, truce gave Scots religious freedoms
- Charles I's inability to put down Scots brought an end to his "Eleven Years' Tyranny" in England
- King recalled Parliament in 1640 to request revenue to continue war with Scotland
- Short Parliament lasted one month as king dissolved it rather than debate his role during Eleven Years as condition of Parliamentary granting of funds.

2nd Bishops' War

- 2nd Bishops' War was continuation of first but ended in equal humiliation for Charles I in Treaty of Ripon, October 1640
- Treaty cost England the price that Scottish Parliament had to pay for its forces
- Defeat by Scots forced king to recall Parliament, this time after being advised to do so by grouping of peers known as Magnum Concilium
- Long Parliament was to last longer than previous one, but still represented downturn in king's fortunes, as English Civil War shortly followed.

5. The candidate evaluates the importance of religious issues in causing the Revolution of 1688 to 1689, using evidence and arguments such as:

Religious issues

- Issue of church governance which arose before Civil War had not been resolved
- Many MPs fearful of continued Stuart dominance of Anglican Church policy
- James II promotion of Roman Catholics to key posts antagonised Presbyterians
- Heir to the throne to be raised as a Roman Catholic
- Divide between Episcopalians and Presbyterians in Scotland created hostility from Scottish Parliament towards monarchy.

Other factors

Political issues

- Divine Right and absolutism as practised by Stuart monarchs
- Status of monarchy questioned by Parliament
- Charles II's dismissal of Parliament resembled Charles I's 11-Year Tyranny
- James II's use of Suspending and Dispensing Powers seen as an abuse by Parliament
- Questions raised over control of the army.

Lines of authority Crown and Parliament

- There were no clear lines of authority
- Questions existed over who held sway in religious matters; Parliament feared a monarch could try to impose Roman Catholicism on country
- Still possible for monarch to be financially independent of Parliament and manipulate succession in favour of Roman Catholic line
- Both Charles II and James II had proved it was possible for monarch to rule without Parliament, influence legislative and judicial procedure, control army for own means, and assert religious and political will on Scotland and Ireland
- Parliament saw need to agree constitutional status for monarchy.

The role of Parliament
- Parliament resented James II's abuses of power but took comfort from thought that he would be succeeded by Protestant daughter Mary
- However, king married again and had son, to be raised as Roman Catholic
- June 1688, Parliament wrote to Mary, by now married to Dutch Prince William of Orange, offering Crown
- They arrived in November with army and on Christmas Day James II fled to France after younger daughter Anne as well as leading generals declared support for Mary
- William and Mary became joint sovereigns on February 13th 1689
- With no Bill of Rights, any future monarchs, including William and Mary, could preach notions of Divine Right, absolutism and passive obedience
- Future limitations on power of monarchy would have to be written into law
- In 1689 Parliament drew up Bill of Rights, which legalised new relationship between Crown and Parliament
- This would ensure no future king or queen could attempt absolutism
- Bill of Rights would be part of wider set of legal provisions for new order in country
- Settlement established that kings and queens should depend upon Parliament for finance, succession would be determined by Parliament and not sitting monarch, judicial system would be controlled by Parliament, and no future monarch could rule without Parliament.

James II
- Ascended throne in 1685 upon death of older brother
- James II, who practised Roman Catholicism, attempted to rule absolutely
- Dismissed Parliament in 1685
- Replaced Anglican advisors with Roman Catholic ones; placed Roman Catholics in important posts at Oxford and Cambridge Universities
- Stationed 13,000-strong army outside London
- Re-established Prerogative Courts in 1686
- 1687, used Suspending Powers to suspend laws against Roman Catholics
- Used Dispensing Powers to dismiss these laws from statute books.

Legacy of Charles II
- Charles II, who had been exiled in France during Interregnum, had accepted limitations on his power when monarchy was restored in 1660
- Prerogative law courts were abolished, non-parliamentary taxation was prohibited, and Triennial Act remained in place
- Loopholes, however, meant king could still make policy
- Puritans lost power in House of Commons
- Towards end of reign Charles II ruled without Parliament for 4 years
- Divine Right preached from pulpits.

6. The candidate assesses the validity of the view that financial reform was the most significant change brought about by the Revolution Settlement, using evidence and arguments such as:

Finance
- In time of James I and Charles I, monarchy could exist financially independently of Parliament. This now impossible
- King and Queen were granted £700,000 for court expenses in 1689
- From then on Parliament voted to give Crown money annually as part of Civil List system
- Procedure of audit established for MPs to check expenditure of monarch

- Fiscal power now in hands of House of Commons
- However monarch would not have to make unpopular moves of raising taxes himself from now on.

Religion
- Before 1688, Crown dictated religious development of country
- After Settlement, hundreds of High Anglicans were expelled from their posts because they refused to recognise authority of William III
- Toleration Act of 1689 passed which provided for free public worship for all except Roman Catholics and Unitarians
- Roman Catholics still ineligible for elected posts in towns or Parliament
- Parliament now held more sway in religious matters
- However monarch still enjoyed political advantages of being head of church.

Legal
- Stuart monarchs had abused legal system and courts
- Legal settlement established Parliamentary control over these areas
- Later, Act of Settlement of 1701 stated judges could only be removed from their positions if Parliament demanded this
- From now on ministers impeached by House of Commons could not be pardoned by Crown
- 1695, Law of Treason altered to give defendants right to be given copy of indictment against them, right to be defended by Counsel and call witnesses in their defence
- An act of treason needed two witnesses against defendant instead of previous one
- Parliament now enforcing own control over judicial procedure
- However monarchs could still appoint judges who might be favourable to them.

Political
- In days before Civil War, Stuart monarchs had been able to rule without Parliament and curtail Parliamentary freedom of speech
- Revolution Settlement provided for another Triennial Act in 1694, which was intended to keep MPs more closely in touch with public opinion
- Licensing Act repealed in 1695, removing restrictions on freedom of press to report Parliamentary criticism of Crown
- William and Mary had to agree to Bill of Rights before they were given throne, legalising new relationship between Crown and Parliament
- This ensured no future king or queen could attempt absolutism
- Members of Parliament could now speak freely when voicing their opinion of monarch
- However, monarch could still dismiss Parliament at will.

The succession
- Before Settlement, monarchs approved own successors
- Bill of Rights declared no Roman Catholic could become king or queen
- Later, Act of Settlement of 1701 stated if William and Mary had no heirs the throne would pass to Sophia of Hanover, Protestant daughter of Elizabeth of Bohemia, sister of Charles I
- Act said all future monarchs should be members of Church of England
- Parliament now governed question of who ascended throne.

Differences between England and Scotland
- Settlement now allowed Scotland to have own church, Presbyterian Kirk
- Scottish Parliament had greater share in government of Scotland.

The status of the army
- Charles I had been able to raise army in 1642
- Revolution Settlement meant Parliament gained partial control of army
- Monarch not given enough money to maintain standing army
- Mutiny Act of 1689 legalised army, this act had to be passed annually by Parliament, which forced king to summon Parliament in order to do so
- Implications for implementation of foreign policy
- Royal authority over military matters now passed to the House of Commons.

Loopholes
- Although Revolution Settlement handed a lot of power from Crown to Parliament, loopholes in agreement meant monarch still held executive power and controlled foreign policy, declaring war and signing treaties
- Monarch still the source of patronage in army and navy
- Monarch still created peers, and could therefore control House of Lords
- Revolution Settlement, therefore, did not completely hand over power to Parliament
- It was a compromise which acted as a halfway-house between Crown and Parliament, and government business was negotiated and conducted between the two.

The Atlantic Slave Trade

7. The candidate assesses the extent to which the slave trade was the major factor in the development of the British economy in the eighteenth century, using evidence and arguments such as:

Evidence that the slave trade was important
- Importance of the slave trade to the development of the economy: profits accruing from tropical crops: financial, commercial, legal and insurance institutions emerged to support the activities of the slave traders. Slave traders became bankers and many new businesses were financed by profits made from slave trading
- The slave trade played an important role in providing British industry with access to raw materials and this contributed to the increased production of manufactured goods
- Ports such as London, Bristol and Liverpool prospered as a direct result of involvement in the slave trade; other ports such as Glasgow profited from trade with the colonies. Thousands of jobs were created in Britain supplying goods and services to slave traders
- Liverpool became a major centre for shipbuilding largely as a result of the trade
- Manchester exported large percentage of cotton goods to Africa
- The slave trade was important to the economic prosperity and well-being of the colonies
- Investment from the slave trade went into the Welsh Slate Industry
- The slave trade was an important training ground for British seamen, providing experienced crews for the merchant marine and the Royal Navy
- Wealth generated by the slave trade meant that domestic taxes could be kept low
- Argument that the slave trade was the vital factor in Britain's industrialisation was put forward in Williams' Capitalism and Slavery thesis.

Evidence that other factors were important
- Changes in agriculture: these created an agricultural surplus which:
  - fed an expanding population
  - produced a labour force in the towns for use in factories

- created a financial surplus for investment in industry and infrastructure.
- Technological innovation: development of water and steam power; new machinery; transport changes
- Mineral and energy resources, particularly iron and coal
- Political stability
- Much of the profits of slavery were dissipated in conspicuous consumption eg landed estates.

8. The candidate evaluates the validity of the view whether the slave trade was too important to the British economy to allow it to be abolished, using evidence and arguments such as:

The importance of the slave trade to the British economy
- It generated finance – West Indian colonies were an important source of valuable exports to European neighbours. Taxes would have to be raised to compensate for the loss of trade and revenue. Abolition would help foreign rivals such as France as other nations would fill the gap left by Britain
- British cotton mills depended on cheap slave produced cotton
- Africa provided an additional market for British manufactured goods
- Individuals, businesses and ports in Britain prospered on the back of the slave trade
- Shipbuilding benefited as did maritime employment.

Other factors

Pressure exerted by vested interests
- Successive British Governments were influenced by powerful vested interests such as MPs and merchants from London, Liverpool and Bristol
- Slave owners and their supporters argued that millions of pounds worth of property would be threatened by the abolition of the slave trade. The slave trade was necessary to provide essential labour on the plantations. Abolition of the slave trade would ruin the colonies.

The events of the French Revolution
- These encouraged the belief among many MPs that the abolitionist cause was associated with revolutionary ideas eg Clarkson openly supported the French Revolution. Radicals used the same tactics as abolitionists to win public support – associations, petitions, cheap publications, public lectures, public meetings, pressure on Parliament. Some abolitionists were linked to radicals and therefore they had to be resisted because of fear that events in France may be repeated in Britain.

Slave rebellion in Saint-Domingue
- Abolition was associated with this symbol of brutal violence and in turn led to an exaggerated, general fear of slave revolts. Toussaint l'Ouverture was denounced. This was linked to fears of Jacobinism
- Slave violence played into the hands of the slave lobby, confirming their warnings of anarchy.
- Britain suffered humiliation when it attempted to take the rebel French Colony, beaten by disease and the ex-slave army.

Propaganda against abolition
- Supporters of slavery and the slave trade could try to claim that the enslaved on plantations were treated at least as well as the working classes in Britain.

Fears over national security
- Abolition could destroy an important source of experienced seamen it was argued thus there was a possibility that Britain would lose its advantage over its maritime rivals. On the other hand, the Triangular Trade was arguably a graveyard for British seamen.

9. The candidate evaluates the significance of the campaign organised by the Anti-Slavery Society in bringing about the abolition of the slave trade, using evidence and arguments such as:

The campaign of the abolitionist movement
- Thomas Clarkson obtained witnesses for the Parliamentary investigations of the slave trade which provided Wilberforce with convincing evidence for his speeches
- Books and pamphlets published eg eyewitness accounts from former slaves such as Olaudah Equiano
- Campaigns to boycott goods produced by slaves in the West Indies such as sugar and rum
- Petitions and subscription lists, public meetings and lecture tours involving those with experience of slave trade eg Olaudah Equiano, churches and theatres used for abolitionist propaganda, artifacts and illustrations eg Wedgwood pottery
- Lobbying of Parliament by abolitionists to extract promises from MPs that they would oppose the slave trade. Effective moderate political and religious leadership among the abolitionists influenced major figures such as Pitt and Fox; abolitionists gave evidence to Parliamentary Commissions.

Other factors

The role of Wilberforce
- Wilberforce put forward the arguments of the Society for the Abolition of the Slave Trade in Parliament for eighteen years
- Wilberforce's speeches in Parliament were graphic and appealing
- Wilberforce's Christian faith had led him to become interested in social reform and link the issues of factory reform in Britain and the need to abolish slavery and the slave trade within the British Empire
- Wilberforce was prepared to work with other abolitionists to achieve his aims, eg Thomas Clarkson.

Effects of slave resistance
- Successful slave rebellion in Saint-Domingue led to an exaggerated, general fear of slave revolts.

Economic factors
- Effects of wars with France – slave trade declined by two-thirds as it was seen as harming the national interest in time of war. The slave trade had become less important in economic terms – there was no longer a need for large numbers of slaves to be imported to the British colonies. There was a world over-supply of sugar and British merchants had difficulties re-exporting it.

Military factors
- Napoleon's efforts to restore slavery in the French islands meant that the abolitionist campaign would help to undermine Napoleon's plans for the Caribbean. The Act banning any slave trade between British merchants and foreign colonies in 1806 was intended to attack French interests.

The Religious Revival
- Role of the Quakers and other non-conformists
- Role of people like John Newton: ex slave ship captain and now clergyman
- Religious arguments against slavery.

Britain 1851 – 1951

10. The candidate assesses the validity of the view that Britain was still far from being a democratic country by 1928, using evidence and arguments such as:

The vote
- In 1867 most skilled working class men in towns got the vote
- In 1884 many more men in the countryside were given the vote

- In 1918 most men over 21 and some women over 30 gained the vote
- Finally in 1928 all men and women over 21 were given the vote.

Fairness
- Secret Ballot 1872 freed voters from intimidation
- Corrupt and Illegal Practices Act 1883 limited the amount spent campaigning
- Re-distribution of seats in 1867, 1885 and 1918 all helped created a fairer system of voting
- The effectiveness of these varied; they were less effective in areas where the electorate was small, or where a landowner or employer was dominant in an area, eg Norwich.

Choice
- Although the working class electorate increased by 1880s there was no national party to express their interests. The Liberals and Conservatives promoted middle, even upper class capitalist values. The spread of socialist ideas and trade unionism led to the creation of the prototype Labour Party – the LRC – by 1900 thereby offering a wider choice to the electorate.

Access to information
- Education – in the later 19th Century there was a great increase in literacy and hence access to information on which to base choice. Also railways spread information nationally and were important to the growth of democracy.

National Party Organisation
- As the size of the electorate grew individual political parties had to make sure their 'message' got across to electorate eg development of National Liberal Federation, Conservative Central Office, Primrose League.

Power of Lords
- From 1911 Lords could only delay bills from the House of Commons for two years rather than veto them. They had no control over money bills.

Widening opportunity to become MP
- The property qualification to be MP was abolished 1858. Payment for MPs began in 1911 enabling working class men to sit
- By 1928 Parliament was much more fully representative of the British people.

Points still to be resolved included
- Undemocratic anomalies – plural votes and the university constituencies – were not abolished until 1948
- In 1949 the two year delaying power of the House of Lords was reduced to only one year, but the power of House of Lords in law making still continues
- Voting system still first past the post in UK.

11. The candidate assesses the extent to which the Liberal reforms of 1906 to 1914 made a significant improvement to the lives of the British people, using evidence and arguments such as:

The young
- Children were thought to be the victims of poverty and unable to escape through their own efforts. In this way they were seen as 'the deserving poor'. Child neglect and abuse were seen as problems associated with poverty
- The Provision of School Meals Act allowed local authorities to raise money to pay for school meals but the law did not force local authorities to provide school meals
- Medical inspections after 1907 for children were made compulsory but no treatment of illnesses or infections found was provided until 1911

- The Children's Charter of 1908 banned children under 16 from smoking, drinking alcohol, or begging. New juvenile courts were set up for children accused of committing crimes, as were borstals for children convicted of breaking the law. Probation officers were employed to help former offenders in an attempt to avoid re-offending
- The time taken to enforce all the legislation meant the Children's Charter only helped improve conditions for some children during the period.

The old
- Rowntree had identified old age as the time when most people dropped below his poverty line. Old age was inescapable so was clearly associated with the problem of poverty
- Old Age Pensions Act (1908) gave people over 70 up to 5 shillings a week. Once a person over 70 had income above 12 shillings a week, their entitlement to a pension stopped. Married couples were given 7 shillings and 6 pence
- The level of benefits was low. Few of the elderly poor would live till their 70th birthday. Many of the old were excluded from claiming pensions because they failed to meet the qualification rules.

The sick
- Illness can be seen as both a cause and consequence of poverty
- The National Insurance Scheme of 1911 applied to workers earning less than £160 a year. Each insured worker got 9 pence in benefits from an outlay of 4 pence – 'ninepence for fourpence'
- Only the insured worker got free medical treatment from a doctor. Other family members did not benefit from the scheme. The weekly contribution was in effect a wage cut which might simply have made poverty worse in many families.

The unemployed
- Unemployment was certainly a cause of poverty
- The National Insurance Act (Part 2) only covered unemployment for some workers in some industries and like (Part 1) of the Act, required contributions from workers, employers and the government. For most workers, no unemployment insurance scheme existed.

Other reforms which could be argued helped address problems associated with poverty
- In 1906 a Workman's Compensation Act covered a further six million workers who could now claim compensation for injuries and diseases which were the result of working conditions
- In 1909, the Trade Boards Act tried to protect workers in the sweated trades like tailoring and lace making by setting up trade boards to fix minimum wages
- The Mines Act and the Shop Act improved conditions.

12. The candidate assesses the validity of the statement that the Labour Government of 1945 to 1951 met the needs of the people 'from the cradle to the grave', using evidence and arguments such as:

Beveridge Report in 1942 identified 5 giants of poverty: Want, Disease, Ignorance, Squalor and Idleness.

Want
- 1946 the first step was made: the National Insurance Act: consisted of comprehensive insurance sickness and unemployment benefits and cover for most eventualities
- It was said to support people from the 'cradle to the grave' which was significant as it meant people had protection against falling into poverty throughout their lives.
- This was very effective as it meant that if the breadwinner of the family was injured then the family was less likely to fall further into the poverty trap, as was common before. However, this act can be criticised for its failure to go far enough
- Benefits were only granted to those who made 156 weekly contributions

- In 1948 the National Assistance Board was set up in order to cover those for whom insurance did not do enough
- This was important as it acted as a safety net to protect these people
- This was vital as the problem of people not being aided by the insurance benefits was becoming a severe issue as time passed. Yet, some criticised this as many citizens still remained below subsistence level showing the problem of want had not completely been addressed
- Family Allowance Act.

Disease:
- Est. of the NHS in 1948 dealt effectively with the spread of disease
- The NHS was the first comprehensive universal system of healthcare in Britain
- Offered vaccination and immunisation against disease, almost totally eradicating some of Britain's most deadly illnesses
- It also offered helpful services to Britain's public, such as childcare, the introduction of prescriptions, health visiting and provision for the elderly, providing a safety net across the whole country: the fact that the public did not have to pay for their healthcare meant that everyone, regardless of their financial situation, was entitled to equal opportunities of health care they had previously not experienced
- NHS could be regarded as almost too successful. The demand from the public was overwhelming, as the estimated amount of patients treated by them almost doubled
- Introduction of charges for prescriptions, etc.

Ignorance
- Reform started by the wartime government: The 1944 Education Act raised the age at which people could leave school to 15 as part of a drive to create more skilled workers which Britain lacked at the time. Introduction of school milk, etc
- Labour introduced a two-tiered secondary schooling whereby pupils were split at the age of 11 (12 in Scotland) depending on their ability. The smarter pupils who passed the "11+ exam" went to grammar and the rest to secondary moderns
- Those who went to grammar schools were expected to stay on past the age of 15 and this created a group of people who would take senior jobs in the country thus solving the skills shortages. Whilst this separation of ability in theory meant that children of even poor background could get equal opportunities in life, in practice the system actually created a bigger division between the poor and the rich
- Labour expanded university education: introduction of grants so all could attend in theory.

Squalor
- After the war there was a great shortage of housing as the war had destroyed and damaged thousands of homes; and the slum cleaning programmes of the 1930s had done little to rectify the situation which was leading to a number of other problems for the government
- Labour's target for housing was to build 200,000 new homes a year. 157,000 pre-fabricated homes were built to a good standard, however this number would not suffice and the target was never met
- Bevan encouraged the building of council houses rather than privately funded construction
- The New Towns Act of 1946, aimed to target overcrowding in the increasingly built up older cities. By 1950, the government had designed 12 new communities
- In an attempt to eradicate slums the Town and Country Planning Act provided local communities more power in regards to building developments and new housing
- By the time Labour left government office in 1951 there was still a huge shortfall in British housing.

Idleness

- Unemployment was basically non-existent so the government had little to do to tackle idleness
- The few changes they did make were effective in increasing the likelihood of being able to find work, because they increased direct government funding for the universities which led to a 60% increase in student numbers between 1945-46 and 1950-51 which helped to meet the manpower requirements of post-war society. This provided more skilled workers and allowed people from less advantaged backgrounds to pursue a higher education, aiming to keep unemployment rates down
- Labour government also nationalised 20 percent of industry – the railways, mines, gas and electricity. This therefore meant that the government were directly involved with people employed in these huge industries which were increasing in size dramatically
- This tackled idleness by the government having control which meant that employees were less likely to lose their job through industries going bankrupt and people were working directly to benefit society
- Marshall Plan: financial aid from U.S.A.

Britain and Ireland 1900 – 1985

13. The candidate assesses how far World War One changed political attitudes towards British rule in Ireland, using evidence and arguments such as:

Irish attitudes to World War I

- Initially war brought prosperity to Ireland - manufacturing and farming, low unemployment thus improving relations between GB and Ireland
- Propaganda – powerful Germany invading helpless and small Catholic Belgium so Ireland supported GB
- Ulster very supportive of Britain to ensure favourable treatment at the end of the war
- Nationalists and Redmond backed war to get Home Rule, urging Irish men to enlist
- Press gave support to the war effort
- Irish Volunteers gave support to help Home Rule be passed after the war
- Recruitment was successful in the south as almost ¼ million men join up.

The Nationalist Movement

- Opposition to war very much a minority in 1914 but supported by Sinn Fein and Arthur Griffith (not powerful at this time), as well as Pearse, Connolly and their supporters and also a section of the Irish Volunteers. This damaged relations with Britain.

Easter Rising

- Rebels saw war as chance to rid Ireland of British by force
- Felt it was opportunity to gain independence by force as Britain had their troops away fighting the Germans in World War I. This greatly strained relations between Britain and Ireland
- Britain had to use force to suppress rebellion, such as using the Gunboat, 'Helga' to sail up the River Liffey and fire on the rebels in the GPO, thus distracting GB's attention and resources away from War effort, thus straining relations
- Strong criticism of Rising initially from the public, politicians, churchmen, as well as press for unnecessary death and destruction. 450 dead, 2500 wounded, cost £2½ million, showing that majority still sided with GB therefore indicating that there was not too much damage to relations between the two countries
- Initial hostility by majority of Irish people to Rising by small group of rebels, majority of people supported Redmond and the Nationalist Party
- Strong hostility and criticism by Dubliners to rebels for destruction of city centre.

Changing attitudes towards British rule after 1916

- The secret court martial, execution of leaders over 10 days as well as imprisonment without trial and at least one execution without a trial saw the rebels gain a lot of sympathy from the Irish public, turning them against British rule
- These political developments meant a growth of sympathy and compassion for rebels who were seen as martyrs and replaced the initial condemnation of the Rising
- Sinn Fein, initially blamed for the Rising, saw a subsequent rise in support for them
- Catholic Church and business community became more sympathetic to the cause of independence.

Anti Conscription Campaign

- Irish opposed conscription and pushed people to Sinn Fein who openly opposed it
- Caused the Nationalists to withdraw from Westminster
- Sinn Fein and Nationalists organised campaign eg general strike April 23rd
- Catholic Church, Mayor of Dublin drew up the National Pledge opposing conscription
- Conscription was not extended to Ireland which Sinn Fein was given credit for
- Conscription campaign drove Sinn Fein underground which improved their organisation.

Decline of Nationalist Party

- Irish Convention failed to reach agreement, which weakened position of Nationalists
- Led to feeling British could not be trusted and Nationalists could not deliver
- Three by-election wins for Sinn Fein gave impression they spoke for people not Nationalists which increased tension between Ireland and Britain politically
- March 1918 Redmond died which accelerated the decline of the Nationalists. Sinn Fein gained influence and popularity as a result
- Many moved from the Nationalist Party as they felt Sinn Fein was doing more for Ireland.

Rise of Sinn Fein

- Release of rebel prisoners from Frongoch meant Sinn Fein's struggle against British Rule in Ireland gained momentum
- Michael Collins was building up IRB and Irish Volunteers when in prison
- Collins ready to encourage anti-British activity in Ireland on release
- Collins and De Valera improved Sinn Fein's leadership
- Opposition to Britain due to martial law, house searches, raids, control of press, arrest of "suspects" without trial, and vigorous implementation of the Defence of the Realm Act
- Hunger striker Thomas Ashe died in 1917. His funeral became a propaganda tool for Sinn Fein.

14. The candidate evaluates the contribution of economic issues to the developing crisis in Northern Ireland up to 1968, using evidence and arguments such as:

Economic issues

- Northern Ireland was left relatively prosperous by World War Two, with the boom continuing into the 1950s. But by the 1960s, as elsewhere in Britain, 'many' industries were in decline, eg Harland and Wolff profitable 'til early' 60s, but government help in 1966. Largely Protestant workforce protected as a result
- Catholic areas received less government investment than their Protestant neighbours. Catholics were more likely to be unemployed or in low-paid jobs than Protestants in Northern Ireland. Catholic applicants also routinely excluded from public service appointments

- The incomes of mainly Protestant landowners were supported by the British system of 'deficiency payments' which gave Northern Ireland farmers an advantage over farmers from the Irish Republic
- Brookeborough's failure to address the worsening economic situation saw him forced to resign as Prime Minister. His successor, Terence O'Neill set out to reform the economy. His social and economic policies saw growing discontent and divisions within his unionist party.

Other factors

The Unionist Ascendancy in Northern Ireland and challenges to it
- Population of Northern Ireland divided: two-thirds Protestant and one-third Catholic: it was the minority who were discriminated against in employment and housing
- In 1963, the Prime Minister of Northern Ireland, Viscount Brookeborough, stepped down after 20 years in office. His long tenure was a product of the Ulster Unionist domination of politics in Northern Ireland since partition in 1921
- Unionist ascendancy: Before 1969 elections not held on a "one person, one vote" basis: gerrymandering used to secure Unionist majorities on local councils. Local govt electoral boundaries favoured Unionist candidates, even in mainly Catholic areas like Derry/Londonderry. Also, right to vote in local elections restricted to ratepayers, favouring Protestants, with those holding or renting properties in more than one ward receiving more than one vote, up to a maximum of six. This bias preserved by unequal allocation of council houses to Protestant families
- Challenges as Prime Minister O'Neill expressed desire to improve community relations in Northern Ireland and create a better relationship with the government in Dublin, hoping that this would address the sense of alienation felt by Catholics towards the political system in Northern Ireland
- Post-war Britain's Labour government introduced the welfare state to Northern Ireland, and it was implemented with few concessions to traditional sectarian divisions. Catholic children in the 1950s and 1960s shared in the benefits of further and higher education for the first time. This exposed them to a world of new ideas and created a generation unwilling to tolerate the status quo
- Many Catholics impatient with pace of reform and remained unconvinced of Prime Minister O'Neill's sincerity. Founding of the Northern Ireland Civil Rights Association (NICRA) in 1967. NICRA did not challenge partition, though membership mainly Catholic. Instead, it called for the end to seven 'injustices', ranging from council house allocations to the 'weighted' voting system.

Role of the IRA
- Rioting and disorder in 1966 was followed by the murders of two Catholics and a Protestant by a 'loyalist' terror group called the Ulster Volunteer Force, who were immediately banned by O'Neill
- Peaceful civil rights marches descended into violence in October 1968 when marchers in Derry defied the Royal Ulster Constabulary and were dispersed with heavy-handed tactics. The RUC response only served to inflame further the Catholic community and foster the establishment of the Provisional IRA by 1970 as the IRA split into Official and Provisional factions
- The Provisional IRA's strategy was to use force to cause the collapse of the Northern Ireland administration and to inflict casualties on the British forces such that the British government would be forced by public opinion to withdraw from Ireland
- PIRA were seen to defend Catholic areas from Loyalist attacks in the summer of 1970.

Cultural and political differences
- The Catholic minority politically marginalised since the 1920s, but retained its distinct identity through its own institutions such as the Catholic Church, separate Catholic schools, and various cultural associations, as well as the hostility of the Protestant majority
- Catholic political representatives in parliament refused to recognise partition and this only increased the community's sense of alienation and difference from the Unionist majority in Northern Ireland
- Nationalists on average 10-12 in NI Parliament compared to average 40 Unionists. In Westminster 10-12 Unionists to 2 Nationalists
- As the Republic's constitution laid claim to the whole island of Ireland, O'Neill's meeting with his Dublin counterpart, Seán Lemass, in 1965, provoked attacks from within Unionism, eg the Rev. Ian Paisley
- Violence erupted between the two communities, in 1966 following the twin 50th anniversaries of the Battle of the Somme and the Easter Rising. Both events were key cultural touchstones for the Protestant and Catholic communities.

The issue of Civil Rights
- From the autumn of 1968 onwards, a wide range of activists marched behind the civil rights banner, adopting civil disobedience in an attempt to secure their goals. Housing activists, socialists, Nationalists, Unionists, Republicans, students, trade unionists and political representatives came together across Northern Ireland to demand civil rights for Catholics in Northern Ireland
- The demand for basic civil rights from the Northern Ireland govt was an effort to move the traditional fault-lines away from the familiar Catholic-Protestant, Nationalist-Unionist divides by demanding basic rights for all citizens of Britain
- Civil rights encouraged by television coverage of civil rights protest in USA and student protests in Europe. Also by widening TV ownership: 1954, 10,000 licences, by 1962 there were 200,000 leading to increased Catholic awareness of the issues that affected them
- As the civil rights campaign gained momentum, so too did unionist opposition. Sectarian tension rose: was difficult to control, and civil disobedience descended into occasions of civil disorder.

15. The candidate evaluates the importance of religious and communal differences between both communities in preventing peace in Ireland between 1968 and 1985, using evidence and arguments such as:

Religious and communal differences
- The Protestant majority in Northern Ireland belonged to churches that represented the full range of reformed Christianity, while the Catholic minority was united in its membership of a Church that dominated life in the Republic and much of Europe. These religious divisions made it very difficult for both communities to come together
- These divisions further enhanced by traditions embraced by both communities, such as the 'marching season', which became a flashpoint for sectarian violence. Also differences in sport, language
- Many Catholic political representatives refused to recognise partition and their views only heightened the Nationalist community's sense of alienation and fostered Unionist hostility towards the Catholic minority
- The speeches and actions of Unionist and Nationalist leaders such as Reverend Ian Paisley and Gerry Adams polarised views in the province, and emphasised the divisions between both communities.

Other factors

Economic differences

- From 1973, the Common Agricultural Policy changed the decision making environment for food prices and farm economics, and employment in the farming sector continued to decline. Traditionally this sector had been dominated by the Unionist community
- Discrimination against Catholic applicants for employment declined steadily during this period as Catholics in the province began to enjoy the same civil rights enjoyed by the population of the rest of the UK.

Hardening attitudes – the role of terrorism

- Paramilitary groups began to operate on both sides of the sectarian divide, while civil rights marches became increasingly prone to confrontation
- In late 1969, the more militant 'Provisional' IRA (PIRA) broke away from the so-called 'Official' IRA. PIRA was prepared to pursue unification in defiance of Britain and would use violence to achieve its aims
- Unionist paramilitaries also organised. The UVF was joined by the Ulster Defence Association, created in 1971
- Examples of terrorist activity: by the end of 1972 sectarian violence had escalated to such an extent that nearly 500 lives were lost in a single year
- PIRA prisoners protest at loss of special status prisoners leading to hunger strikes Second hunger strike in 1981, led by Bobby Sands. Sands was put forward for a vacant Westminster seat and won. Sands and nine other hunger strikers died before the hunger strikes called off in October 1981
- Sinn Fein won the by-election following Sands' death in June 1983, these electoral successes raised the possibility that Sinn Fein could replace the more moderate SDLP as the political voice of the Catholic minority in Northern Ireland
- Indiscriminate terrorism meant Eire public opinion turned against PIRA
- In 1985 the violence of Northern Ireland's paramilitary groups still had more than a decade to run and the sectarian divide remained as wide as it had ever been.

British government policies – Internment

- New Prime Minister Brian Faulkner reintroduced internment ie detention of suspects without trial, in 1971 in response to unrest. Policy a disaster, both in its failure to capture any significant members of the PIRA and in its sectarian focus on Nationalist rather than Loyalist suspects. The reaction was predictable, even if the ferocity of the violence wasn't. Deaths in the final months of 1971 over 150.

Direct Rule

- A number of reforms had followed on from the Downing Street Declaration, ie on allocation of council housing, investigate the recent cycle of violence and review policing, such as the disbanding of the hated 'B Specials' auxiliaries
- The British government, now led by Prime Minister Edward Heath, decided to remove control of security from the government of Northern Ireland and appointing a secretary of state for the province leading to resignation of Stormont government. Direct rule imposed
- Despite attempts to introduce some sort of self-rule, such as the Sunningdale agreement of 1973, which failed in the face of implacable Unionist opposition and led to the reintroduction of direct rule. It would last for another 25 years.

The role of the British Army

- The so-called 'Battle of Bogside' in 1969 only ended with the arrival of a small force of British troops at the request of Chichester Clark. An acknowledgement that the govt. of Northern Ireland had lost its grip on the province's security

- By 1971 policing the province was fast becoming an impossible task, and the British Army adopted increasingly aggressive policies on the ground
- On 30 January 1972, the army deployed the Parachute Regiment to suppress rioting at a civil rights march in Derry. Thirteen demonstrators were shot and killed by troops, with another victim dying later of wounds. Appalling images of 'Bloody Sunday; led to increased recruitment by Provisional IRA
- The British Army's various attempts to control the PIRA, such as house-to-house searches and the imposition of a limited curfew, only served to drive more recruits into the ranks of the paramilitaries.

The role of the Irish government

- Irish government's role in The Anglo-Irish Agreement, signed in November 1985, confirmed that Northern Ireland would remain independent of the Republic as long as that was the will of the majority in the north. Also gave the Republic a say in the running of the province for the first time
- The agreement also stated that power could not be devolved back to Northern Ireland unless it enshrined the principle of power sharing.

HISTORICAL STUDY: EUROPEAN AND WORLD HISTORY

The Crusades, 1071 – 1204

16. The candidate evaluates the importance of religious factors in the decision of Europeans to go on crusade, using evidence and arguments such as:

Religious motives

- It was generally believed that the Remission of Sins offered by Pope Urban was an attractive solution to the dilemma of knights. Salvation was a constant worry for those trained to kill. Urban successfully resolved the need to protect Christianity from the Muslim threat and the general desire to re-establish the pilgrimage routes to the Holy Lands
- The promise of remission of current sins was also a great relief to those knights worried about their eternal soul. Tancred's biographer wrote about both his worry over this dilemma and his relief at Urban's suggestion
- The appeal of the People's Crusade shows the power of the belief that they were doing good and helping God
- Of the leaders of the Princes' Crusade, Raymond of Toulouse, is often held up as an example of a knight riding to the defence of the Holy Lands. His decision to take Tripoli in 1100 casts a shadow over this interpretation of his motives
- In later Crusades many of the religious aspects of the Crusade are adopted and modified by the growing idea of chivalric codes.

Other factors

The desire to acquire territory in the Holy Land

- Many of the great magnates on this expedition had intentions to acquire new estates for themselves. The motives of many of the leaders of the Princes' Crusade have been put down to this
- Bohomend and Baldwin in particular showed little zeal in carrying on with the Crusade once they had acquired Antioch and Edessa respectively.

Peer pressure

- The pressure put on knights by their families to take the cross was at times severe. Noblemen's wives tended to be keenly aware of the politics at court and had a role in influencing the decisions of some
- Stephen of Blois had married Adela, daughter of William I of England. It would have been unthinkable for such a notable knight not to go on the Crusade.

Seeking of fame and riches

- Some knights did go seeking glory. The Crusade had provided the solution to the problem of knights and their need for salvation. Killing was only wrong if you killed Christians. Urban indicated that the killing of a Muslim was a just act, and the equivalent to prayer or penance
- Seeking of riches per se was uncommon; land was the real source of wealth and power.

The sense of adventure

- Going on crusade was exciting and engendered a sense of adventure
- Pilgrimages had always been seen as important, and the idea of this as an armed pilgrimage was very appealing. It offered a way out for many serfs from their lives in bondage, or perhaps a chance to see the Holy Land.

Overpopulation and famine

- Many were forced to leave because of the lack of available farmland in an already overcrowded Europe.
- Several famines have also been suggested as a possible motive. It was popularly believed that the Holy Land was a land of plenty.

17. The candidate assesses the validity of the view that while Richard was a greater military leader and Saladin was a better diplomat, using evidence and arguments such as:

Diplomatic strengths and weaknesses

Saladin's strengths as a diplomat

- Despite being a Sunni Muslim in Shi'ite-dominated Egypt, he was successful in bringing much needed stability to the troubled court. His religious tolerance and fair judiciary earned him the respect of the Shi'ite citizens
- While ruler of Egypt Saladin was able to keep Nur-ed-Din at bay by evading the main contentious issue of religious conformity. When Nur-ed-din died in 1174, Saladin was able to step in and take over from his 10 year old son
- Saladin brought effective military leadership and central authority to Egypt and Syria for the first time
- In 1180 Saladin had successfully limited the attacks from Outremer by negotiating a peace treaty with Baldwin IV
- The capture of Jerusalem in 1187 made Saladin the hero of Islam. The eventual negotiated surrender saved much bloodshed.

Richard's weaknesses as a diplomat

- Many historians have pointed out that Richard, like his father Henry II, had something of a fiery temper. However it is questionable as to what extent this lost him the prize, Jerusalem. There is evidence that Richard was a poor diplomat; certainly at times he failed to understand the nature of his allies but he was perhaps better at understanding the nature of his enemy. His temper did result in the loss of potential allies. His treatment of Leopold of Austria, the leader of the much-reduced German contingent, resulted in an injury to the pride of Leopold and the loss of his German knights to the cause
- Richard's inability to share the spoils taken during this attack on Cyprus with Philip Augustus helped persuade the ill king of France that he was needed at home. The one thing Richard had wished to do was keep Philip with him on the Crusade; now he had to worry about French incursions into his Angevin Empire
- Against advice Richard backed Guy de Lusignan to become King of Jerusalem, against the popular Conrad of Montferrat, perhaps because he was the favourite of Philip. This continued support of Guy resulted in a compromise that no one liked. The assassination of Conrad was even whispered by some to be Richard's fault. The end result was

the withdrawal of the support of Conrad's forces and those of the Duke of Burgundy's remaining French knights.

Richard's strengths as a diplomat

- Richard proved himself in the art of diplomacy during the Crusade, when he successfully negotiated with Al-Adill, Saladin's brother. The two instantly got on, and a bond was forged between them. Saladin was increasingly concerned when Richard knighted one of Al-Adill's sons and even offered his sister in marriage. Al-Adill's connection to Richard was enough of an incentive for Saladin to agree to a truce with Richard.

Saladin's diplomatic weaknesses

- Not all of his supporters were happy with the peace treaty of 1180. Many felt that this contradicted the jihad and gave support to the Christian claim to Jerusalem
- Saladin was panicked into peace with Richard. Saladin was worried over the close relationship between Al-Adil and Richard. If he had held out it was probable that Richard would have had to return to England anyway without the peace treaty.

Military strengths and weaknesses

Richard's leadership

- Richard had established himself as an able leader prior to the Crusade
- Richard was good at motivating troops, and his arrival at the siege of Acre galvanised the troops in a way that Philip had been unable to do. Even when confined to his bed due to illness he was still able to direct the operations.

Richard's victories

- While journeying to the Holy Lands Richard captured Cyprus
- Richard, despite being lured into a trap, won the Battle of Arsuf with an impressive charge of knights that routed Saladin's men. Saladin was defeated in battle and it helped raise morale; the great defeat of Hattin had been erased from the minds of the Crusaders
- Richard won the Battle of Jaffa against overwhelming odds. Saladin had failed to defeat Richard in battle, and he lost control of his men at Jaffa; they refused to obey his orders.

Saladin's leadership

- Saladin brought effective military leadership and central authority to Egypt and Syria for the first time.

Saladin's victories

- In 1168 while Caliph of Egypt he destroyed the combined Crusader/Byzantium invasion fleet/army at the port city of Damietta
- In 1170 he followed this up with an attack on Gaza, massacring the Christian inhabitants of the city
- Saladin's victory at the Battle of Hattin (1187) was all consuming. The military orders were devastated, King Guy had been captured, many of the nobles executed or taken into slavery. One by one the great forts and cities fell to Saladin's army
- The capture of Jerusalem in 1187 made Saladin the hero of Islam. The eventual negotiated surrender saved much bloodshed.

Use of tactics

- 1180 Saladin had successfully limited the attacks from Outremer by negotiating a peace treaty with Baldwin IV
- Saladin's tactics leading up to Hattin were masterly. He provoked Guy of Lusignan into an unnecessary sally to aid a castle that was not seriously threatened. He avoided a pitched battle till the Crusaders were debilitated by heat and thirst, then further disabled them by lighting fires.

18. The candidate assesses how far the crusading ideal had declined by the Fourth Crusade in 1204, using evidence and arguments such as:

The Fourth Crusade
- The initial inspiration of the Forth Crusade had a strong crusading ideology behind it. Pope Innocent III was a highly effective pope. He had managed to settle the problem of the investiture contest with Germany, and hoped to sort out the issue of the Holy Lands as well. Innocent believed that the inclusion of medieval monarchs had caused the previous two Crusades to fail, unlike the First Crusade that was nominally under the command of Bishop Adhemar. This Crusade would fall under the command of six papal legates. These men would hold true to the ideal of the Crusade and not be bound by earthy greed of politics
- However, the Fourth Crusade has also been described as the low point of the crusading ideal. Hijacked by the Venetians, the Crusade instead became a tool for their growing political and economic ambitions
- While attacking Zara, Alexius, son of the deposed emperor of Byzantium, arrived with a new proposal for the Crusaders. He asked them to reinstate his father, who had been imprisoned by his brother, and if they agreed they would be handsomely rewarded. He also promised to return control of the Byzantine Church to Rome. The church was against such an attack on another Christian city, but the prospect of wealth and fame led the Crusade to Constantinople
- When the Crusaders discovered that Alexius and his father could not, or would not, meet the payment as agreed, the Crusaders stormed the city. The murder, looting and rape continued for three days, after which the crusading army had a great thanksgiving ceremony
- The amount of booty taken from Constantinople was huge: gold, silver, works of art and holy relics were taken back to Europe, mostly to Venice. Most Crusaders returned home with their newly acquired wealth. Those that stayed dividing up the land amongst themselves, effectively creating several Latin Crusader States where Byzantium had once stood.

Role of Venice
- By 1123 the city of Venice had come to dominate maritime trade in the Middle East. They made several secret trade agreements with Egypt and North African emirs, as well as enjoying concessions and trade agreements within the Kingdom of Jerusalem. Byzantium however, remained a constant rival for this dominance of trade and in 1183 Venice was cut off from the lucrative trading centres of the empire
- Venice's participation in the Crusade was only secured when the Pope agreed to pay huge sums of money to Venice for the use of its ships, and supplies as well as half of everything captured during the Crusade on land and sea
- Venice's leader, the Doge Enrico Dandolo, had sold the Crusaders three times as much supplies and equipment as required for the Crusade. The crusading leader, Boniface of Montferrat, found that he was unable to raise enough money to pay, and the Crusaders were all but imprisoned on an island near Venice. Dandolo's proposal to pay off the Crusaders' debt involved attacking Zara, a Christian city that had once belonged to Venice but was now under the control of the King of Hungary, a Christian monarch. Thus the Crusade had become a tool of the Venetians
- The Fourth Crusade's intended target, Egypt, was totally unsuitable from a Venetian perspective. Thus when the Pope's representative approached the Venetians in 1201 they agreed to help transport the Crusaders, hoping to divert the Crusade to a less friendly target. The final target for the Fourth Crusade was therefore determined by politics and economics.

Coexistence of Muslim and Crusading states
- Attempts at peace between Muslim and the Crusading states during the reign of Baldwin IV, before his death and the fall of Jerusalem
- Also other examples, such as the treaty of mutual protection signed between King Alric of Jerusalem and the Emir of Damascus prior to the Second Crusade.

The corruption of the crusading movement by the Church and nobles
- Popes were willing to use crusades against Christians, such as the Albegensian Crusade against the Cathar heretics of Languedoc (Toulouse and southern France) in 1209-1229. The Cathars did not believe in the hierarchy of Rome, all you needed was to be able to read the Bible. This is only the first of many such Crusades in Europe, seen as diluting the crusading ideal, ie killing Muslims
- Examples of nobles using the Crusade for their own ends are all over the place, from Bohemond and Baldwin in the First Crusade, to arguably Richard in the Third. The Fourth Crusade is littered with examples.

Effects of trade
- Trade links directly into the Fourth Crusade and the influence of Venice
- Pisa and Genoa both had a lot of influence in events during the Third Crusade, they both had favoured candidates for the vacant throne of Jerusalem for example and used trade rights as a bargaining chip to get what they wanted.

The American Revolution 1763 – 1787

19. The candidate evaluates the importance of the rejection of the Olive Branch petition in the colonists' declaration of independence in 1776, within a wide context of factors, using evidence and arguments such as:

Rejection of Olive Branch Petition
- George III rejected the colonists' last attempt at compromise
- 2nd Continental Congress had written appeal to king pledging its allegiance to crown and bitterness towards Parliament, yet appeal fell on deaf ears as George III declared colonists to be in rebellion
- Many colonists started to consider independence as only means of changing relationship with Britain
- However, petition was expression of loyalty to George III which masked many colonists' intentions to declare greater autonomy for themselves, regardless of king's reaction
- George III rejected the Olive Branch Petition, possibly as a consequence of increased colonist military activity, eg Lexington and Bunker Hill.

Other factors

Disputes over taxation
Stamp Act
- This first form of taxation on colonies, in 1765, was objected to by colonists because they were not represented in British Parliament which imposed these taxes
- "No taxation without representation" became familiar protest during this time
- Act stated that official stamp had to be bought to go on any printed matter, and colonists subsequently refused to pay for this
- Colonists stated that they already paid financial dues to British through Navigation Acts and other restrictions, and that they had their own militia and did not need to pay for the British Army to protect them
- However, British said taxation would contribute to costs of Seven Years War and also pay for continued presence of British Army in America to protect colonies.

Townshend Duties

- After Stamp Act was repealed in 1766, these Duties, which were on glass, tea, paper and lead, were imposed in 1767
- Colonists challenged right of Parliament to impose duties that seemed designed purely to raise revenue
- However, British insisted that duties be paid in order to maintain costs of acting as Mother Country to protect colonies.

Boston Massacre

- Massacre occurred in 1770
- Although 5 working-class men died, including one black man, reports of 5 middle-class white men dying caused outrage amongst politically-minded colonists
- Committees of Correspondence meant that news of Massacre spread quickly around 13 colonies
- Acquittal of British soldiers led many colonists to fear for their personal liberty and believe that they would one day be enslaved by British
- However Massacre was an incident which animated people mainly in New England area, something which later caused George III to voice his belief that problems in America were "localised".

Punishment of Massachusetts

- Tax remained on tea from 1770 in order to maintain British right to tax colonists
- Boston Tea Party in December 1773 was expression of some colonists' frustrations at British policy towards them
- The British response to the Boston Tea Party, in a series of acts starting in March 1774, known to colonists as Intolerable Acts – closing port of Boston, altering constitution of legislature of Massachusetts, billeting British troops in colonial homes, and suspending trial by jury in colony
- Other colonists acted in sympathy with Massachusetts and showed unity at First Continental Congress in September 1774
- However, British spoke of punishments as Coercive Acts, which were an attempt to get colonists to see that acts of hostility towards Britain would not be tolerated.

British intransigence

- Britain retained an uncompromising attitude in face of continued colonist protest and pleas for compromise.

Influence of Thomas Paine

- Republican pamphlet 'Common Sense' was published in January 1776 and sold 100,000 copies.

20. The candidate evaluates the extent to which the colonists' advantage of fighting on home ground led to their eventual victory in the American Revolution, using evidence and arguments such as:

Colonists' advantage of fighting on home ground

- Land war fought on American soil: this gave the Continental Army an advantage, as the colonists' knowledge of the theatre of war meant they handled the terrain better than the British
- Local people burned their crops rather than let them fall into British hands, reducing potential supplies for the British.

Other factors

George Washington

- Washington was an inspirational leader, a self-made Virginian whose choice as Commander of the Continental Army gave heart to many
- Washington fought guerrilla warfare effectively. He taught his troops to fire accurately from distance in open battle. He had experience of the British Army during the Seven Years War
- Washington's speeches to troops offered them the incentive of independence if they won the war

- Washington benefited from luck on several occasions, such as when inefficiency led the British into traps or when the French arrived at Yorktown.

French entry into the war

- Franco-American Treaty of Alliance in February 1778 was a turning point in the war
- France contributed troops, ammunition, expertise and supplies to the colonists
- Strength of the French navy meant Britain had to spread its forces worldwide, thus reducing its effort in the colonies
- French intervention on the part of Admiral de Grasse preceded the final British surrender at Yorktown
- Entry of France into the war may have encouraged Spain and Holland to follow suit within the next two years
- However, the war had been taking place for over eighteen months by the time France entered. France's main contribution was at sea rather than on land.

British military inefficiency

- On several occasions British generals did not act appropriately to orders received. Orders from London were misinterpreted; eg Howe marching south to Brandywine instead of north into New England, thus isolating Burgoyne who subsequently surrendered his forces at Saratoga
- Petty jealousies obstructed co-operation amongst British military leaders
- Changes in personnel holding high office hindered progress
- However, in many instances the British were forced into bad decisions by the tactics of Washington's army
- Distance between Britain and the colonies caused a delay in communications between London and the generals, with orders from Britain often overtaken by events by the time they reached America.

British political mistakes

- The government ignored pleas by those such as Chatham (Pitt the Elder) to reconcile with America
- Burke's attempts in the House of Commons to persuade the government to make peace were also dismissed
- George III and British ministers treated Americans as rebels and therefore ignored arguments for the colonies' rights to autonomy, self-legislation and self-taxation.
- George III and British ministers' dismissal of Olive Branch Petition in 1775 led colonists to believe the war must be won
- Inefficiences at the Admiralty under Lord Sandwich's tenure as First Lord meant Royal Navy was ill-prepared for attacks on Britain by French and Spanish which diverted British efforts in America
- Lord North's attempts to conciliate the colonists later in the war were too little too late; the colonists were motivated by independence.

Control of the seas

- Spanish and Dutch entry into the war – they stretched British resources even further and made the British less effective in the colonies.
- Armed League of Neutrality – Russian, Danish and Swedish willingness to fire on the Royal Navy placed extra pressure on Britain.

21. The candidate assesses the accuracy of the statement that the American Constitution of 1787 was an answer to the problems highlighted by the experience of British rule, using evidence and arguments such as:

The experience of rule by Britain

- As part of the British Empire, colonists had been ruled by the King and the British Parliament, who together made key policy decisions, set laws and taxes, and enforced the law; there were no checks and balances

- Colonists feared the potentially tyrannical power of a monarch, and designed the Constitution to prevent any such future threat
- Branches of government were to be predominantly elective, to ensure the participation of the people.

Significance of the Constitution

- When the colonists drew up their Constitution, they built in a separation of powers providing checks and balances within the political system. The Bill of Rights established liberty for individuals in states within a federal union of all states, and set out clear lines of authority between federal government and individual states. This would avoid central government exerting a controlling power over people's lives
- The hierarchy which existed under rule by Britain was altered by the Constitution, which stated that 'all men are created equal' and that everyone was entitled to 'life, liberty and the pursuit of happiness'. Now people would be asked to ratify many of the stages within the democratic processes at state and national level. However, women and blacks were excluded from the franchise, and in reality only one-fifth of eligible voters turned out for national elections.

Executive: role of President

- Executive power was vested in the elected President, and his Vice-President and Cabinet. The President acted as head of state and Commander-in-Chief but would have no vote in the law-making process, although he could veto legislation. The President would make all key decisions and establish policy. Members of the Executive could be removed from office by the electorate or the other branches of government if it was felt they were not doing their job properly.

Legislature: Congress

- Legislative power lay in the hands of an elected Congress which was divided into two Houses, the Senate and Representatives. Congress passed laws and raised taxes, as well as having responsibility for international trade, war and foreign relations. No one in the legislature could serve in the judiciary or executive without first resigning from the legislature. Congressional elections were held regularly to ensure that Congressmen remained in touch with the people they served.

Judiciary: Supreme Court

- Judicial power was granted to the Supreme Court of the United States. The Supreme Court acted as the highest court of appeal in the country. It also debated the legality of new laws passed by Congress. Supreme Court judges were nominated by the President and their appointment was ratified by Congress after a rigorous checking process. Appointees to the Supreme Court could be removed from their position if they acted improperly.

The French Revolution, to 1799

22. The candidate evaluates the extent to which revolution broke out in France in 1789 as a result of the economic crisis of 1788 to 1789, using evidence and arguments such as:

The economic crisis of 1788/9

- Bad harvests and grain shortages inspired unrest among the peasantry and the urban workers in Paris and in provincial cities throughout France, exerting critical pressures on the Ancien Régime
- There was less demand for manufactured goods, which led to unemployment increasing amongst the urban workers
- The nobility were increasingly blamed as peasants started to take political action
- The economic crisis clearly created an environment in which the Ancien Régime was struggling to survive.

Other Factors

Financial problems of the Ancien Régime

- Because of exemptions the crown was denied adequate income. The privileged orders were an untapped source of revenue but it would require reforms to access it
- This created resentment amongst the 3rd Estate
- Exacerbated divisions that already existed between the estates
- Tax-farming meant not all revenues were reaching the government
- By the 1780s France faced bankruptcy due to heavy expenditure and borrowing to pay for wars
- Government failed to gain agreement on tax reform
- This was arguably the biggest threat facing the Ancien Régime. The opposition which this generated not only led to Calonne's dismissal in 1787 but more importantly to the convocation of the Estates General in 1788. When it met in May 1789 the long-standing divisions between the three Estates unleashed forces which culminated in the overthrow of the Ancien Régime.

Influence of the Enlightenment

- The Enlightenment encouraged criticism, and freedom of thought, speech and religion, and was seen as the end of man's self-imposed irrationality at the hands of the Church in particular
- Ideas of philosophes like Voltaire who attacked god, Montesquieu who favoured a British system of government and Rousseau who put forward the idea of direct democracy
- Very much appealed to the middle-classes, who led the revolution.

The American Revolution

- This war contributed to the financial crisis which came to a head in France post–1786 but for many in France at the time they also represented the practical expression of the enlightened views of the Philosophes in terms of the rights of the individual, no taxation without representation and freedom from tyrannical government. The wars inspired many of the lesser nobility and the bourgeoisie to seek the same freedoms.

The political crisis of 1788/9

- The convocation of the Estates General in August 1788 sharpened divisions between the three Estates which came to a head between May and August 1789. The Cahiers des Doleances revealed the depth of dissatisfaction with the existing order, especially among the bourgeoisie and the peasantry. The creation of the National Assembly, the abolition of feudalism and the Declaration of the Rights of Man and the Citizen all contributed to a revolutionary change in French government, society and economy.

Actions of Louis XVI

- Louis was largely under the influence of his wife, Marie Antoinette who, although strong minded, failed to grasp the serious nature of situation and was also unpopular as she was Austrian
- Louis XVI's handling of the Estates-General contributed towards the start of the Revolution. He wanted to make reform difficult by making the three Estates meet separately, in the hope that the First and Second Estates would vote the third down
- This backfired: opposition to the King grew, the Third Estate refused to act separately, and many of the clergy changed sides, changing the balance of power
- Louis allegedly closed the meeting halls, which led to the Tennis Court Oath from members of the Third Estate. He later agreed to a constitution when the Third Estate representatives occupied the royal tennis courts

• The King had lost more political ground than if he had just listened to the grievances of the middle classes and the Third Estate from the start.

Role of Bourgeoisie

• As part of the Third Estate resented paying the taxation
• Dominated the Third Estate representatives in the Estates-General
• Were outside the political process unless they bought a noble title: wanted access to power
• Very attracted to ideas of a constitutional monarchy as advocated by people like Montesquieu
• Provided the leadership for the revolution.

23. The candidate evaluates the extent to which army intervention in politics brought about Napoleon's coup of 1799, by using evidence and arguments such as:

Increasing intervention of the army in politics

• Even before the 1795 constitution was ratified the army had been used to quell sans-culottes insurgents who sought to invade the Convention and to repel an émigré invasion at Quiberon
• Napoleon's use of a 'whiff of grapeshot' to put down the disturbances in October merely underlined the parlous nature of politics at the time
• The deployment of the army in May 1796 to put down the left-wing Babeuf Conspiracy was followed by the Coup of Fructidor in September 1797 when the first 'free' Convention elections returned a royalist majority.

Other factors

Role of Sieyes

• Afraid that France would descend into anarchy as a result of the on-going political conflict and deeming the 1795 constitution unworkable, Sieyes enlisted the aid of Bonaparte in mounting a coup against it
• The Convention, the Directory and the legislative councils had run their course and few, if any, mourned their passing.

Political instability

• In the late summer of 1794 France was emerging from two years of increasing radicalisation and resulting bitterness between opposing factions
• The Jacobins under Robespierre had been overthrown and a 'White Terror' was soon to sweep the country in revenge for the excesses of the radical left during the Terror
• France had been torn apart by civil war, threatened by foreign armies egged on by émigré nobles seeking to overthrow the Revolution and riven by religious conflict occasioned by the State's opposition to the primacy of the Catholic Church.

The Constitution of 1795

• Policy-makers framed a new constitution which sought to reconcile the bitterness of the preceding years by imposing checks and balances against the emergence of one dominant individual, group or faction. In so doing, many historians argue that the new constitution was a recipe for instability in the years which followed
• A bi-cameral legislature was established wherein each chamber counter-balanced the power of the other. By so doing it inhibited strong and decisive government
• To ensure continuity, the new Convention was to include two-thirds of the outgoing deputies from the old. This enraged sections of the right who felt that the forces of left-wing radicalism still prevailed in government
• The resulting mass protests in October 1795 were put down by the army under Bonaparte. The principle of using extra-parliamentary forces to control the State had been established with Bonaparte right at the heart of it. It was to prove a dangerous precedent

• Annual elections worked against consistent and continuous policy-making
• So did the appointment of an Executive – the Directory – one of whose members rotated on an annual basis
• Again, the counter-balance between the legislature and the executive may have been commendable but it was to prove inherently unstable in practice.

Role of Bonaparte

• A supreme self-propagandist, he seemed to offer the strength and charisma which the Directory and the legislative councils singularly lacked
• Afraid that his spectacular victories in Italy during 1795 might be jeopardised by the election of a right-wing government less sympathetic to conducting a war against monarchical states, Bonaparte threw his support behind the Directory who effectively annulled the election results by purging right-wing deputies
• The 1788 and 1799 elections were similarly 'adjusted'
• The Consulate – with Bonaparte as First Consul – came into being. A notably more authoritarian constitution was promulgated by referendum, supported by a populace tired of weak and ineffectual government and the instability it had brought between 1795 and 1799.

24. The candidate assesses the validity of the statement that the Bourgeoisie gained most from the French Revolution, by using evidence and arguments such as:

The impact of the Revolution on the bourgeoisie

• The Revolution instigated a fundamental shift in political and economic power from the First and Second Estates to the Bourgeoisie
• The ending of feudalism in August 1789 heralded profound social and economic change (eg facilitating the development of capitalism) whilst the Declaration of the Rights of Man and the Citizen later in the month did the same for political life. In both cases the main beneficiaries were the Bourgeoisie
• Successive constitutions and legislative reforms throughout the 1790s favoured the Bourgeoisie above all other social groups by emphasising the notion of a property-owning democracy with voting rights framed within property qualifications, whilst the ending of trade restrictions and monopolies favoured an expanding business and merchant class
• France had moved from a position of privileged estates to one where increasingly merit was what counted. It was the educated Bourgeoisie who were best placed to benefit from this profound change in French society.

The impact on other sections of Society

The peasantry

• In contrast to the Catholic Church and the nobility the position of the peasantry was in many ways strengthened by the Revolution. The ending of feudalism in August 1789 removed many of the legal and financial burdens which had formed the basis of peasant grievances in the Cahiers des Doleances presented to the Estates-General in 1789
• The revolutionary land settlement, instigated by the nationalisation of church lands in November 1789, had transferred land from the nobility and the clergy to the peasantry to their obvious advantage. It should be noted, however, that not all peasants benefited equally from this. Only the well-off peasants could afford to purchase the Church lands which had been seized by the National Assembly.

The urban workers

• At key points throughout the Revolution overt demonstrations of discontent by the urban masses – particularly in Paris – impacted on key events as successive regimes framed policy with an eye to appeasing the mob. However, any modest gains by the urban poor were short-lived. A decade of almost continuous wars in the 1790s had created shortages and inflation which hit the urban poor particularly hard

- The passing of the Chapelier Law in May 1791, by a bourgeois-dominated National Assembly protecting the interests of industrialists, effectively banned the formation of trade unions and thereafter the Revolution brought few tangible economic or political gains for urban workers.

The impact of the Revolution on the First Estate

- The Catholic Church was a key pillar of the Ancien Regime. The Upper Clergy (usually drawn from the ranks of the traditional nobility) enjoyed considerable wealth and status based on a raft of privileges and tax exemptions. These privileges and exemptions were swept away by the Revolution and the position of the Catholic Church within France by 1799 was far less assured than it had been under the Ancien Regime
- The Civil Constitution of the Clergy (July 1790) polarised attitudes towards the place of the Catholic Church within French society and promoted conflict between opposing factions through the rest of the period to 1799. In November 1789 Church lands were nationalised, stripping the Church of much of its wealth. The net result of all of this was that the Church never regained its primacy within the French state and can be seen to have lost far more than it gained.

The impact of the Revolution on the Second Estate

- The aristocracy had enjoyed similar privileges and tax exemptions to those of the Catholic Church under the Ancien Regime. Advancement in the key positions of the State, the Army and, indeed the Church, depended more often on birth than merit. The traditional nobility monopolised these key positions and sought at all times to defend its favoured position. Again, the Revolution swept away aristocratic privilege even more completely than that of the clergy
- The ending of feudalism in August 1789 marked the prelude to a decade when the status of the nobility in France effectively collapsed. In 1790 outward displays of 'nobility' such as titles and coats of arms were forbidden by law and in 1797, after election results suggested a pro-royalist resurgence, the Convention imposed alien status on nobles and stripped them of French citizenship
- The Revolution brought in a regime where careers were open to talent regardless of birth or inheritance and the traditional aristocracy simply ceased to exist. Having said that, some nobles simply transformed themselves into untitled landlords in the countryside and continued to exercise significant economic and political power.

Germany 1815 – 1939

25. The candidate assesses how strong nationalism was in Germany, using evidence and arguments such as:

Supporters of nationalism

- Liberal nationalists – a united Germany should have a Liberal constitution that would guarantee the rights of citizens
- Cultural nationalists – unity was more important than individual rights and that what mattered was the preservation of German identity and culture
- Economic nationalists – unity would remove the trade barriers between states and this would allow economic growth and prosperity
- To encourage trade Prussia formed a customs union in 1818 that by the 1830s was called the Zollverein; the Zollverein helped nationalist ideas to spread
- Nationalist ideas were spread by philosophers, historians, poets and dramatists who influenced the literate middle classes and especially the students: Jahn and the burschenschaten movement; Wartburg in 1817; Hamburg in 1832; Young Germany in 1833; the Rhine Movement in 1840
- Fichte described 'Germany' as the Fatherland where all people spoke the same language and sang the same songs
- German poets and authors, such as the Grimm brothers, and composers such as Beethoven, encouraged feelings of national pride in the German states
- In 1830 anti-French feelings promoted 'the watch on the Rhine' and nationalist festivals such as Hambach (1832) also encouraged nationalist feelings.

Opponents of nationalism

- One-fifth of the population of the Austrian empire were German; the Austrian Emperor feared nationalism would encourage them to break away and join Germany; this would leave Austria weaker and cause other national groups in the Empire to demand their independence
- In 1815 Metternich became worried about the growth of liberal and nationalist student societies
- In 1819 Carlsbad Decrees banned student societies and censored newspapers
- The following year the power of the Diet was increased so that soldiers could be ordered to stop the spread of new ideas in any of the German States
- The particularism of the various German states – autonomous and parochial in many ways
- Popular apathy – most Germans had little desire to see a united Germany
- France and Russia feared that a strong, united Germany would be a political, economic and military rival to them.

Attitudes of peasants

- Golo Mann wrote that most Germans 'seldom looked up from the plough'. He doubted the influence of artists and intellectuals whom most Germans knew little or nothing about; nationalism attracted mainly the educated/business/ middle classes
- But by the late 1840s peasants were demanding that remaining feudal dues should be cancelled by their German princes.

Political turmoil in the 1840s

- Trade depression, unemployment and high food prices because of bad harvests led to revolutions throughout Europe
- In the German Confederation nationalists and liberals saw their chance; the rulers of the small states fled; elections were held to local assemblies and then to a national convention to create a united Germany; this convention or parliament met at Frankfurt.

The Frankfurt Parliament, divisions

- This was the first serious attempt to challenge Austria's political power in Germany and Austrian opposition to the liberals and nationalists
- Failure of the Frankfurt Parliament – lack of clear aims and no armed force to enforce its decisions
- Nationalists could not agree on the size of a new Germany – should it include Austria and the Hapsburg lands and Prussia's Polish possessions?
- Should it be governed by a King or be a republic or a mixture of both?
- The Protestants of the North distrusted the Southern Catholics.

The collapse of the revolution in Germany, 1848-1849

- Frankfurt Parliament failed to satisfy the needs of the starving workers who had helped create the revolution
- Parliament had to rely on the Prussian army to put down a workers' revolt

- Self-interest of German rulers led to opposition to the actions at Frankfurt
- Frederick William, King of Prussia, tried to take advantage of the defeat of the 1848 revolution to increase Prussian power to exclude Austria from the Confederation – the Erfurt Parliament
- Austria was still too strong in 1850 and was able to force Prussia to back down; at Olmutz it was agreed to return to the Constitution of 1815.

26. The candidate evaluates the extent to which the weaknesses of the Weimar Republic were the major reason for the rise of the Nazi Party between 1919 and 1933, using evidence and arguments such as:

Weaknesses of the Weimar Republic
- 'A Republic without Republicans'/'a Republic nobody wanted' – lack of popular support for the new form of government after 1918
- 'Peasants in a palace' – commentary on Weimar politicians
- Divisions among those groups/individuals who purported to be supporters of the new form of government eg the socialists
- Alliance of the new government and the old imperial army against the Spartacists – lack of cooperation between socialist groups – petty squabbling rife
- The Constitution/Article 48 ('suicide clause') - arguably Germany was too democratic. 'The world's most perfect democracy – on paper'
- Lack of real, outstanding Weimar politicians who could strengthen the Republic, Stresemann excepted
- Inability (or unwillingness) of the Republic to deal effectively with problems in German society
- Lukewarm support from the German Army and the Civil Service.

Other factors

Resentment towards the Treaty of Versailles
- The Treaty of Versailles: acceptance by Republic of hated terms
- Land loss and accepting blame for the War especially hated
- Led to growth of criticism; 'November Criminals', 'Stab in the back' myth.

Social and Economic difficulties
- Over-reliance on foreign investment left the Weimar economy subject to the fluctuations of the international economy
- 1922/23 (hyperinflation) - severe effects on the middle classes, the natural supporters of the Republic; outrage and despair at their ruination
- The Great Depression of 1929 – arguably without this the Republic might have survived. Germany's dependence on American loans showed how fragile the recovery of the late 1920s was. The pauperisation of millions again reduced Germans to despair
- Propaganda posters with legends such as "Hitler – our only hope" struck a chord with many
- The Depression also polarised politics in Germany – the drift to extremes led to a fear of Communism, which grew apace with the growth of support for the Nazis.

Appeal of the Nazis after 1928
- Nazi Party had attractive qualities for the increasingly disillusioned voting population: They were anti-Versailles, anti-Communist [the SA took on the Red Front in the streets], promised to restore German pride, give the people jobs
- The Nazis put their message across well with the skilful use of propaganda under the leadership of Josef Goebbels
- The SA were used to break up opponents meetings and give the appearance of discipline and order

- Gave scapegoats for the population to blame from the Jews to the Communists.

The role of Hitler
- Hitler was perceived as a young, dynamic leader, who campaigned using modern methods and was a charismatic speake
- He offered attractive policies which gave simple targets for blame and tapped into popular prejudice.

Weaknesses and mistakes of others
- Splits in the left after suppression of Spartacist revolt made joint action in the 1930s very unlikely.
- Roles of von Schleicher and von Papen. Underestimation of Hitler
- Weakness/indecision of Hindenburg.

27. The candidate evaluates the validity of the statement that the 'Nazis gave the people what they wanted' as a reason for the Nazis maintaining power between 1933 and 1939, using evidence and arguments such as:

Success of Economic policies
- Nazi economic policy – attempted to deal with economic ills affecting Germany, especially unemployment
- Nazis began a massive programme of public works; work of Hjalmar Schacht
- Nazi policy towards farming eg Reich Food Estate – details of various policies
- Goring's policy of 'guns before butter'. Popular once foreign policy triumphs appeared to justify it.

Other factors

Social policies
- Creation of the *volksgemeinschaft* (national community)
- Nazi youth policy
- Nazi education policy
- Nazi policy towards the Jews-first isolate, then persecute and finally destroy
- Nazi family policy – Kinder, Kirche, Kuche
- Kraft durch Freude programme
- A Concordat with the Catholic Church was reached; a Reichsbishop was appointed as head of the Protestant churches.

Success of foreign policy
- Nazi success in foreign policy attracted support among Germans; Rearmament, Rhineland, Anschluss
- 'Much of Hitler's popularity after he came to power rested on his achievements in foreign policy' (Welch).

Establishment of totalitarian state
- Political parties outlawed; non-Nazi members of the civil service were dismissed
- Nazis never quite able to silence opposition to the regime
- Speed of takeover of power and ruthlessness of the regime made opposition largely ineffective
- Anti-Nazi judges were dismissed and replaced with those favourable to the Nazis
- Acts Hostile to the National Community (1935) – all-embracing law which allowed the Nazis to persecute opponents in a 'legal' way.

Fear and state terrorism
- The use of fear/terror through the Nazi police state; role of the Gestapo
- Concentration camps set up; the use of the SS.

Crushing of opposition
- Opponents liable to severe penalties, as were their families
- Opponents never able to establish a single organisation to channel their resistance – role of the Gestapo, paid informers

• Opposition lacked cohesion and a national leader; also lacked armed supporters
• Lack of cooperation between socialists and communists – role of Stalin considered.

Propaganda
• Use of Nuremburg Rallies
• Use of Radio
• Cult of the Leader: the Hitler myth
• Use of the Cinema: Triumph of the Will, the Eternal Jew, etc
• Role of Goebbels.

Italy 1815 – 1939

28. The candidate assesses the success of supporters of Italian nationalism up to 1850, using evidence and arguments such as:

Supporters of nationalism

Educated middle class
• Risorgimento saw 'patriotic literature' from novelists and poets including Pellico, and Leopardi. These inspired the educated middle class
• Gioberti, Balbo and Mazzini promoted their ideas for a national state, this inspired nationalism amongst the middle classes.

Liberals
• Some liberals and business classes were keen to develop an economic state. Napoleon Bonaparte had built roads and encouraged closer trading. One system of weights, measures and currency appealed.

Popular sentiment
• French revolutionary ideals had inspired popular sentiment for a national Italian state.
• There was a growing desire for the creation of a national state amongst students; many joined Mazzini's 'Young Italy'
• Operas by Verdi and Rossini inspired growing feelings of patriotism
• The use of Tuscan as a 'national' language by Alfieri and Manzoni spread ideas of nationalism
• Membership of secret societies such as the Carbonari grew. Members were willing to revolt and die for their beliefs which included desire for a national state.

Opponents

Austria
• Resentment against Austria and its restoration of influence in the Italian peninsula and their use of spies and censorship, helped increase support for the nationalist cause. However, any progress made by nationalists was firmly crushed by the Austrian army. Strength of the Quadrilateral. Austrians never left Italian soil. Carbonari revolts in Kingdom of Naples 1820-1821, Piedmont 1821, Modena and the Papal States 1831 all crushed by Austrian army. During 1848-1849 revolutions, Austrian army defeated Charles Albert twice – Custoza and Modena, retook Lombardy and destroyed the Republic of St Mark.

Italian princes and rulers
• Individual rulers were opposed to nationalism and used censorship, police and spies as well as the Austrian army, to crush revolts 1820-1821, 1830 and 1848-1849.

Attitude of the peasants
• The mass of the population were illiterate and indifferent to politics and nationalist ideas. They did revolt during bad times as can be seen in 1848 – but their revolts were due to bad harvests and bad economic times and were not inspired by feelings of nationalism.

Position of the Papacy
• Pope Pius IX. Nationalist movement had high hopes of New Pope Pius IX, initially thought of as a liberal and sympathetic to nationalist cause. Hopes dashed when Pope Pius IX denounced the nationalist movement during 1848-49 revolutions.

Failures of 1848 – 1849 revolutions
• These showed that nationalist leaders would not work together, nor did they seek foreign help thus hindering progress. Charles Albert's 'Italia farad a se' declared that Italy would do it alone – she did not. Lombardy and Venetia suspected Charles Albert's motives and were reluctant to work with him. Venetians put more faith in Manin
• All progress was hampered when Pope Pius IX denounced nationalism. Charles Albert hated Mazzini and would not support the Roman Republic. Austrian military might based on the Quadrilateral defeated Charles Albert twice – at Custoza and Modena, retook Lombardy and destroyed the Republic of St Mark
• The French crushed the Roman Republic.

29. The candidate evaluates the accuracy of the claim that the appeal of fascism was the main reason why Mussolini came to power in Italy by 1925, using evidence and arguments such as:

Appeal of the Fascists
• They exploited weaknesses of other groups by excellent use of Mussolini's newspaper 'Il Popolo D'Italia'
• The Fascio Italiano di Combattimento began as a movement not a political party and thus attracted a wide variety of support giving them an advantage over narrower rivals
• By 1921 – fascism was anti-communist, anti-trade union, anti-socialist and pro-nationalism and thus became attractive to the middle and upper classes
• Fascism became pro-conservative, appealed to family values, supported church and monarchy; promised to work within the accepted political system. This made fascism more respectable and appealing to both the monarchy and the papacy
• Squadristi violence was directed against socialism so it gained the support of elites and middle classes
• Violence showed fascism was strong and ruthless. It appealed to many ex-soldiers
• Fascists promised strong government. This was attractive after a period of extreme instability
• Fascists promised to make Italy respected as a nation and thus appealed to nationalists
• Fascist policies were kept deliberately vague to attract support from different groups.

Other factors

Role of Mussolini
• Key role in selling the Fascist message: Powerful orator – piazza politics
• He seized his opportunities. He changed political direction and copied D'Annunzio
• He used propaganda and his newspaper effectively and had an ear for effective slogans
• He dominated the fascist movement kept support of Fascist extremists (Ras)
• He relied on strong nerve to seize power and to survive the Matteotti crisis
• Mussolini manipulated his image, kept out of violence himself but exploited the violence of others.

Weaknesses of Italian governments
• Parliamentary government was weak – informal 'liberal' coalitions. Corruption was commonplace (trasformismo). Liberals were not a structured party. New parties formed: PSI (socialists), PPI (Catholic Popular Party) with wider support base threatening existing political system

- WWI worsened the situation; wartime coalitions were very weak. 1918; universal male suffrage and 1919 Proportional Representation; relied on 'liberals' – unstable coalitions. Giolitti made an electoral pact with Mussolini (1921); Fascists gained 35 seats then refused to support the government. Over the next 16 months, three ineffective coalition governments
- Fascists threatened a 'March on Rome' – King refused to agree to martial law; Facta resigned; Mussolini was invited to form coalition. 1924 Acerbo Law.

Resentment against the Peace Settlement
- Large loss of life in frustrating campaigns in the Alps and the Carso led to expectation that these would be recognised in the peace settlement; Wilson's commitment to nationalist aims led to the creation of Yugoslavia and a frustration of Italian hopes of dominating the Adriatic
- 'Mutilated victory' – Italian nationalists fuelled ideas that Italy had been betrayed by her government.

Role of the King
- The King gave in to Fascist pressure during the March on Rome. He failed to call Mussolini's bluff
- After the Aventine Secession the King was unwilling to dismiss Mussolini.

Economic difficulties
- WWI imposed serious strain on the Italian economy. The government took huge foreign loans and the National Debt was 85 billion lira by 1918. The Lira lost half of its value, devastating middle class savers. Inflation was rising; prices in 1918 were four times higher than 1914. This led to further major consequences:
  - no wage rises
  - food shortages
  - two million unemployed 1919
  - firms collapsed as military orders ceased.

Social and economic divisions
- Membership of trade unions and PSI rose – strikes, demonstrations, violence. 1919/20 'Biennio Rosso' in towns – general strike 1920; army mutiny; occupation of factories
- Industrialists/middle classes were fearful of revolution. Governments failed to back the police so law and order broke down
- In the countryside, there was seizure of common land – peasant ownership increased.

Weaknesses and mistakes of opponents
- D'Annunzio's seizure of Fiume was not stopped by the government
- Government failed to get martial law to stop fascist threat. Some liberals supported the Acerbo Law
- Socialist General Strike July 1922 – failed. Socialists' split weakened them; refused to join together to oppose fascism
- Liberals fragmented into four factions grouped around former PMs. They were too weak to effectively resist. Hoped to tame Fascists
- PPI were divided over attitude to fascism – right wing supported fascism. Aventine Secession backfired; destroyed chance to remove Mussolini.

30. The candidate evaluates how important the use of fear and intimidation was in maintaining Fascist control over Italy between 1922 and 1939, using evidence and arguments such as:

Fear and intimidation
- Mussolini favoured complete State authority with everything under his direct control. All Italians were expected to obey Mussolini and his Fascist Party

- The squadristi were organised into the MVSN – *Milizia Voluntaria per la Sicurezza Nazionale* – the armed local Fascist militia (Blackshirts). They terrorised the cities and provinces causing fear with tactics such as force-feeding with toads and castor oil
- After 1925–6 around 10,000 non-Fascists/opposition leaders were jailed by special tribunals
- The Secret police, OVRA was established in 1927 and was lead by Arturo Bocchini. Tactics included abduction and torture of opponents. 4000 people were arrested by the OVRA and sent to prison
- Penal colonies were established on remote Mediterranean islands such as Ponza and Lipari. Conditions for those sentenced to these prisons were primitive with little chance of escape
- Opponents were exiled internally or driven into exile abroad
- The death penalty was restored under Mussolini for serious offences but by 1940 only ten people had been sentenced to death.

Other relevant factors

Establishment of the Fascist state
- Nov/Dec 1922 Mussolini was given emergency powers. Nationalists merged with PNF 1923. Mussolini created MSVN (fascist militia) – gave him support if the army turned against him – and Fascist Grand Council – a rival Cabinet. These two bodies made Mussolini's position stronger and opposition within PNF weaker. The establishment of a dictatorship began:
- 1926 – opposition parties were banned. A one party state was created
- 1928 – universal suffrage abolished
- 1929 – all Fascist Parliament elected.

Crushing of opposition
- Liberals had divided into four factions so were weakened
- The Left had divided into three – original PSI, reformist PSU and Communists – they failed to work together against Fascists
- Pope forced Sturzo to resign and so PPI (Catholic Popular Party) was weakened and it split
- Acerbo Law passed. 1924 elections – Fascists won 66% of the vote
- Opposition parties failed to take advantage of the Matteotti crisis. By walking out of the Chamber of Deputies (Aventine Secession) they gave up the chance to overthrow Mussolini; they remained divided – the Pope refused to sanction an alliance between PPI and the socialists. The King chose not to dismiss Mussolini
- Communists and socialists did set up organisations in exile but did not work together. Communist cells in northern cities did produce some anti-fascist leaflets but they suffered frequent raids by OVRA
- PPI opposition floundered with the closer relationship between Church and State (Lateran Pacts).

Social controls
- Workers were controlled through 22 corporations, set up in 1934; overseen by National Council of Corporations, chaired by Mussolini
- Corporations provided accident, health and unemployment insurance for workers, but forbade strikes and lock-outs
- There were some illegal strikes in 1930s and anti-Fascist demonstrations in 1933 but these were limited
- The majority of Italians got on with their own lives conforming as long as all was going well. Middle classes/elites supported fascism as it protected them from communism

- Youth knew no alternative to fascism, were educated as Fascists and this strengthened the regime. Youth movements provided sporting opportunities, competitions, rallies, camps, parades and propaganda lectures – 60% membership in the north.

Propaganda

- Press, radio and cinema were all controlled
- Mussolini was highly promoted as a 'saviour' sent by God to help Italy – heir to Caesar, world statesman, supreme patriot, a great thinker who worked 20 hours a day, a man of action, incorruptible.

Foreign policy

- Mussolini was initially extremely popular, as evidenced by huge crowds who turned out to hear him speak
- Foreign policy successes in the 1920s, such as the Corfu Incident, made him extremely popular. He was also able to mobilise public opinion very successfully for the invasion of Abyssinia
- Mussolini's role in the Munich Conference of 1938 was his last great foreign policy triumph
- As Mussolini got more closely involved with Hitler his popularity lessened. His intervention in Spain proved a huge drain on Italy's resources. The invasion of Albania was a fiasco. The Fascist Grand Council removed him in 1943.

Relations with the Papacy

- Lateran treaties/Concordat with Papacy enabled acceptance of regime by the Catholic majority
- Many Catholics supported Mussolini's promotion of 'family values'.

Economic and social policies

- Fascists tried to develop the Italian economy in a series of propaganda-backed initiatives eg the 'Battle for Grain'. While superficially successful, they did tend to divert resources from other areas
- Development of transport infrastructure, with building of autostrade and redevelopment of major railway terminals eg Milan
- One major success was the crushing of organized crime. Most Mafia leaders were in prison by 1939
- Dopolavoro had 3.8 million members by 1939. Gave education and skills training; sports provision, day-trips, holidays, financial assistance and cheap rail fares. This diverted attention from social/economic problems and was the Fascist state's most popular institution.

Russia 1881 – 1921

31. The candidate evaluates the importance of working class discontent in causing the 1905 revolution in Russia, using evidence and arguments such as:

Discontent of Working Class

- At the start of the 1900s there was industrial recession which caused a lot of hardship for the working class
- The working class complaints were long hours, low pay, poor conditions, the desire for a constitutional government and an end to the war with Japan
- There was a wave of strikes in Jan 1905 with nearly half a million people on strike (10 times the number in the previous decade)
- In October there were two and half million people on strike as well as demonstrations
- Soviets were speaking for the workers and expressing political demands.

Other Factors

Discontent with Repressive Government and its policies

- There was discontent amongst various factions in Russian society
- The middle class and some of the gentry were unhappy with the government at the time
- The middle class was aggrieved at having no participation in government, and angry at the incompetence of the government during the war with Japan
- There was propaganda from middle class groups, Zemstva called for change, the Radical Union of Unions was formed to combine professional groups
- Students rioted, and carried out assassinations
- The gentry tried to convince the Tsar to make minor concessions
- Political groups did not really play a role although they encouraged peasant unrest, and strikes in the urban areas
- The Mensheviks had influence in the soviets and the Bolsheviks were involved in the Moscow Rising
- Russification: The National minorities were aggrieved at the lack of respect for their culture language and religion, and the imposition of the Russian language
- The National minorities harboured a great desire for independence or at least greater autonomy and began to assert themselves, such as Georgia which declared its independence.

Economic problems

- Worsening economic conditions such as famines in 1897, 1898 and 1901 had led to shortage and distress in the countryside. Urban workers conditions and pay also dreadful
- Economic recession between 1899 and 1903 led to growing unemployment throughout the Empire.

Discontent amongst the Peasants

- The peasants had several grievances such as Redemption payments, high taxes, Land Hunger and poverty
- There was a wave of unrest in 1902 and 1903, which had gradually increased by 1905 There were various protests like timber cutting, seizure of lords' land, labour and rent strikes, attacks on landlord's grain stocks, landlords estates seized and divided up
- There were claims that peasants should boycott paying taxes, redemption payments and refuse to be conscripted to the army.

War with Japan

- The war with Japan was a failure and humiliation for the country and moreover this was compounded by the heavy losses suffered by the Russian army
- The war was initially to distract the public from domestic troubles by rallying patriotism
- The incompetence of the government during the war made social unrest worse rather than dampening it
- Troops suffered from low morale after the defeat and there were complaints about poor pay and conditions
- There were some sporadic but uncoordinated revolts although nothing too major
- There were mutinies by troops waiting to return from the war and on the Trans Siberian Railway
- In June there was the Potemkin mutiny although the planned general mutiny did not follow
- Generally though most of the troops remained loyal (unlike 1917).

Bloody Sunday

- 22nd Jan 1905 Father Gapon, an Orthodox priest attempted to lead a peaceful March of workers and their families to the Winter Palace to deliver a petition asking the Tsar to improve the conditions of the workers

- Marchers were fired on and killed by troops
- Many of the people saw this as a brutal massacre by the Tsar and his troops
- Bloody Sunday greatly damaged the traditional image of the Tsar as the "Little Father", the Guardian of the Russian people
- Reaction to Bloody Sunday was strong and was nationwide with disorder strikes in urban areas, terrorism against government officials and landlords, much of which was organised by the SRs
- The situation was made worse by the defeat to Japan in 1905
- The assassination of government minister Plehve.

32. The candidate evaluates the extent to which the Bolsheviks gained power due to the weaknesses of the Provisional Government, using evidence and arguments such as:

Weaknesses of the Provisional Government
- The Provisional Government was an unelected government; it was a self-appointed body and had no right to exercise authority, which led it into conflict with those bodies that emerged with perceived popular legitimacy
- The Provisional Government gave in to the pressure of the army and from the Allies to keep Russia in the War
- Remaining in the war helped cause the October Revolution and helped destroy the Provisional Government as the misery it caused continued for people in Russia
- General Kornilov, a right wing general, proposed to replace the Provisional Government with a military dictatorship and sent troops to Petrograd
- Kerensky appealed to the Petrograd Soviet for help and the Bolsheviks were amongst those who helped
- Some Bolsheviks were armed and released from prison to help put down the attempted coup.

Other Factors

Appeal of the Bolsheviks
- Lenin returned to Russia announcing the April Theses, with slogans such as "Peace, Land and Bread" and "All Power to the Soviets" which were persuasive
- Lenin talked of further revolution to overthrow the Provisional Government and his slogans identified the key weaknesses of the Provisional Government
- The Bolsheviks kept attending the Petrograd Soviet when most of the others stopped doing so and this gave them control of the Soviet, which they could then use against the Provisional Government
- The Bolsheviks did not return their weapons to the Provisional Government after they defeated Kornilov
- Bolsheviks were able to act as protectors of Petrograd.

Dual power – The role of the Petrograd Soviet
- The old Petrograd Soviet re emerged and ran Petrograd
- The Petrograd Soviet undermined the authority of Provisional Government especially when relations between the two worsened
- Order No.1 of the Petrograd Soviet weakened the authority of the Provisional Government as soldiers were not to obey orders of Provisional Government that contradicted those of the Petrograd Soviet.

Economic problems
- The workers were restless as they were starving due to food shortages caused by the war
- The shortage of fuel caused lack of heating for the workers in their living conditions
- The shortage of food and supplies made the workers unhappy and restless
- The Bolsheviks' slogans appealed to them such as the workers control of industry.

The Land Issue
- All over Russia peasants were seizing nobles land and wanted the Provisional Government to legitimise this
- The failure of the Provisional Government to recognise the peasants' claims eroded confidence in the Provisional Government
- Food shortages caused discontent, and they were caught up by revolutionary slogans such as "Peace, Land And Bread".

The July Days
- The Bolsheviks staged an attempt to seize power, rising in support of the Kronstadt sailors who were in revolt
- The revolt was easily crushed by the Provisional Government but showed increasing opposition to the PG, especially from the forces
- The revolt also showed that the PG was still reasonably strong and able to crush opposition such as the Bolsheviks who now appeared to be weakened.

33. The candidate evaluates how important the use of terror by the Reds was in allowing them to win the Civil War, using evidence and arguments such as:

Terror (Cheka)
- The Cheka was set up to eradicate any opposition to the Reds
- There was no need for proof of guilt for punishment to be exacted
- There was persecution of individual people who opposed the Reds as well as whole groups of people, which helped to reduce opposition due to fear, or simply eradicate opposition
- The Cheka group carried out severe repression
- Some of the first victims of the Cheka were leaders of other political parties
- 140,000 were executed by 1922 when Lenin was happy that all opposition had been suppressed.

Other Factors

Organisation of the Red Army
- The Red Army was better organized than the White Army and better equipped and therefore able to crush any opposition from the White forces
- Use of ex-officers from old Imperial Army
- Reintroduction of rank and discipline
- Role of Commissars.

Role of Trotsky
- Trotsky had a completely free hand in military matters
- HQ was heavily armed train, which he used to travel around the country
- He supervised the formation of the Red Army, which became a formidable fighting force of three million men
- He recruited ex-Tsar army officers and used political commissars to watch over them, thus ensuring experienced officers but no political recalcitrance
- He used conscription to gain troops and would shoot any deserters
- Trotsky helped provide an army with great belief in what it was fighting for, which the Whites did not have.

Disunity among Whites
- The Whites were an uncoordinated series of groups whose morale was low
- The Whites were a collection of socialists, liberals, moderates etc who all wanted different things and often fought amongst themselves due to their political differences. All of the Whites shared a hatred of Communism but other than this they lacked a common purpose
- No White leader of any measure emerged to unite and lead the White forces whereas the Reds had Trotsky and Lenin.

Superior Red resources
- Once the Reds had established defence of their lines they were able to repel and exhaust the attacks by the Whites until they scattered or surrendered
- With the major industrial centres in their land (Moscow and Petrograd) the Reds had access to factories to supply weapons etc and swiftly move due to their control of the railways.
- Control of the Railways meant they could transport troops and supplies quickly and efficiently and in large numbers to the critical areas of defence or attack
- The decisive battles between the Reds and Whites were near railheads
- The Reds were in control of a concentrated area of western Russia, which they could successfully defend due to the maintenance of their communication and supply lines
- Having the two major cities of Moscow and Petrograd in their possession meant that the Reds had the hold of the industrial centres of Russia as well as the administrative centres
- Having the two major cities gave the Reds munitions and supplies that the Whites were unable to therefore obtain.

Foreign Intervention
- The Bolsheviks were able to claim that the foreign "invaders" were imperialists who were trying to overthrow the revolution and invade Russia
- The Reds were able to stand as Champions of the Russian nation from foreign invasion
- The help received by the Whites from foreign powers was not as great as was hoped for
- The Foreign Powers did not provide many men due to the First World War just finishing and their help was mostly restricted to money and arms.

Propaganda
- Whites were unable to take advantage of the brutality of the Reds to win support as they often carried out similar atrocities
- The Whites were unable to present themselves as a better alternative to the Reds due to their brutality
- The Reds kept pointing out that all of the land that the peasants had seized in the 1917 Revolution would be lost if the Whites won. This fear prevented the peasants from supporting the Whites.

Leadership of Lenin
- Introduction of War Communism
- By forcing the peasants to sell their grain to the Reds for a fixed price the Reds were able to ensure that their troops were well supplied with and well fed
- The Whites' troops were not as well supplied and fed as the Reds' troops
- Skilled delegation and ruthlessness.

USA 1918 – 1968

34. The candidate evaluates how far it can be argued that the activities of the Ku Klux Klan as the most important obstacle to the achievement of Civil Rights for black people up to 1941, using evidence and arguments such as:

Activities of the Ku Klux Klan
- Founded in 1860s to prevent former slaves achieving equal rights
- Suppressed by 1872, but in the 1920s there was a resurgence
- Black population in South terrified to campaign for civil rights by actions of KKK
- By 1925 it had three million members, including the police, judges and politicians
- Secret organisation with powerful members

- 1923 Hiram Wesley Evans became the Klan's leader
- Methods horrific: included beatings, torture and lynching
- Roosevelt refused to support a federal bill to outlaw lynching in his New Deal in 1930s – feared loss of Democrat support in South
- Activities took place at night – men in white robes, guns, torches, burning crosses
- The 'second' Klan grew most rapidly in urbanizing cities which had high growth rates between 1910 and 1930, such as Detroit, Memphis, Dayton, Atlanta, Dallas and Houston
- Klan membership in Alabama dropped to less than 6,000 by 1930. Small independent units continued to be active in places like Birmingham.

Other Factors

Legal impediments
- 'Jim Crow Laws' – separate education, transport, toilets etc – passed in Southern states after the Civil War
- 'Separate but Equal' Supreme Court Decision 1896, when Homer Plessey tested their legality
- Attitudes of Presidents eg Wilson 'Segregation is not humiliating and is a benefit for you black gentlemen'.

Lack of political influence
- 1890s: loopholes in the interpretation of the 15th Amendment were exploited so that states could impose voting qualifications
- 1898 case of Mississippi v Williams – voters must understand the American Constitution
- Grandfather Clause: impediment to black people voting
- Most black people in the South were sharecroppers they did not own land and some states identified ownership of property as a voting qualification
- Therefore black people could not vote, particularly in the South, and could not elect anyone who would oppose the Jim Crow Laws.

Divisions in the black community
- Booker T Washington, accomodationist philosophy, regarded as an 'Uncle Tom' by many
- In contrast W E B De Bois founded the NAACP – a national organisation whose main aim was to oppose discrimination through legal action. 1919 he launched a campaign against lynching, but it failed to attract most black people and was dominated by white people and well off black people
- Marcus Garvey and Black Pride – he founded the UNIA (Universal Negro Improvement Association) which aimed to get blacks to 'take Africa, organise it, develop it, arm it, and make it the defender of Negroes the world over'.

Popular prejudice
- After the institution of slavery the status of Africans was stigmatised, and this stigma was the basis for the anti-African racism that persisted
- The relocation of millions of African Americans from their roots in the Southern states to the industrial centres of the North after World War I, particularly in cities such as Boston, Chicago, and New York (Harlem). In northern cities, racial tensions exploded, most violently in Chicago, and lynchings – mob-directed hangings, usually racially motivated – increased dramatically in the 1920s.

35. The candidate evaluates the importance of the emergence of effective black leaders in the growing demand for Civil Rights between 1945 and 1968, using evidence and arguments such as:

The emergence of effective black leaders
- Martin Luther King – inspirational. Linked with SCLC. Peaceful non violence and effective use of the media
- Malcolm X – inspirational, but more confrontational. Articulate voice of Nation of Islam

- Stokely Carmichael – Black power and rejection of much of MLK's non violent approach. A direct ideas descendant of Marcus Garvey
- All leaders attracted media coverage, large followings and divided opinion across USA
- Black Panthers attracted attention but lost support by their confrontational tactics
- Other leaders and organisations eclipsed by media focus on main personalities.

Other factors

Effective black organisations formed
- 1957 Martin Luther King and other black clergy formed the Southern Christian Leadership Conference (SCLC) to coordinate the work of Civil Rights groups
- King urged African Americans to use peaceful methods
- 1960 a group of black and white college students organised Non-violent Coordinating Committee (SNCC) to help the Civil Rights movement
- They joined with young people from the SCLC, CORE and NAACP in staging sit-ins, boycotts marches and freedom rides
- Combined efforts of the Civil Rghts groups ended discrimination in many public places including restaurants, hotels, and theatres.

Continuing racial discrimination pushed many black Americans to demand civil rights
- The experience of war emphasised freedom, democracy and human rights yet in USA Jim Crow laws still existed and lynching went unpunished
- The Emmet Till murder trial and its publicity
- Education: 1954 Brown v Board of Education of Topeka; 1957 Little Rock Central High School
- Transport: 1955 Rosa Parks and the Montgomery Bus Boycott.

Influence of Second World War
- Black soldiers talked about 'the Double-V-Campaign': Victory in the war and victory for Civil Rights at home
- Philip Randolph is credited with highlighting the problems faced by black Americans during World War Two
- Planned March on Washington in 1941 to protest against racial discrimination
- Roosevelt's response – Executive order 8802
- Roosevelt also established the Fair Employment Practices Committee to investigate incidents of discrimination
- Creation of the Congress of Racial Equality (CORE) 1942
- Beginning of a mass movement for Civil Rights.

36. The candidate assesses the extent to which the Civil Rights campaigns of the 1950s and 1960s resulted in significant improvements in the lives of black Americans, using evidence and arguments such as:

Aims of Civil Rights movement
- Were mainly pacifist and intended to bring Civil Rights and equality in law to all non-white Americans
- More radical segregationist aims of Black Radical Movements.

Role of NAACP
- Work of NAACP in the Brown v Topeka Board of Education, 1954
- Work of NAACP in the Montgomery Bus Boycott, 1955.

Role of Congress of Racial Equality [CORE]
- Organised sit-ins during 1961 and freedom rides
- Helped organise march on Washington
- Instrumental in setting up Freedom Schools in Mississippi.

Role of SCLC and Martin Luther King
- Emergence of Martin Luther King and the SCLC
- Little Rock, Arkansas - desegregation following national publicity
- Non-violent protest as exemplified by Sit-ins and Freedom Rides
- Birmingham, Alabama 1963: use of water cannon: Reaction of Kennedy
- March on Washington, August 1963 - massive publicity
- Martin Luther King believed that the Civil Rights Act of 1964 'gave Negroes some part of their rightful dignity, but without the vote it was dignity without strength'
- March 1965, King led a march from Selma to Birmingham, Alabama, to publicise the way in which the authorities made it difficult for black Americans to vote easily.

Changes in Federal Policy
- Use of executive orders: Truman used them to appoint black appointments, order equality of treatment in the armed services: Kennedy signed 1962 executive order outlawing racial discrimination in public housing, etc
- Eisenhower sent in army troops and National Guardsmen to protect nine African-American students enrolled at Little Rock Central High School: Kennedy sent troops to Oxford, Mississippi to protect black student: James Meredith
- Johnson and the 1964 Civil Rights Act banning racial discrimination in any public place, Voting Rights Act of 1965: by end of 1965 over 250,000 Blacks newly registered to vote, Affirmative Action, etc.

Social, Economic and Political changes
- Civil Rights Acts of 1964 and 1965 irrelevant to the cities of the North
- Economic issues more important in the North
- Watts riots and the split in the Civil Rights movement
- King and the failure in Chicago
- Urban poverty and de facto segregation still common in urban centres – failure of King's campaign to attack poverty.

Rise of black radical movements
- Stokely Carmichael and Black Power
- Malcolm X publicised the increasing urban problems within the ghettos of America
- The Black Panthers were involved in self-help schemes throughout poor cities
- Kerner commission 1968 recognised US society still divided.

Appeasement and the Road to War, to 1939

37. The candidate assesses the extent to which fascist powers used diplomacy to achieve their aims using evidence and arguments such as:

Fascist diplomacy as a means of achieving aims:
- Aims can be generally accepted as destruction of Versailles, the weakening of democracies, the expansion of fascist powers and countering communism
- Diplomacy and the protestation of 'peaceful' intentions and 'reasonable' demands
- Appeals to sense of international equality and fairness and the righting of past wrongs eg Versailles
- Withdrawal from League and Disarmament Conference
- Anglo German Naval Treaty 1935 - Germany allowed to expand navy. Versailles ignored in favour of bi lateral agreements. A gain for Germany
- Prior to Remilitarisation of Rhineland Hitler made offer of 25 year peace promise
- Diplomacy used to distract and delay reaction to Nazi action.

Economic reasons
- Use of economic influence and pressure, eg on south-eastern European states

- Aid supplied to Franco (Spain) was tactically important to Hitler. Not only for testing weapons but also access to Spanish minerals.

Pacts and alliances
- The German-Polish Non-Aggression Pact between Nazi Germany and Poland signed on January 26, 1934 – normalised relations between Poland and Germany, and promised peace for 10 years. Germany gained respectability and calmed international fears
- Rome-Berlin axis – treaty of friendship signed between Italy and Germany on 25 October 1936
- Pact of Steel an agreement between Italy and Germany signed on May 22, 1939 for immediate aid and military support in the event of war
- Anti-Comintern Pact between Nazi-Germany and Japan on November 25th, 1936. The pact directed against the Communist International (Comintern) but was specifically directed against the Soviet Union. In 1937 Italy joined the Pact Munich Agreement – negotiations led to Hitler gaining Sudetenland and weakening Czechoslovakia
- Nazi Soviet Non-Aggression Pact August 1939 – both Hitler and Stalin bought time for themselves. For Hitler it seemed war in Europe over Poland unlikely. Poland was doomed. Britain had lost the possibility of alliance with Russia.

Rearmament
- Open German rearmament from 1935
- The speed and scale of rearmament, including conscription
- The emphasis on air power and the growing threat from the air
- By 1939, Hitler had an army of nearly 1 million men, over 8,000 aircraft and 95 warships
- Mussolini embarked on a rearmament programme to protect Italy from worldwide depression. His building of a modern navy seriously threatened British domination of the Mediterranean as a result.

Military threat and force
- Italy's naval ambitions in the Mediterranean – 'Mare Nostrum'
- Italian invasion of Abyssinia – provocation, methods, and relatively poor performance against very poorly equipped enemy
- German remilitarisation of Rhineland – Hitler's gamble and timing, his generals' opposition, lack of Allied resistance
- Spanish Civil War – aid to Nationalists, testing weapons and tactics, aerial bombing of Guernica
- Anschluss – attempted coup 1934; relations with Schuschnigg; invasion itself relatively botched militarily; popularity of Anschluss in Austria
- Czechoslovakia – threats of 1938; invasion of March 1939
- Italian invasion of Albania – relatively easy annexation of a client state
- Poland – escalating demands; provocation, invasion
- The extent to which it was the threat of military force which was used rather than military force itself – eg Czechoslovakia in 1938; and the extent to which military force itself was effective and/or relied on an element of bluff – eg Rhineland.

38. The candidate assesses the validity of the statement that the Munich agreement of 1938 was a "reasonable settlement under the circumstances", using evidence and arguments such as:

Munich reasonable under circumstances
- Czechoslovakian defences were effectively outflanked anyway following the Anschluss
- Britain and France were not in a position to prevent German attack on Czechoslovakia in terms of difficulties of getting assistance to Czechoslovakia
- British public opinion was reluctant to risk war over mainly German-speaking Sudetenland

- Military unpreparedness for wider war – especially Britain's air defences
- Lack of alternative, unified international response to Hitler's threats
- Failure of League of Nations in earlier crises
- French doubts over commitments to Czechoslovakia
- US isolationism
- British suspicion of Soviet Russia
- Strong reservations of rest of British Empire and Dominions concerning support for Britain in event of war
- Attitudes of Poland and Hungary who were willing to benefit from the dismemberment of Czechoslovakia
- Munich bought another year for rearmament which Britain put to good use
- Views of individuals, politicians and media at this time.

Munich not reasonable
- A humiliating surrender to Hitler's threats
- Another breach in the post-WW1 settlement
- A betrayal of Czechoslovakia and democracy
- Czechoslovakia wide open to further German aggression as happened in March 1939
- Further augmentation of German manpower and resources
- Furtherance of Hitler's influence and ambitions in Eastern Europe
- Further alienation of Soviet Union
- Poland left further exposed
- A British, French, Soviet agreement could have been a more effective alternative
- Views of individuals, politicians and media at this time.

39. The candidate evaluates the extent to which the occupation of Czechoslovakia in March 1939 led to the outbreak of World War Two six months later, using evidence and arguments such as:

The occupation of Bohemia and the collapse of Czechoslovakia
- British and French realisation, after Hitler's breaking of Munich Agreement and invasion of Czechoslovakia in March 1939, that Hitler's word was worthless and that his aims went beyond the incorporation of ex-German territories and ethnic Germans within the Reich
- Promises of support to Poland and Rumania
- British public acceptance that all attempts to maintain peace had been exhausted
- Prime Minister Chamberlain felt betrayed by the Nazi seizure of Czechoslovakia, realised his policy of appeasement towards Hitler had failed, and began to take a much harder line against the Nazis.

Other factors

British abandonment of the policy of Appeasement
- Events in Bohemia and Moravia consolidated growing concerns in Britain
- Czechoslovakia did not concern most people until the middle of September 1938, when they began to object to a small democratic state being bullied. However, most press and population went along with it, although level of popular opposition often underestimated
- German annexation of Memel (largely German population, but in Lithuania) further showed Hitler's bad faith
- Actions convinced British government of growing German threat in south-eastern Europe
- Guarantees to Poland and promised action in the event of threats to Polish independence.

Importance of Nazi-Soviet Pact
- Pact – diplomatic, economic, military co-operation; division of Poland
- Unexpected – Hitler and Stalin's motives

- Put an end to British-French talks with Russia on guarantees to Poland
- Hitler was freed from the threat of Soviet intervention and war on two fronts
- Hitler's belief that Britain and France would not go to war over Poland without Russian assistance
- Hitler now felt free to attack Poland
- But, given Hitler's consistent, long-term foreign policy aims on the destruction of the Versailles settlement and lebensraum in the east, the Nazi-Soviet Pact could be seen more as a factor influencing the timing of the outbreak of war rather than as one of its underlying causes
- Hitler's long-term aims for destruction of the Soviet state and conquest of Russian resources - lebensraum
- Hitler's need for new territory and resources to sustain Germany's militarised economy
- Hitler's belief that British and French were 'worms' who would not turn from previous policy of appeasement and avoidance of war at all costs
- Hitler's belief that the longer war was delayed the more the balance of military and economic advantage would shift against Germany.

British diplomacy and relations with the Soviet Union
- Stalin knew that Hitler's ultimate aim was to attack Russia
- Lord Halifax, the British Foreign Secretary was invited by Stalin to go to Russia to discuss an alliance against Germany
- Britain refused as they feared Russian Communism, and they believed that the Russian army was too weak to be of any use against Hitler
- In August 1939, with war in Poland looming, the British and French eventually sent a military mission to discuss an alliance with Russia. Owing to travel difficulties it took five days to reach Leningrad
- The Russians asked if they could send troops into Poland if Hitler invaded. The British refused, knowing that the Poles would not want this. The talks broke down
- This merely confirmed Stalin's suspicions regarding the British. He felt they could not be trusted, especially after the Munich agreement, and they would leave Russia to fight Germany alone. This led directly to opening talks with the Nazis who seemed to be taking the Russians seriously by sending Foreign Minister von Ribbentrop and offering peace and land.

The position of France
- France had signed an agreement with Czechoslovakia offering support if the country was attacked. However, Hitler could all but guarantee that in 1938, French would do nothing as their foreign policy was closely tied to the British
- French military, and particularly their airforce, allowed to decline in years after 1919
- After Munich, French more aggressive towards dictators and in events of 1939 were keen on a military alliance with the Soviet Union, however despite different emphasis on tactics were tied to the British and their actions.

Developing crisis over Poland
- Hitler's long-term aims for the destruction of Versailles, including regaining of Danzig and Polish Corridor
- British and French decision to stick to their guarantees to Poland.

Invasion of Poland
- On 1 September 1939, Hitler and the Nazis faked a Polish attack on a minor German radio station in order to justify a German invasion of Poland. An hour later Hitler declared war on Poland stating one of his reasons for the invasion was because of "the attack by regular Polish troops on the Gleiwitz transmitter"

- France and Britain had a defensive pact with Poland. This forced France and Britain to declare war on Germany, which they did on September 3.

The Cold War 1945 – 1989

40. The candidate assesses how effectively the Soviet Union controlled Eastern Europe up to 1961, using evidence and arguments such as:

The international context
- 1955 - emergence of Nikita Khrushchev as leader on death of Stalin. He encouraged criticism of Stalin and seemed to offer hope for greater political and economic freedom across the Eastern European satellite states
- Speech to 20th Party Congress, Feb 1956: Khrushchev attacked Stalin for promoting a cult of personality and for his use of purges and persecution to reinforce his dictatorship. Policy of de-Stalinisation
- Development of policy of peaceful co-existence to appeal to the West
- Development of policy of different roads to Socialism to appeal to satellite states in Eastern Europe who were becoming restless.

Demands for change and reaction: Poland (1956)
- Riots sparked off by economic grievances developed into demands for political change in Poland
- On the death of Stalinist leader Boleslaw Bierut in 1956 he was replaced by Wladyslaw Gromulka, a former victim of Stalinism which initially worried the Soviets
- Poles announced their own road to Socialism and introduced extensive reforms
- Release of political prisoners (and Cardinal Wyszynski, Archbishop of Warsaw); collective farms broken up into private holdings; private shops allowed to open, greater freedom to factory managers
- Relatively free elections held in 1957 which returned a Communist majority of 18
- No Soviet intervention despite concerns
- Gromulka pushed change only so far. Poland remained in the Warsaw Pact as a part of the important 'buffer zone'. Political freedoms were very limited indeed. Poland was a loyal supporter of the Soviet Union until the 1980s and the emergence of the Solidarity movement.

Demands for change and reaction: Hungary (1956)
- Hungarians had similar complaints: lack of political freedom, economic problems and poor standard of living
- Encouraged by Polish success, criticism of the Stalinist regime of Mátyás Rákosi grew and he was removed by Khrushchev
- Popular upsurge of support for change in Budapest led to a new Hungarian government led by Imre Nagy, who promised genuine reform and change
- Nagy government planned multi-party elections, political freedoms, the withdrawal of Hungary from the Warsaw Pact and demands for the withdrawal of Soviet forces
- Nagy went too far. The Soviet Union could not see this challenge to the political supremacy of the Communist Party and the break-up of their carefully constructed buffer zone. They intervened and crushed the rising brutally
- Successful intervention, but lingering resentment from mass of Hungarian people, through some economic flexibility allowed the new regime of Janos Kadar to improve economic performance and living standards.

Demands for change and reaction: Berlin (1961)
- Problem of Berlin – a divided city in a divided nation
- Lack of formal boundaries in Berlin allowed East Berliners and East Germans to freely enter the West which they did owing to the lack of political freedom, economic development and poor living standards in the East

- Many of those fleeing (2.8 million between 1949 and 1961) were skilled and young, just the people the communist East needed to retain. This was embarrassing for the East as it showed that Communism was not the superior system it was claimed to be
- Concerns of Ulbricht and Khrushchev: attempts to encourage the Western forces to leave Berlin by bluster and threat from 1958 failed
- Kennedy of America spoke about not letting the Communists drive them out of Berlin. Resultant increase in tension could not be allowed to continue
- Building of barriers: barbed wire then stone in August 1961 to stem the flood from East to West
- Success in that it reduced the threat of war and the exodus to the West from the East to a trickle
- Frustration of many in East Germany. Propaganda gift for the US and allies.

Military and ideological factors
- Buffer zone could not be broken up as provided military defence for Soviet Union
- Use of force and Red Army to enforce control in late 40s and early 50s
- Need to ensure success of Communism hence policy.

Domestic pressures
- Intention to stop any further suffering of Soviet Union in aftermath of WW2 made leadership very touchy to change
- Some economic freedoms were allowed, but at the expense of political freedoms
- Need to stop spread of demands for change.

41. The candidate evaluates the extent to which the superpowers' attempts to manage the Cold War between 1962 and 1985 were prompted by the economic cost of the arms race, using arguments and evidence such as:

Economic cost of arms race
- Developments in technology raised the costs of the arms race
- The development of Anti-Ballistic Missile technology and costs of war led to SALT 1 and the ABM treaty
- Limiting MIRV and intermediate missile technology led to SALT 2
- The cost of 'Star Wars' technology also encouraged the Soviet Union to seek better relations
- Khrushchev's desire for better relations between the Superpowers in the 50s and 60s was, in part, about freeing up resources for economic development in the USSR. He hoped this would show the superiority of the Soviet system
- Gorbachev wanted to improve the lives of ordinary Russians and part of this was by reducing the huge defence budget eg Intermediate Nuclear Forces Treaty, December 1987.

Other factors

Mutually Assured Destruction
- The development of vast arsenals of nuclear weapons from 1945 by both Superpowers as a deterrent to the other side; a military attack would result in horrific retaliation
- So many nuclear weapons were built to ensure that not all were destroyed even after a first-strike, and this led to a stalemate known as MAD. Arms race built on fear.

Dangers of military conflict as seen through Cuban Missile Crisis
- The threat of nuclear war seemed very close on the discovery of Soviet nuclear missiles on Cuba in 1962. Before Khrushchev backed down nuclear war was threatened. It also illustrated the lack of formal contact between the Superpowers to defuse potential conflicts

- Introduction of a 'hot-line' between the Kremlin and White House in order to improve communication between the Superpowers. Khrushchev and Kennedy also signed the Limited Nuclear Test Ban Treaty, the first international agreement on nuclear weapons.

Technology: The importance of verification
- American development of surveillance technology (U2 and satellites) meant that nuclear weapons could be identified and agreements verified
- Example of U2 flight over Cuba where Anderson photographed nuclear sites
- Also U2 and satellite verification to make sure the Soviets were doing as promised at the negotiating table
- Some historians think Arms Control would never have taken root, but for the ability of the sides to verify what the other was doing.

Co-existence and Détente
- Policies of co-existence and détente developed to defuse tensions and even encourage trade
- Role of others like Brandt in West Germany in defusing tension through their policies of Ostpolitik, etc.

42. The candidate evaluates the role of Gorbachev in ending the Cold War using evidence and arguments such as:

Role of President Mikhail Gorbachev
- Gorbachev saw that the USSR could not afford a new arms race. The Soviet economy was at breaking point. Commitments to the arms race and propping up allied regimes meant consumer goods and other things such as housing that mattered to Russian people were neglected
- Gorbachev implemented policies of Perestroika and Glasnost which aimed to reform the Soviet economy and liberalise its political system
- Gorbachev worked to improve relations with the USA. He took ideology out of his foreign policy, as exemplified by arms agreements to allow the USSR to concentrate on internal matters: Intermediate Nuclear Forces Treaty, Dec 1987, Nuclear Weapons Reduction Treaty, 1989
- Gorbachev told leaders of the satellite East European states in March 1989 that the Soviet army would no longer help them to stay in power.

Other factors

Role of President Ronald Reagan
- Unlike many in the US administration Reagan actively sought to challenge Soviet weakness and strengthen the west in order to defeat Communism. In 1983 he denounced the Soviet Union as an 'Evil Empire'
- Programme of improving US armed forces, including nuclear weapons and he proposed a Star Wars missile shield to challenge the belief in MAD (SDI). He was very charming when he met Gorbachev and visited the Soviet Union.

Western economic strength
- Allowed America to embark on the Star Wars weapons programme
- Perception of the affluent West through television and consumer goods undermined Communist claims of the superiority of their economic system.

Withdrawal of the Soviet Union from Afghanistan
- Symptom of the problems of Soviet Union
- Intervention in Dec 1979: conflict with the Mujaheddin. Russian army morale crumbled when over 20,000 Soviet soldiers died, as did support at home
- The conflict showed the weaknesses of the Soviet economy. War led to a slump in living standards for ordinary Russians
- Russians began to question the actions of their own government. Gorbachev withdrew troops in 1988.

Failure of Communism in Eastern Europe

• Strong Polish identity and history of hostility with Russia. By 1970s, Poland in economic slump. Emergence of opposition around Gdansk in 1980: industrial workers strike led by Lech Walesa, who argued for the creation of an independent trade union. Solidarity grew to nine million members in a matter of months. Movement suppressed in 1981 by General Jaruzelski's government

• Multiparty elections in Poland, after Soviet troops left, victory for Solidarity.

• Czechoslovakia, political prisoners released in November 1989 and by the end of the month, the communist government had gone. No Soviet intervention

• Opening of the Berlin Wall: division of Germany finally came to an end

• Soviet domination ended

• Perestroika and Glasnost and end of Communist rule in USSR.

HIGHER HISTORY PAPER 2 2012

SPECIAL TOPIC 1: THE WARS OF INDEPENDENCE, 1286 – 1328

1. The candidate makes a judgement on the extent to which **Sources A** and **B** agree about the Scots' attempts to protect their independence in terms of:

Overall both sources generally agree that the Scottish Guardians were concerned about maintaining the independence of Scotland. **Source B** offers a more detailed summary of how the kingdom would function under a dual monarchy and seems to suggest more optimism than the frank statements of the actual treaty.

Source A	*Source B*
• No one of the kingdom of Scotland shall be held to answer outwith that kingdom for any agreement entered into, or for any crime committed, or in any other cause contrary to the laws and customs of that kingdom	• Persons in Scotland who had been accused of a crime or sued at law should not have to answer in a court outside their country
• The rights and liberties and customs of Scotland shall be wholly preserved	• The guardians above all anxious to do nothing that might impair the "rights" or the integrity of Scotland
• We promise that the kingdom of Scotland shall remain separate and divided from the kingdom of England	• The treaty envisaged two feudal kingdoms – England and Scotland – ruled separately
• We grant that no tenant-in-chief of the king of Scotland shall be forced to go outside the kingdom to do homage or fealty.	• Tenants in chief of the Scots Crown need do homage for their lands in Scotland only.

2. The candidate makes a judgement as to how useful **Source C** is as evidence of the subjugation of the Scots by Edward I in 1296 in terms of:

Points from the source which show the candidate has interpreted the significant views:

• **Origin** – Primary source written in the early 14th century by the canon of Guisborough Priory in the Bruce lands of Yorkshire. The chronicle details events throughout the period of the Scottish wars (though there is a gap between 1316 and 1326); it is generally considered a reliable document. Events detailed during the reign of Edward I are a contemporary record of events.

• **Possible purpose** – Walter's work is a record of English history, dating from the conquest in 1066, as with many chronicles it is an attempt to set the world in context. The Guisborough Priory suffered during the Scottish wars, and housed many refugees from other religious houses during the wars. There could be a trace of bias due to this.

• **Content –**
  • When the city was taken more than 8,000 were killed
  • Taking of hostages like Lord William Douglas
  • Taking the oaths of loyalty from two hundred men.

Points from recall which support and develop those from the source:
- Despite the Scots' early confidence, and the fortification of Berwick, the city fell quickly to Edward's more professional and experienced army
- The garrison of the castle surrendered under the laws of chivalry and Edward allowed them to go, but the townsmen and Burghers were slaughtered
- Edward forced the women and children to abandon their homes and re-populated Berwick with people from Northumbria.

Points from recall which offer a wider contextualisation such as:
- The Earl of Surrey defeated the Scottish army at Dunbar, many Scottish knights and nobles were captured
- Edward I captured important castles such as Roxburgh, Edinburgh and most importantly Stirling, there was no attempt at resistance at Stirling
- Edward's march northward to Elgin, and the acceptance of oaths of loyalty from nobles along the way (Ragman's Roll)
- King John's humiliating surrender at Kincardine Castle (Toom Tabard)
- Edward's removal of the Stone of Destiny and Scottish legal documents to prevent an inauguration of a future king
- The appointment of the Earl of Surrey as Lieutenant of Scotland
- Any other relevant points.

3. The candidate makes a judgement as to how far **Source D** shows the changing military balance between Scotland and England, 1298-1301 in terms of:

Points from the source which show the candidate has interpreted the significant views:
- The Scots army is forced to retreat north, deploying scorched earth tactics. It can be surmised that this would have had a negative impact on the people living in the area as well as the local economy
- Edward seized and repaired Stirling Castle, a vital stronghold in the defence of Scotland
- Edward holds a parliament at Carlisle and divides Scottish land out amongst his supporters
- Wallace is forced to resign as Guardian because he cannot work with the jealous nobles.

Points from recall which support and develop those in the source:
- It was not Wallace's decision to attack that was the mistake, but his tactics at the Battle of Falkirk that cost him his victory and his position as Guardian of Scotland
- Wallace understood the power of the English cavalry. His tactics of fortifying the positions of the schiltrons behind stakes and ropes meant that they were essentially impregnable as far as the English cavalry were concerned, but easy targets for the Welsh archers
- Despite the crushing defeat at Falkirk, there was no capitulation before Edward, as there had been after Dunbar.

Points from recall which offer a wider contextualisation such as:
- New Guardians were chosen, including Bruce and Comyn, and later Bishop Lamberton
- They planned to attack Roxburgh castle, still in English hands, but a pre-emptive strike by Edward forced them to retreat to their own lands and organise their defences. Unlike Wallace who had no lands to defend, these lords were concerned about more than just the independence of Scotland
- The Scots did have some success, Bruce, Comyn and Lamberton were able to capture Stirling Castle in late 1299 and succeeded in harassing Edward's armies with small forces operating out of Scotland's rugged terrain. In the Southwest the Galloway hills and in the central borders, Selkirk Forrest offered ideal bases for hit and run activities

- However, they also had their share of misfortunes. The highly important castle of Caerlaverock was captured in 1300 by Edward; its fall meant that the Scots army had to flee across the moors to avoid destruction
- Distrust and arguments between Bruce and Comyn
- Bruce eventually resigned his Guardianship and instead settled for defending his lands in the south west
- By the end of 1300 the Scottish resistance was in balance. Edward had succeeded in defeating the Scots at Falkirk and thus had forced Wallace's resignation, but the Scots continued to fight tenaciously. However the arguments in the Scottish camp weakened their ability to present a united front against Edward
- Any other relevant points.

4. The candidate makes a judgement on how fully **Source E** explains the reasons for the ultimate success of Bruce in maintaining Scotland's independence in terms of:

Points from the source which show the candidate has interpreted the significant views:
- Robert rewarded his followers from lands of his enemies and thus ensured their loyalties
- Robert raided northern England to try and force the English king to negotiate
- Robert negotiated an uneasy truce with England in 1323
- Robert negotiated a mutual defence treaty with France in 1326 as part of his policy to ensure a stable inheritance for his son.

Points from recall which support and develop those in the source:
- Bannockburn represented a major victory for Robert, it was the start of his fearful reputation as a great warlord who couldn't be beaten
- Bannockburn had more of an impact on domestic politics in Scotland than any real long term military benefits. Robert passed legislation forbidding nobles holding land in both England and Scotland
- Robert took land from the disinherited at Cambuskenneth and shared it among his supporters to gain loyalty
- The war in the north of England was a significant and often overlooked aspect of the Scottish wars.

Points from recall which offer a wider contextualisation such as:
- As well as the 1315 invasion, Robert attacked England no fewer than 5 times (1316, 1318, 1322, 1323 and 1328)
- The campaign of 1322 was particularly impressive and culminated in the battle of Old Byland, which almost saw a repeat of Bannockburn and the capture of Edward II
- In 1320 the Declaration of Arbroath, a rebuttal to the papal decrees against Robert, was dispatched to Rome along with other letters. It is often seen as a key defence against English insistence that the papacy intervene on their behalf. By 1323 papal attitude to Scotland had significantly improved
- The campaign of 1328, following the murder of Edward II by Isabella and Mortimer is a final decisive move by Robert
- He re-opened his Irish campaign with a new army invading Ulster, at the same time his most trusted lieutenants raided northern England, skilfully running rings around Mortimer and the young newly crowned Edward III
- Robert's announcement that he intended to annex Northumbria eventually forced Isabella and Mortimer to sign the Treaty of Edinburgh 1328
- Edward Bruce invaded Ireland to take war to English and create a pan-Celtic alliance. Overran Ulster quickly, but became bogged down
- Any relevant recall 1306 – 14
- Any other relevant points.

SPECIAL TOPIC 2: THE AGE OF REFORMATION, 1542-1603

1. The candidate makes a judgement on how far **Sources A** and **B** agree about the changes brought about by the Treaty of Edinburgh in terms of:

Overall both sources look at and agree about the changes brought about by the Treaty of Edinburgh of 1560 signed between England and France.

However, **Source A** says that while Scottish nobles and people had to fulfil and observe the terms set out in the treaty while **Source B** says that king and queen were obliged to fulfil their treaty obligations due to the Scots' obedience and loyalty.

Source A	*Source B*
• All warlike operations shall cease	• Truce arranged between England and France
• All military forces of each party shall withdraw from the realm of Scotland	• All foreign soldiers were to withdraw from Scotland
• King Francis and Queen Mary shall abstain from using or carrying the said title or arms of the kingdom of England or Ireland	• Francis II and Mary, Queen of Scots, would abstain from displaying the English arms with those of Scotland
• Francis and Mary will fulfil all those things which were granted to the nobility and people of Scotland provided that the nobility and people of Scotland fulfil and observe what was contained in those conventions and articles.	• Francis and Mary would fulfil all their treaty obligations since the Scots had spontaneously and freely professed and acknowledged their obedience and loyalty towards their king and queen.

2. The candidate makes a judgement on how useful **Source C** is in explaining Mary's difficulties in ruling Scotland, in terms of:

Points from the source which show the candidate has interpreted the significant views:

- **Origin** – The source was written by James Melville, a trusted member of Mary's household who witnessed the murder of David Riccio.
- **Possible Purpose** – To explain the reasons behind the murder of David Riccio and the difficulties Mary faced from the nobles within her court.
- **Content**
  - David Riccio as Mary's secretary was envied and hated by the nobility
  - Mary's husband, Darnley, agreed to the murder of Riccio which Scottish Lords had planned so that they could control the court and parliament
  - Mary was unable to save Riccio and kept as captive.

Points from recall which support and develop those in the source:
- As the Queen's husband, Darnley wanted the 'crown matrimonial'. Mary refused as she believed he was unfit to rule
- As Darnley became more resentful, ambitious Scottish nobles encouraged his anger and Darnley joined a plot to murder Riccio
- George Douglas took Darnley's knife to strike the first blow. He left the knife in Riccio's body to show that Darnley was involved in the murder
- During the struggle, Mary was seized and threatened. Her life was in danger and so was the life of her unborn child.

Points from recall which offer a wider contextualisation:
- Many nobles including Mary's half-brother, the Earl of Moray hated Darnley and they viewed the marriage unfavourably. This led to the Chaseabout Raid in 1565 and although Mary demonstrated her authority over the nobles, she lost the support of many powerful men
- Mary had called a Parliament to punish said nobles by confiscating their titles and property. They offered to help Darnley if he intervened to prevent this. The murder took place two days after the Parliament opened
- While some nobles hoped to benefit from her death; others planned to imprison her and make her child their ruler because they would gain from another minority
- Rivalry between noble families would be one of the main sources of trouble in Mary's reign
- Religion was the most serious problem of Mary's reign. A Catholic Queen ruling a Protestant country was viewed with suspicion by the Kirk
- Mary favoured French influences and often preferred to hide away with servants
- Queen Elizabeth viewed Mary, her cousin and heir, with suspicion. Mary feared that her cousin might assist Scottish Protestants to rise against her
- Mary a woman
- Any other relevant points.

3. The candidate makes a judgement on how far **Source D** illustrates the efforts of James VI to control the Kirk in terms of:

Points from the source which show the candidate has interpreted the significant views:
- When local feuding between the Catholic Earl of Huntly and the Protestant Earl of Moray led to the latter's murder, the incident was used by the Kirk to gain concessions in the Golden Act
- Despite the Golden Act, James never conceded the principle of royal supremacy over the Kirk
- James made a number of successful efforts to tighten royal control over the general assembly and re-establish diocesan episcopacy
- James appears frustrated by the lack of respect he receives from his subjects and is determined to bring Scotland's remote localities under more direct royal control.

Points from recall which support and develop those in the source:
- Relations with the Kirk deteriorated after 1592, leading to conflict in 1596
- James' belief in the divine right of monarchs clashed with Melvillians' view that the Monarch should be accountable to the authority of the Kirk
- In his writings, James asserted that no human institution could limit the powers of a monarch
- Extreme Presbyterians/Melvillians were marginalised on account of James' views
- Further detail of Trew Law and Basilikon Doron.

Points from recall which offer a wider contextualisation such as:
- The Second Book of Discipline (1578) had proposed a Presbyterian Kirk which could make the church independent of the King and his nobility
- By 1581 plans to establish 13 Presbyteries appeared to challenge royal authority
- In 1584, all ministers were required to accept the 'Black Acts' abolishing Presbyteries and asserting royal authority over the Kirk
- In 1592 the 'Golden Act' accepted the recovery of Presbyterian influence within the Kirk, but did not reduce the power of the King

- James sought to extend the power of the monarch and bishops over the Kirk by: having bishops recognised as moderators of Presbyteries; allowing them to hear cases of excommunication and deposition of ministers
- Elders were excluded from Presbyteries and the monarch had the power to determine time and place of the General Assembly
- James would have the General Assembly meeting in Perth or Aberdeen where he could expect more ministers would support the King
- As a result of rebellion in December 1596, James fled from Edinburgh, but this made him more determined to control the Kirk
- 1597 riot in Edinburgh after a sermon preached against the King. James VI had the ministers of Edinburgh briefly imprisoned. The King ordered that no minister was to be appointed without his consent
- In 1597, Andrew Melville was deposed as rector of St Andrews
- James attended every General Assembly from 1597 to 1603, by which time assemblies were becoming more agreeable to the King's aims
- James preferred form of Church government was by bishops and in 1600 he appointed three bishops to Parliament
- Any other relevant points.

4. The candidate makes a judgement on how fully **Source E** explains the impact of the Reformation on the lives of the people of Scotland in terms of:

Points from the source which show the candidate has interpreted the significant views:
- There was a new religious fervour demonstrated by support for Presbyterian beliefs
- Congregations had the right to choose their own minister
- The place of music in the lives of people generally and in the church services was to suffer
- There remained a compassionate attitude towards representatives of the Catholic faith.

Points from recall which support and develop those in the source:
- Emphasis was placed upon attendance at daily and Sunday services. There were to be no distractions which might detain a congregation from their duties
- The *Second Book of Discipline* led indirectly to a regular meeting of ministers from 10 to 20 parishes for discussion of doctrine, which became the presbytery
- The Kirk removed all organs from places of worship
- It proved impractical to dispossess the Catholic clergy of their benefices so they were allowed to retain two-thirds of their revenues for life
- Concessions made to Catholic clergy, on the grounds of old age or ill-health.

Points from recall which offer a wider contextualisation such as:
- At the beginning of 1560, Scotland was a Catholic country with a Protestant minority. By 1603, it was a Protestant country with a small Catholic minority
- The Reformation did not lead to a significant transfer of wealth from the Church and much of the lands of the Catholic Church remained in the hands of the nobility
- The new church still had the problem of not having enough revenue for the parishes
- James VI was reluctant to enforce anti-Catholic laws
- Kirk sessions were instruments of moral and religious control
- The elaborate interiors of Catholic churches were replaced with plain, whitewashed parish kirks

- Observance of Catholic festivals and saints' days and festivals were discouraged
- Literary works and Kirk sermons were conducted in English rather than Latin. (The only Protestant Bibles available to lowland Scots were in English)
- Assistance given to the poor from the friaries ended. New plans to help the poor by the Presbyterian church faced difficulty
- The aim of a school in every parish not achieved but some advances were made in central Scotland
- Literacy rates improved during this period
- Many of the issues prevalent within the Catholic Church prior to the Reformation remained, such as: attendance; poverty of some parishes; and poor quality of preaching
- Scots merchants continued to trade with England and trading ports across the North Sea
- Scots focused on trade with the Protestant Dutch
- Trade with France continued despite the change in religion – although pro-French foreign policy was replaced with pro-English under James
- Any other relevant points.

SPECIAL TOPIC 3: THE TREATY OF UNION, 1689-1740

1. The candidate makes a judgement on how far **Sources A** and **B** agree about worsening relations between Scotland and England in terms of:

Overall **Source A** and **Source B** agree that Scotland's economy was affected by England; **Source A** attributes this to a combination of factors and **Source B** suggests that English actions were responsible.

Source A	*Source B*
• Scotland tipped over the edge of an economic abyss	• Scots aware of sinking economic condition of their nation
• English wars leading to damaging loss of French trade	• Visible damage both to trade and wealth of Scotland
• Protective tariffs blocked the export of certain Scottish goods	• Problems owing to the disadvantage of tariffs
• Outcome was incorporating union with England.	• One way for Scots to restore themselves was incorporating union and alliance with England.

2. The candidate makes a judgement on how useful **Source C** is as evidence of attitudes towards the union, in terms of:

Points from the source which show the candidate has interpreted the significant views:
- **Origin** – Petition sent by Stirling Town Council during debates.
- **Possible purpose** – To give reasons for opposing union with England.
- **Content** –
  - Treaty will bring insupportable taxation which will ruin manufacturing
  - Burghs will lose right to be represented in legislative power
  - Scotland will be suppressed as its parliament is extinguished with fatal consequences.

Points from recall which support and develop those in the source:
- Royal burghs would be deprived of rights
- Fear of loss of European trade
- British parliament would favour English trade over Scottish.

Points from recall which offer a wider contextualisation such as:

Attitudes against union:
- English currency, weights and measures to be introduced
- Public opinion against union
- Reduction in status of Scottish nobility in British parliament
- Scots Episcopalians opposed union and Hanoverian succession – only Stuart dynasty might restore episcopacy to Scottish church
- Protestants feared a British parliament dominated by Anglican Episcopalian church with bishops' seats in the House of Lords
- Fear of 'Scotlandshire'
- Scots' liberties at risk.

Attitudes for union:
- Advantages in commerce and trade
- Economy would improve – national product would increase
- Scotland's trade would catch up with other European nations'
- Free trade with English colonies
- Protection of being in Great Britain
- Common interests already with England
- Advantages of Scottish politicians being part of the court of the king in London
- Hanoverian succession offered security to Protestantism
- Threat from "Popery" reduced
- Property preserved
- Any other relevant points.

3. The candidate makes a judgement on how far **Source D** explains the passage of the Treaty of Union through the Scottish Parliament in terms of:

Points from the source which show the candidate has interpreted the significant views:
- Opposition was divided and poorly led by unpredictable Hamilton
- Hamilton may have been bribed by the Court party
- Hamilton refused to participate in planned walkout of parliament
- Failure of armed rising proved that opponents of union were not willing to engage in violence.

Points from recall which support and develop those in the source:
- Hamilton divided opponents of union and obstructed arguments against union
- Bribery of Scottish ministers/politicians
- Disagreement amongst opponents of union unable to act together
- Political management was vital to make the outcome certain
- Court party fundamental to final victory.

Points from recall which offer a wider contextualisation such as:
- The Equivalent: £398,085.10s to cover the taking on of English debt
- Expectation of the Equivalent influenced support for treaty in parliament
- Those who lost out to Darien failure were beneficiaries
- Payment made to wool industry as well as payment of Scottish public debt
- Unspecified payments made to Scottish Commissioners for Union
- £20,000 paid to various Scottish politicians through Earl of Glasgow
- Court members voted consistently through all Articles of the Treaty
- Promise of favours, pensions, military patronage, high-ranking positions and cash ensured government majorities
- Threats of loss of civil list pension
- Squadrone Volante's hold on balance of power key to Court party's success

- Some Squadrone members believed they would share the Equivalent
- Assurances that new parliament would support Scots economy over taxation
- Scottish parliament given incentive of free trade with England and its colonies
- Last minute concessions from English on issues such as salt, wool and liquor
- Seats in House of Lords for 16 Scottish peers
- Other Scots peers to retain privileges – Treaty appealed to self-interest
- Act of Security for the Kirk would allow Church of Scotland to continue
- Rights of burghs and Royal Burghs to remain
- Inherited offices for Lords to continue
- Scots laws and Scottish courts to remain
- Security of liberty and stability under one parliament
- English forces moving north and fear of invasion if no treaty was agreed
- Peace secured by being part of Great Britain
- Role of Daniel Defoe in informing the English government during Treaty's passage through the Scottish Parliament
- Any other relevant points.

4. The candidate makes a judgement on how fully **Source E** explains the effects of Union up to 1740 in terms of:

Points from the source which show the candidate has interpreted the significant views:
- Scotland not extinguished, it retained identity, attitudes, ideas; traditions were not eradicated
- Treaty did exert strong Anglicising influence
- Guarantees to Scottish legal system and Church had influence on Scotland
- Continuation of Scottish systems of education and local government were significant achievement of Union.

Points from recall which support and develop those in the source:
- Scottish tradition still evident in culture, music, art, literature, law, religion, education; Scottish Enlightenment, Scott, Smith, Hume, Burns
- Influence of English agricultural techniques and innovations.

Points from recall which offer a wider contextualisation such as:
- Political effects: 1711 – parliament banned Scottish peers with English titles
- Highland clans divided between Hanoverian and Jacobite loyalties
- 1713 – motion to repeal Act of Union defeated by 4 votes
- Whig election victory in 1715 led to government delaying Malt Tax
- 1725 – Secretary of State for Scotland replaced by Home Secretary
- Economic effects: Scottish industry could not compete with English competition; only small number of Scots engaged successfully with colonies
- Taxes led to increases in smuggling and loss of revenue for government
- Paper industry failed; Scottish linen industry suffered
- Merchant shipping benefited, particularly trade with Baltic and Caribbean
- Tobacco industry developed in Glasgow
- Agriculture improved; increased investment; 1727 – Royal Bank of Scotland
- 1730s – favourable economic climate; industries such as linen recovered
- Jacobite reaction: Jacobites led national sentiment in literature and songs
- 1708 – abortive French-sponsored invasion by the Old Pretender

- Jacobite rising of 1715; Earl of Mar played leading role; Battle of Sheriffmuir in November 1715 claimed as victory by both government and Jacobites
- 1716 Disarming Act banned holding of weapons by Highlanders
- 1719 – failed attempt at rising in north-west Scotland by Earl Marischal
- Other effects: claims of the unpopularity of union made vocally by opponents
- 1712 – House of Lords became court of appeal for Scottish cases
- 1724 – outbreak of fence-smashing by levellers; 1725 – Shawfield riots in response to Malt Tax; 1736 – Porteous riots in Edinburgh
- Military road-building; establishment of forts in Highlands
- 1710 – Tories in parliament failed to remove Church of Scotland's privileges; 1711 – Greenshields case; 1712 – Toleration Act and Patronage Act
- 1722 Marrow affair in Church of Scotland; 1733 secession from state church
- Initial dissatisfaction with the Equivalent being unpaid
- Scots joined East India Company in large numbers
- Increased Baltic trade
- Any other relevant points.

SPECIAL TOPIC 4: MIGRATION AND EMPIRE, 1830–1939

1. Overall: The sources agree about the push factor of poverty and the pull factor of prosperity. Although almost a hundred years apart both sources remark on the poverty of life in rural Scotland with high unemployment and the difficulty of providing for families. In contrast both sources comment on the opportunities to be had in Canada, particularly the availability of employment and land for farming.

Source A	Source B
• Occupying a farm that does not pay him in Scotland	• The pay is good as experienced men can at the very start earn £5 to £6 a month in Canada
• Quite unable to support his family in Scotland	• The inability of the crofts to satisfy the hunger of the families in Scotland
• So much land lies in Canada to occupy	• The men also have the prospect of becoming tenant farmers and later on owners of their own farms in Canada
• A farmer continuing to remain in Scotland even when unemployed.	• Lack of employment generally in Scotland.

2. The candidate makes a judgment on how useful **Source C** is as evidence of the assimilation of immigrants into Scottish society in terms of:

Points from source which show the candidate has interpreted the significant views:
- **Origin** – memories of an immigrant child and his assimilation into Scottish society in the 1920s and 30s.
- **Possible purpose** – to record the experiences of his family arriving in Glasgow in the 1920s and how they became established in their new home.
- **Content** –
  - I found myself surrounded by classmates chanting at me because I was a foreigner
  - Our family moved house a few times in an effort to improve our lot
  - In no time at all I was a complete Glaswegian.

Points from recall which support and develop those in the source:
- Assimilation of Italians helped by popularity of ice cream parlours and fish and chip shops
- Young Italians soon adopted local speech patterns due to frequency of contact in catering trade
- Some tension between Catholic Italians and Presbyterian Scots. Italian cafés criticised by Scottish Presbyterian church leaders for opening on the Sabbath
- Italian café owners also met with criticism from local people who claimed the cafés were sometimes the scenes of unruly behaviour. Glasgow Herald article claimed ice cream parlours were morally corrupt and reported the 'ice cream hell'
- There was a greater degree of acceptance of Italian cafés from the Temperance Movement as the cafés chose not to sell alcohol.

Points from recall which offer a wider contextualisation such as:

Catholic Irish:
- Often resented as competition for jobs
- Blamed for spread of diseases and poverty
- Catholic Irish workers were also accused of being strike-breakers and being willing to work for less money than Scottish workers
- Often blamed for being 'benefit scroungers' claiming poor relief after 3 years residence
- The Education (Scotland) Act 1918 allowed Catholic schools into the state system funded through education rates. It also gave the schools the right to give Catholic religious instruction and select their own teachers
- The Catholic Irish had a shared experience with the Scottish worker in that they were affected by industrialisation, urbanisation, as well as fighting together during the First World War
- Even into the 1930s Catholic Irish faced persecution, sometimes organised by Church of Scotland.

Protestant Irish:
- Irish Protestants had a lot in common with the average Scot – long term and deeply embedded cultural interaction between Ulster and lowland Scotland
- Much easier assimilation because of religion
- The first Scottish Orange Lodge opened in 1800 in the weaving centre of Maybole in Ayrshire. The growth of the lodge system in Scotland shows the spread of Irish Protestantism.

Jews:
- Prejudice and discrimination affected the Jews in Scotland – The Daily Record – Aug 1905 'Alien Danger: Immigrants infected with loathsome disease'
- Anti-Semitism never that widespread, possibly owing to low numbers of Jewish immigrants in relation to other groups
- Very few Jews received any help from local poor relief. It was members of the Jewish community that helped each other eg The Glasgow Jewish Board of Guardians and the Hebrew Ladies Benevolent Society in 1901 were dealing with 500 cases of needy Jews.

Lithuanians:
- Between 1860s and 1914 about 7000 Lithuanians decided to settle in Scotland
- Scots complained about the Lithuanians being dirty and immoral but soon most were accepted
- Settlements in mining areas of central Scotland such as Coatbridge
- At first Lithuanians used as strike breakers but soon Lithuanians joined with the local workers and joined the strikes
- Many Lithuanians integrated by changing surnames to Scottish names

- During Great War Lithuanians between eighteen and forty-one faced the choice of conscription into the British Army or deportation for military service in Russia. Of the 1,800 Lithuanians who were called up, 700 joined the British Army and 1,100 chose to be deported to Russia
- Any other relevant points.

3. The candidate makes a judgement on how far **Source D** shows the contribution of Scots to the growth and development of the Empire in terms of:

Points from the source which show the candidate has interpreted the significant views:
- The most obvious field of Scottish achievement in Australia was farming/sheep grazing and the wool trade
- Scots also invested heavily in mining/the Gold Rush of the 1850s brought to Australia a considerable number of Scottish miners
- Shipping and trade were other areas of enterprise in which Scots excelled; example of McIllwrath McEachan and Burns Phillips
- Scots played large part in creating the sugar boom of the 1880s in Northern Queensland.

Points from recall which support and develop those in the source:
Examples of Scots contributing to economic growth and development in Australia:
- Many Scots sheep and cattle farmers squatted on land until allowed to buy squatters licenses
- After gold discovered in Victoria and New South Wales, many gold camps were recognisably "Scottish"
- Role of Church of Scotland in developing education in Australia, eg Australia College, Scots College in Melbourne, and influence of development of Melbourne and Sydney universities.

Points from recall which offer a wider contextualisation such as:
Examples of Scots contributing to Canada:
- Scots gave a thorough and honest character to Canadian business and financial life
- George Stephen organising finance and creation of Canadian Pacific Railroad
- Scots' control of the fur trade
- Contribution to laws and learning/education (eg McGill University).

Examples of Scots contributing to New Zealand:
- Scots founded banks and financial institutions as well as having a political impact
- Scottish influence on NZ education.

Examples of Scots contributing to India:
- Scots' impact on education, the development of the banking system.
- Many Indian institutions such as elite schools, universities and press owed much to Scottish emigrants
- Scots' contribution to development of tea plantations and the jute industry
- Any other relevant factors.

4. The candidate makes a judgement on how fully **Source E** explains the effects of migration and Empire on Scottish society, in terms of:

Points from the source which show the candidate has interpreted the significant views:
- The movement of the Irish changed the population balance of several lowland towns
- A huge reservoir of Irish labour which … was ready and willing to move anywhere and do anything to find work
- Huge construction schemes of nineteenth century relied on this vast labour

- The Irish presence vital to an understanding of Scottish culture as Catholic Irish have played such an influential role in the evolution and shaping of Scottish society ranging from literature to music and on to football.

Points from recall which support and develop those in the source:
- Details of economic contribution of Irish immigrants to Scottish industrial development
- Development of Celtic, Edinburgh Hibernian, Dundee United, etc
- The Education (Scotland) Act 1918 allowed Catholic schools into the state system funded through education rates. It also gave the schools the right to give Catholic religious instruction and select their own teachers. Resentment in Scotland for 'Rome on the Rates'
- Sectarian divisions, Orange v Green.

Points from recall which offer a wider contextualisation such as:
- One in four immigrants from Ireland were Protestant and brought their own distinct culture which had an impact in Scotland, especially through the Orange Lodge
- Large numbers of poorer Jews arrived between 1880 and 1914 – by 1919 over 9000 lived in Glasgow alone. Most lived in the Gorbals and maintained separate identity – eg spoke Yiddish, the Jewish language
- Jewish immigrants tended to work in particular jobs such as peddling and hawking (selling door to door)
- Sweated labour was associated with immigrants and Jews in particular: tailoring and cigarette making
- Impact of Lithuanians to the economy through the coal-mining industry around Coatbridge
- In 1861 there were about 120 Italians in Scotland, by 1901 the Italian population was 4051
- Italians were usually found in catering trades, especially ice cream and fish and chips
- Italian businesses met with success – number of Italian cafés/takeaways in Glasgow increased: 1903 – 89, 1905 – 337, broadening the average Scots social experience
- In addition to catering, Italians became established as hairdressers – they established the College of Italian Hairdressers in Glasgow in 1928 adding another distinct contribution to Scotland
- Role of Empire in making Scots rich
- Role of Empire as a market for Scottish goods and emigrants
- Empire helped the export orientated Scottish economy to develop, at least up until 1914, especially in production of shipping, locomotives, etc
- Empire as a source of competition to Scottish economy: farm produce from Australia, Jute mill development in India, etc
- Any other relevant points.

SPECIAL TOPIC 5: THE IMPACT OF THE GREAT WAR, 1914 – 1928

1. The candidate makes a judgement as to how far **Sources A** and **B** agree about the experience of Scots on the Western Front in terms of:

Overall: **Source A** and **Source B** offer some similar and some contrasting opinions on the experience of Scots on the Western Front with regard to the taking of Hill 70. **Source A** reflects the tenacity and dogged determination required by the Scots during a long and difficult attack whilst **Source B** skirts over difficulties and gives the impression of an easier, successful attack. Both agree that the pipes played during the attack and that no reinforcements arrived.

Source A	Source B
• We made for the top of Hill 70 through murderous rifle and machine gun fire	• For a time there was a kind of Bank Holiday crowd on Hill 70 as the German machine gunners … initially dared not fire
• We made for the top to the sound of the pipes and led by our brave old colonel	• Shriller than the scream of shells was the skirl of pipes going with them
• We were desperate for reinforcements but no help could we see	• We must hold on until the reinforcements arrive. None came
• Shows determination of Scots; "A Cameron never can yield". This time we meant to do or die.	• Shows determination, 'to go all out and press onto Hill 70.'

2. The candidate makes a judgement on how useful **Source C** is as evidence of the impact of the war on Scottish women in terms of:

Points from source which show the candidate has interpreted the significant views:
- **Origin** – Glasgow Herald, daily Scottish newspaper. Contemporary source.
- **Possible purpose** – To report on the opposition in Glasgow to increased rents and the eviction of tenants.
- **Content –**
  - Reports on the first attempt to enforce eviction of a woman in Merryland Street, Glasgow who had not been paying her rent
  - Role of Mrs Barbour of the GWHA addressing demonstration of strikers
  - Details methods used by demonstrators, mainly women.

Points from recall that support and develop those in the source:
- Rent Strikes took place following large increases in rents and increased cost of living. Women at home with men away particularly vulnerable
- Rent Strikes began in May 1915; 25,000 tenants joined the movement by the end of the year
- Rent Strikes saw a prominent role played by women – formation of tenants' strike committees, Glasgow Women's Housing Association and many local "Women's Housing Associations"
- Roles of Mary Barbour, Helen Crawfurd, Agnes Dollan and Jessie Stephens
- Agitation, Rent Strikes and role of women in other areas such as Aberdeen and Dundee.

Points from recall which offer a wider contextualisation such as:
- Migration of thousands of workers into munitions districts had led to acute housing shortages
- War led to women being more involved in local politics and changing male attitudes
- The war led to dilution of labour and the employment of more women for example at Gretna in the huge munitions works
- Anti-war groups formed like the No Conscription League: leading role of women in these groups
- Role of women as workers on the land, etc
- Any other relevant points.

3. The candidate makes a judgement on how far **Source D** illustrates the economic difficulties faced by Scotland after 1918 in terms of:

Points from the source which show the candidate has interpreted the significance views:
- Many of the changes brought by the war were temporary
- The war shifted the balance of international trade against Scottish shipbuilders
- War shifted the balance against textile manufacturers
- The war demonstrated the fragility of the Scottish heavy industry base.

Points from recall which support those in the source:
- War affected Britain's ability to trade. Loss of markets had a long term effect on industry
- Concentration on a narrow group of heavy industries meant Scotland was affected badly when the post-war boom turned into a slump. Exemplification, such as decline in shipbuilding
- Dundee jute companies saw price collapse with removal of trade restrictions on India
- The textile industry in Scotland had a varied experience – wool price rose but falling exports of cotton and woollen goods.

Points from Recall which offer a wider contextualisation such as:
- War delayed long-standing structural problems for the Scottish economy and its reliance on a narrow range of heavy industries that were reliant on exports
- Initial post-war boom in some industries like ship-building – warship yards built passenger liners and merchant ships to replace those lost
- Mines were nationalised and the miners made good wages. After the war the mines returned to their original owners. Lack of investment and fierce foreign competition resulted in decline
- The Admiralty cancelled the cost-plus system and went back to competitive tendering for orders. The demand for ships, and therefore steel, declined
- Yards suffered because of labour disputes and a shortage of material
- Wages were cut in autumn of 1921, men were laid off and Yarrow's closed. Industrial unrest and late delivery of ships damaged the Clyde's reputation
- Other countries increased their steel-making as well as their ship-building capacity. Falling demand for ships affected steel
- Jute prices collapsed after the war. Trade restrictions removed. Competition from abroad. Resulting in unemployment, social misery and discontent
- In Dundee, several firms went into liquidation others amalgamated, to form Jute Industries Ltd
- The collapse of foreign markets for herring from Germany, Poland, Czechoslovakia, Bulgaria, Russia and the Baltic greatly affected the industry. European countries started to compete
- Cheap foreign imports of food like refrigerated meat from Argentina and frozen lamb and tinned fruit from Australia and New Zealand competed with indigenous agriculture when trade was resumed after the war
- Any other relevant points.

4. The candidate makes a judgement on how fully **Source E** describes the impact of the war on political developments in Scotland in terms of:

Points from the source which show the candidate has interpreted the significance views:
- The war years showed that support for Scottish home rule continued
- Arthur Henderson and the Labour leadership in London were forced to concede a separate Scottish Council of Labour

- The war undermined the organisation of Scottish Liberalism, but also much of its moral authority
- The ILP was able to emerge as the natural successor to liberal radicalism.

Points from recall which support those in the source:
- Home rule still prominent. September 1918 the Scottish Home Rule Association formed
- The Labour Party manifesto of 1918 included a commitment to home rule for Scotland
- The ILP MPs from Clydeside elected November 1922 were committed to home rule
- Initial instances of radicalism after war: 1919 – George Square
- In the 1922 election Labour made the breakthrough as the second political party
- ILP members' activities – involved in resisting the Munitions Act of 1915; in opposing the introduction of the dilution of labour; anti-conscription…
- ILP in Scotland had many women prominent in the party such as Mary Barbour, Agnes Dollan and Helen Crawfurd.

Points from recall which offer a wider contextualisation such as:
- It was difficult for Home Rule to make progress in Westminster parliament
- Private members' Home Rule bills failed
- Support for Home Rule waned within the Labour Party
- Glasgow University Scottish National Association formed 1926
- 1927 Jon McCormack and Roland Muirhead, formed the National Party of Scotland. It distanced itself from the Labour Party. Drew support from intellectuals like Hugh McDiarmid
- Some Liberals and Conservatives formed the Scottish Party at the end of the 1920s and proposed some form of devolution in an effort to attract Liberal and Unionist supporters
- The Labour Party emerged as an important political force with seven seats in Scotland, winning as many votes as the Conservatives. Continued success in the 1922 election
- The role of Manny Shinwell, Willie Gallacher, John MacLean
- In Scotland the ILP was to the fore, campaigning on major issues. Membership increased
- Clydeside ILP MPs confronted Conservatives and Liberals, even leadership of PLP. MPs on issues of poverty and unemployment
- The Conservative Party was strengthened as they worked hard to gain middle class support, helped by Presbyterian churches. Scottish legal system also had strong links with the Conservatives
- Events in Ireland – growing fears in Scotland of extremism
- Any other relevant points.

HIGHER HISTORY PAPER 1 2013

1. Each question is marked out of 20.

2. In Paper 1 candidates will be rewarded according to:

   (a) **Knowledge and Understanding – 6 marks are allocated for** the relevant knowledge they use to address the question. Marks will be awarded for each accurate, full point they make; these points may be further developed, as in the following example, relating to the effectiveness of the Liberal Reforms:

      Old age pensions *(0 marks for stating this)* **were given to all people over 70** *(1 mark)***; married couples received 7/6 and single people 5s** *(a second mark for knowledge)*. **This provision was not enough to live on, but old people were able to help pay their families if they lived with them** *(no further mark for knowledge, but an argument which would receive credit under the category Argument and Evaluation)*.

   (b) **Argument/Evaluation – 10 marks are allocated for** the quality of thought revealed in their answers by the arguments and evaluation demonstrated. This should be taken as including the extent to which the candidate:

      - gives an answer which is relevant to the question and relates explicitly to the question's terms;
      - argues a case;
      - makes the various distinctions required by the question;
      - responds to all the elements in the question, and to any isolated factor in particular;
      - explains, analyses, debates and assesses rather than simply describes or narrates;
      - answers with clarity and fluency and in language appropriate to historical writing at this level.

   (c) **Structure – 4 marks are allocated for** the appropriateness of the organisation of the answer, according to the degree to which the response

      - establishes the context of the question and the relevant factors to be considered in the introduction
      - demonstrates a development of the issue
      - responds to the question in the form of a balanced conclusion based on the evidence and arguments deployed.

3. The following descriptions provide additional guidance on the marks awarded to essays displaying various characteristics. Many essays will exhibit some, but not all, of the features listed; others will be stronger in one area than another.

KNOWLEDGE – Up to 6 marks can be awarded
These are for substantive points and points further developed which are relevant and accurate.

STRUCTURE – Up to 4 marks can be awarded if:
The introduction clearly sets the issue in its wider context, indicates relevant factors and demonstrates a solid line of argument.
There is a coherent development directly focused on the question.
The conclusion is balanced, summarising the arguments and coming to an overall judgement directly related to the question.

ARGUMENT – Up to 10 marks can be awarded if:
The evidence is integrated into a sustained analysis.
The argument is sustained and balanced, with some awareness of alternative interpretations and/or historical debate.

Historical Study: British History

Church, State and Feudal Society

1. The candidate assesses the extent the secular church was more important than the regular church in terms such as:

Arguments to suggest the secular church was more important:

Religious Importance
- The offer of salvation in the afterlife was the key cornerstone in the power of the church, and many historians have argued that the all the other aspects of the Church's power derived from this.
- The church taught everyone of the power of the saints, and how their remains (relics) could have strong spiritual power. Masses believed and travelled far to witness the miracles performed by such relics.
- Even entire kingdoms adopted the help and guidance of saints, and patron saints became popular.
- This led to the idea of pilgrims and pilgrimages, enforcing the religious power of the church over a wider audience.
- The church performed important religious services, marriage, christenings etc.

Political Importance
- The secular church provide an important contact point with ordinary people, this was used by both the kings and clergy to influence the population.
- The church had its own courts; members of the clergy (roughly 1 in 3 in England) couldn't be tried in the kings court.
- The church was an integral part of the Feudal System in England, and could even raise troops from their own lands.
- Clerics were used by the government as scribes and accountants.
- Kings believed that the church was so powerful politically that they should have the right to invest vacant church positions; the Investiture Contest between monarchs and the Pope.

Economic Importance
- The tithe. People were expected to pay this tax to the church, typically 10% of their income, though it was usually paid in kind.
- After the king, the church was the biggest landholder in England.

Arguments to suggest the Regular Church as more important:

Religious Importance
- Monasteries seen as more religious than other areas of the church, vows of poverty and chastity etc.
- Ideas that the monasteries were "Prayer Factories" and could help pray for souls.
- Monks were supposed to devote their lives to god and hard work.
- Kings founded monasteries to pray for their souls, i.e. William the Conqueror and David I.

Political Importance
- Many monasteries were founded by monarchs.
- David I founded monasteries at Dunfermline (1128) and Kelso (1128) to help bring order to less developed areas of Scotland.
- Abbots and monks were strong supporters of law and order, they offered support and advice to nobles and monarchs.

Economic Importance
- Monasteries became very wealthy as land was granted in the hope for salvation.

- Cistercian monasteries were usually built in remote areas and they helped to cultivate the land for the first time.
- Monasteries came to dominate local industries, such as Melrose and the Scottish wool trade and Fountains Abbey and metal working.

2. The candidate evaluates the validity of the view that the desire to develop law and order was the main factor in the development of centralised monarchy, using evidence and arguments such as:

Law and order
- Throughout England and Scotland the justice system was liable to change depending on which lord held sway over that part of the land. Money often bought justice and archaic trial by ordeal or combat was still common.
- Royal justice was usually reserved for more serious crimes. Issues of land, an important aspect of justice, were often poorly judged or unfairly settled.

Other factors

The growth of the nobility
- In both England and Scotland the power of the monarchies was threatened by the growth in power of the nobility.
- During the time of the civil war in England the barons had increased in political importance due to both sides vying for their support. As a result barons built castles without royal permission, increased the numbers of knights beyond limits agreed by their charters, acquired land illegally and many hired large armies of Flemish mercenaries.
- The Mormaers in Scotland were semi-independent and held almost autonomous power over large parts of Scotland. The Earls of Moray had a long tradition of independence, even going so far as to usurp the crown during the reign of Macbeth. The common army of Scotland was summoned by the Mormaers not the king, and was directly under their control.

The cost of warfare
- Throughout the 12th Century kings were finding it increasingly more expensive to raise the costs to build castles or raise feudal armies.
- Constant warfare during the period of civil war in England drained the treasury.

The need to develop the economy
- In England the issue of revenue became apparent during the civil war between Stephen and Matilda.
- Sheriffs had become increasingly lax in paying their taxes. Sheriffs kept the taxes collected in their region for themselves, or only a small amount found its way into the royal treasury.
- Prior to David I, revenue in Scotland was mostly limited to the incomes from royal demesnes.
- The lack of royal burghs limited international trade and early medieval Scottish kings lacked the financial resources to tackle the Mormaers directly without the Community of the Realm backing them.

The effects of foreign influence
- David I spent a considerable time in the English court and saw the benefits of the feudal system for increasing the power and authority of the monarchy. His introduction of feudalism allowed him to increase the number of loyal barons and create a new feudal court.

3. The candidate evaluates how important changing social attitudes were in causing the decline of feudal society, using evidence and arguments such as:

Changing social attitudes

- Social mobility was increasing for a number of reasons, including the move to an economy based more on cash than service. In England the wars against France had brought riches to some, and enabled them to climb the social ladder.
- Peasants who could afford to purchase or rent extra land could move up the social ladder. E.g. the de la Poles family in Hull rose from traders to become royal bankers, and the Pastson family rose out of serfdom to become country gentry.
- It became impossible to tell the difference from "knave and Knight", because they dressed alike.

Other factors

The Black Death

- The decline in the population meant that the survivors, particularly of the lower classes, could demand and often received better wages for their labour. Wage levels in England roughly doubled. Indeed, the shortage of labourers is often seen as causing the decline of serfdom in Western Europe.
- Landowners for the first time needed to negotiate for their serfs' services, leading to higher wages and better living conditions for those that survived.

The Peasants' Revolt

- In England, the attempts of the Statute of the Labourers in 1351 to force peasants back into serfdom were widely and strongly resisted. The extent of the revolt and the impressive way in which it was organised shows that the old feudal consensus had broken down.
- There is an argument that the Peasants' Revolt was a reaction to the attempts to force peasants to return to the old ideas of labour services.

The growth of towns

- Many found the freedom of burgh life allowed them to develop trade without the burden of labour services or restrictions in movement.

The growth of trade/mercantilism

- With markets for their goods fluctuating considerably, many nobles came to understand their weak economic position. For some it was better to let their peasants become tenants who rented their land than to continue as their feudal protector.
- Others discovered that sheep were a far more profitable resource than peasants could ever be. The monasteries in particular turned over large areas to sheep pasture to capitalize on the strong demand for wool.
- Peasants who could afford to purchase or rent extra land could propel themselves upwards on the social ladder.

The Century of Revolutions 1603 – 1702

4. The candidate assesses the validity of the view that the policies of Charles I led to problems ruling Scotland, using evidence and arguments such as:

1st Bishops' War

- 1st Bishops' War took place in 1639
- Charles I could not raise enough money to fight war effectively, was forced to agree to truce in June as part of Pacification of Berwick
- As well as conceding military failure, truce gave Scots religious freedoms
- Charles I's inability to put down Scots brought an end to his "Eleven Years' Tyranny" in England
- King recalled Parliament in 1640 to request revenue to continue war with Scotland
- Short Parliament lasted one month as king dissolved it rather than debate his role during Eleven Years as condition of Parliamentary granting of funds

2nd Bishops' Wars

- 2nd Bishops' War was continuation of first but ended in equal humiliation for Charles I in Treaty of Ripon of October 1640
- Treaty cost England price that Scottish Parliament had to pay for its forces
- Defeat by Scots forced king to recall Parliament, this time after being advised to do so by grouping of peers known as Magnum Concilium
- Long Parliament was to last longer than previous one, but still represented downturn in king's fortunes, as English Civil War shortly followed

Religious policy

- Charles I introduced William Laud, the Archbishop of Canterbury, to Scotland in 1633
- Laud proceeded to oversee Anglican practice in Scottish churches
- Many resented influence of Laud
- King approved of unification of churches without consulting Privy Council
- 1635 Book of Canons declared that monarch had authority over Church of Scotland and introduced new Service Book, a Scottish bishops' variation of English Prayer Book
- 23 July 1637 English Prayer Book was read at St. Giles Cathedral by Dean Hannay.
- In chaos that ensued, Bishop he was shouted down by crowd
- Across Scotland people declared opposition to Service Book, placing Charles I's Privy Council in difficult position, caught between king and his rivals

The Covenanters

- Covenanting movement challenged Charles I over religious policies and was active politically
- Covenanters wanted to preserve Presbyterianism in Scotland
- National Covenant was signed in 1638
- Covenant designed to promote a church free from monarchical meddling
- Charles I's failed to suppress Covenanters, contributing to outbreak of War of the 3 Kingdoms
- During war, English Parliament's treaty of alliance with Scottish Covenanters- the Solemn League and Covenant of 1643- was key feature of positive change in fortunes of king's enemies

Political challenge

- Charles I's policies which took power and land from Scottish nobles
- King did not visit Scotland until 1633 when he was crowned there
- Appointed bishops rather than nobles to Scottish Privy Council
- John Spottiswoode appointed Chancellor, first non-secular official in this position since Reformation
- Charles I gave increasing power to bishops, undermining status of Scottish nobility
- Stuart notion of Divine Right of Kings was brought to an end by Scots opposition to Charles I's attempts to impose his will on Scottish people

5. The candidate evaluates how important the role of the Army was in the failure to find an alternative form of government between 1649 and 1658, using evidence and arguments such as:

The role of the Army

- Army extremists pushed for greater martial authority.
- Army officers formed the Council of State with the Rump Parliament. Extremists in the army opposed too great an involvement of Parliament in governing the country.

• The creation of a military dictatorship from 1653 drew comparisons with the Stuart monarchs' martial law, as did the formation of the first Protectorate in September 1654 and the drawing up of military districts under the governance of major-generals during the second Protectorate from October 1656.

• Parliamentarians resented the influence of the Army on constitutional affairs throughout the Interregnum.

Other factors

Legacy of Civil War

• The civil war was deeply divisive of society, and caused lasting bitterness, as well as causing high casualties and destruction of property. Royalist exiles intrigued for a return to power, while parliament's supporters feared plots everywhere. This engendered an atmosphere of suspicion and mistrust which intensified tension and made compromise more difficult.

• All of the pre-Civil War problems such as religious, political, legal and economic issues, plus additional foreign policy issues, meant that Cromwell was always going to encounter difficulties.

The effects of execution of the king

• After the execution of Charles I in 1649, the Council of State abolished the monarchy and declared a Republic, or Commonwealth. Previously problems could be tackled by monarch and Parliament. However, now there was no check on Parliamentary power.

• Royalists accused Cromwell of regicide and refused to acknowledge his authority.

• In Scotland, Charles II was crowned king and some of his supporters wanted him to ascend the throne in England also. Without a king, Cromwell ruled on his own for two different periods during the Interregnum, drawing comparisons with Charles I's eleven year tyranny.

Cromwell's dominance

• Cromwell dominated politics and was in a unique position to influence the direction of the country. However, he was a contrary character, who espoused democratic principles but acted in a dictatorial manner, as he knew an elected government would contain his enemies and could lead to independence for Scotland and Ireland. His roots were in Parliament but his rise to the rank of general during the Civil War meant that he favoured the military during the Interregnum.

• He was naturally conservative, but many of his policies were ahead of time, such as relief for the poor and the insane during the Barebones Parliament. Cromwell was a Puritan but passed progressive reforms, such as civil marriages, which horrified many.

• He was heavily preoccupied with foreign matters early on in the Interregnum, relied heavily on the Army, ignored Parliamentary concerns and suffered from the absence of a monarch to act as a check on his actions such as passing unpopular legislation

The role of Parliament

• The Rump Parliament consisted of MPs who had failed to avert Civil War in 1642 and who now had to address the same problems in 1649. Puritans amongst them were keen on church reform and viewed this as their priority. Parliament was opposed to the role of the Army, and wanted to have a greater say in drawing up the constitution.

• Quarrels between MPs and army officers were a feature of the Interregnum. Parliament stood in the way of toleration and thus prevented religious wounds healing.

Unpopular legislation

• The Treason Law and Censorship Law were introduced in 1649. In 1650 the Oath of Allegiance was imposed for all men over 18. He abolished the High Court in 1654 which caused a backlog of 23,000 cases.

• The Barebones Parliament consisted of many well-intentioned but inexperienced figures who proved incapable of using power effectively; it was accused of introducing too many reforms in too short a space of time. The constitution was drawn up solely by army officers which drew further criticism. Roman Catholics and Anglicans were excluded from voting by the First Protectorate, which also introduced strict Moral Codes that curtailed popular forms of entertainment and enforced the Sabbath.

• The Commission of Triers and Committee of Ejectors, who oversaw the appointment of clergymen and schoolmasters, proved unpopular with the church.

• A 10% land tax was resented by the aristocracy. Taxation in general increased to fund wars with Spain.

• Cromwell's approval of his son Richard as his successor led many to feel that Cromwell viewed himself as a monarchical figure.

Foreign policy

• Faced with possible invasion, Cromwell was forced to fight several battles to control Scotland.

• He had to put down rebellions in Ireland by Royalists and Catholics brutally, which caused further resentment and hostility.

• War was waged on Holland to enforce the Navigation Acts. In the mid-1650s war with Spain caused increased taxes.

• Distractions caused by foreign affairs may have led to social issues such as coal shortages in the winter of 1652-3 not being addressed appropriately and therefore increasing instability in England.

6. The candidate assesses the success of the Revolution Settlement in addressing the key issues between Crown and Parliament, using evidence and arguments such as:

Religion

• Before 1688 the Crown dictated the religious status of the country. After the Settlement, hundreds of High Anglicans were expelled from their posts because they refused to recognise the authority of William III. The Toleration Act of 1689 was passed which provided for free public worship for all except Roman Catholics and Unitarians. Roman Catholics were still ineligible for elected posts in towns or Parliament. Parliament now held more sway in religious matters. However the monarch still enjoyed political advantages of being head of the church.

Finance

• In the time of James I and Charles I the monarchy could exist financially independently of Parliament. Now this was impossible. The king and queen were granted £700,000 for court expenses in 1689, and from then on Parliament voted to give the Crown money annually as part of the Civil List system. A procedure of audit was established for MPs to check the expenditure of the monarch. Fiscal power was now in the hands of the House of Commons. However the monarch would not have to make the unpopular moves of raising taxes himself from now on.

Legislation

• Stuart monarchs had abused the legal system and the courts. The legal settlement established Parliamentary control over these areas, and later the Act of Settlement of 1701 stated that judges could only be removed from their positions if Parliament demanded this. From now on ministers impeached by the House of Commons could not be pardoned by the Crown. In 1695 the Law of Treason was altered to give defendants the right to be given a copy of the indictment against them, the right to be defended by Counsel, and to be able to call witnesses in their defence. An act of treason needed two witnesses against the defendant instead of one as previously. Parliament was now enforcing its own control over judicial procedure. However monarchs could still appoint judges who might be favourable to them.

Parliament

- In the days before the Civil War, Stuart monarchs had been able to rule without Parliament and curtail Parliamentary freedom of speech. The Revolution Settlement, however, provided for another Triennial Act in 1694, which was intended to keep MPs more closely in touch with public opinion. In addition, the Licensing Act was repealed in 1695, removing restrictions on the freedom of the press to report Parliamentary criticism of the Crown.
- William and Mary had to agree to the Bill of Rights before they were given the throne, legalising the new relationship between Crown and Parliament. This ensured that no future king or queen could attempt absolutism. Members of Parliament could now speak freely when voicing their opinion of the monarch. However, the monarch could still dismiss Parliament at will.

The succession

- Before the Settlement, monarchs approved their own successors. The Bill of Rights declared that no Roman Catholic could become king or queen. Later, the Act of Settlement of 1701 stated that if William and Mary had no heirs the throne would pass to Sophia of Hanover, Protestant daughter of Elizabeth of Bohemia, sister of Charles I. The Act said that all future monarchs should be members of the Church of England. Parliament now governed the question of who ascended the throne.

Scotland

- The Claim of Right asserted that James had been deposed; Parliament gave the Crown to William and Mary ie power flowed upwards from the people.
- The Settlement confirmed the position of the Kirk in Scotland as the Presbyterian Church.
- The abolition of the Committee of the Articles gave the Scottish Parliament a much greater share in the government of Scotland.

Ireland

- Roman Catholics in Ireland had been persecuted by monarchs in the past. The Settlement stated that Roman Catholics would enjoy the same freedoms as they had done under Charles II, although this promise was broken by the Penal Laws of 1693-94 which excluded Roman Catholics from the learned professions and elected positions. Soldiers who had fought for James II against William's troops in 1690 were allowed to flee to France.

The status of the army

- Charles I had been able to raise an army in 1642. The Revolution Settlement meant that Parliament gained partial control of the army. The monarch was not given enough money to maintain a standing army. The Mutiny Act of 1689 legalised the army, and this act had to be passed annually by Parliament, which forced the king to summon Parliament in order to do so. Royal authority over military matters had now passed to the House of Commons.

Loopholes in the Settlement.

- Although the Revolution Settlement handed a lot of power from the Crown to Parliament, there were loopholes in the agreement which meant the monarch still held executive

power and controlled foreign policy, declaring war and signing treaties. The monarch was still the source of patronage in the army and navy. The monarch still created peers, and could therefore control the House of Lords. The Revolution Settlement, therefore, did not completely hand over power to Parliament. It was a compromise which acted as a halfway-house between Crown and Parliament, and government business was negotiated and conducted between the two.

The Atlantic Slave Trade

7. The candidate assesses the importance of the slave trade to the development of the British economy in the 18th century, using evidence and arguments such as:

Evidence that the Slave Trade was important

- Importance of the slave trade to the development of the economy: financial, commercial, legal and insurance institutions emerged to support the activities of the slave traders. Slave traders became bankers and many new businesses were financed by profits made from slave trading.
- The slave trade played an important role in providing British industry with access to raw materials and this contributed to the increased production of manufactured goods.
- Ports such as London, Bristol and Liverpool prospered as a direct result of involvement in the slave trade; other ports such as Glasgow profited from trade with the colonies. Thousands of jobs were created in Britain supplying goods and services to slave traders.
- Liverpool became a major centre for shipbuilding largely as a result of the trade.
- Manchester exported large percentage of cotton goods to Africa.
- The slave trade was important to the economic prosperity and well-being of the colonies.
- Investment from the Slave trade went into the Welsh Slate Industry.
- The slave trade was an important training ground for British seamen, providing experienced crews for the merchant marine and the Royal Navy.
- Wealth generated by the slave trade meant that domestic taxes could be kept low.
- Argument that the slave trade was the vital factor in Britain's industrialisation was put forward in Williams' Capitalism and Slavery thesis.

Evidence that other factors were important

- Changes in agriculture: these created an agricultural surplus which:
  - fed an expanding population
  - produced a labour force in the towns for use in factories
  - created a financial surplus for investment in industry and infrastructure.
- Technological innovation: development of water and steam power; new machinery; transport changes.
- Mineral and energy resources, particularly iron and coal.
- Political stability.
- Much of the profits of slavery were dissipated in conspicuous consumption e.g. landed estates.

8. The candidate assesses the extent to which African Societies benefited from the slave trade, using evidence and arguments such as:

Development of slave based states and economies

- Africans could become slaves as punishment for a crime, as payment for a family debt, or most commonly of all, by being captured as prisoners of war. With the arrival of European and American ships offering trading goods in exchange for captives, Africans had an added incentive to enslave each other, often by abducting unfortunate victims.

- Some societies preyed on others to obtain captives in exchange for European firearms, in the belief that if they did not acquire firearms in this way to protect themselves, they would be attacked and captured by their rivals and enemies who did possess such weapons. This led to the growth of states such as Dahomey whose raison d'etre was the slave trade.

Destruction of society

- Rich and powerful Africans were able to demand a variety of consumer goods and in some places even gold for captives, who may have been acquired through warfare or by other means, initially without massive disruption to African societies.
- By the end of 17th century European demand for African captives, particularly for the sugar plantations in the Americas, became so great that they could only be acquired through initiating raiding and warfare; large areas of Africa were devastated and societies disintegrated.
- It is estimated that around 10 million people were transported from Africa over the eighteenth century. This was a huge drain on the most productive and economically active sections of the population and this led to economic dislocation and falls in production of food and other goods.

Slave sellers and European 'factories' on West African Coast

- Europeans seldom ventured inland to capture the millions of people who were transported from Africa as captives. In the areas where slavery was not practised, such as among the Xhosa people of southern Africa, European slave ship captains were unable to buy African captives.
- Development of European 'factories' on coast to control the slave trade.

Development of foreign colonies

- West Africa was impoverished by its relationship with Europe while the human and other resources that were taken from Africa contributed to the economic development and wealth of Europe and the European colonies in the New World. The transatlantic trade also created the conditions for the subsequent colonial conquest of Africa by the European powers.

Role played by African societies in continuing the trade

- African slave sellers grew wealthy by selling African captives to European traders on the coast. They were able to deal on equal terms with European traders who built 'factories' on the West African coast to house captives before selling them onto the slave ship captains who in turn transported the captives to the colonies of the New World.
- On the African side, the slave trade was generally the business of rulers or wealthy and powerful merchants, concerned with their own selfish or narrow interests, rather than those of the continent. At that time, there was no concept of being African - identity and loyalty were based on kinship or membership of a specific kingdom or society, rather than to the African continent.
- States based on slavery, particularly Dahomey, grew in power and influence.

9. The candidate evaluates the extent to which the decline in economic importance of slavery resulted in abolition of the Slave Trade, using evidence and arguments such as:

The decline in the economic importance of slavery

- Effects of wars with France – slave trade declined by two-thirds as it was seen as harming the national interest in time of war.
- The slave trade had become less important in economic terms – there was no longer a need for large numbers of slaves to be imported to the British colonies.

- There was a world over-supply of sugar and British merchants had difficulties re-exporting it.

Other factors
The religious revival

- The religious revival of the late eighteenth century was at the heart of the anti-slavery movement. Many of the early leaders particularly were Quakers. The revival also took on board humanitarian considerations.

The role of Wilberforce

- Wilberforce put forward the arguments of the Society for the Abolition of the Slave Trade in Parliament for eighteen years.
- Wilberforce's speeches in Parliament were graphic and appealing.
- Wilberforce's Christian faith had led him to become interested in social reform and link the issues of factory reform in Britain and the need to abolish slavery and the slave trade within the British Empire.
- Wilberforce was prepared to work with other abolitionists to achieve his aims, including the Quakers, Thomas Clarkson and Olaudah Equiano.

The effects of slave resistance

- Successful slave rebellion in Saint-Domingue led to an exaggerated, general fear of slave revolts. There was an argument that if conditions were not ameliorated by, for example, the abolition of the slave trade, further revolts would follow. Already on Jamaica a substantial number of runaways lived outside the control of the authorities.

The campaign of the Anti-Slavery Society

- Thomas Clarkson obtained witnesses for the Parliamentary investigations of the slave trade which provided Wilberforce with convincing evidence for his speeches.
- Books and pamphlets published eg eyewitness accounts from former slaves such as Olaudah Equiano.
- Campaigns to boycott goods produced by slaves in the West Indies such as sugar and rum.
- Petitions and subscription lists, public meetings and lecture tours involving those with experience of slave trade eg John Newton, churches and theatres used for abolitionist propaganda, artefacts and illustrations eg Wedgwood pottery.
- Lobbying of Parliament by abolitionists to extract promises from MPs that they would oppose the slave trade. Effective moderate political and religious leadership among the abolitionists influenced major figures such as Pitt and Fox; abolitionists gave evidence to Parliamentary Commissions.

Military factors

- Napoleon's efforts to restore slavery in the French islands meant that the abolitionist campaign would help to undermine Napoleon's plans for the Caribbean. The Act banning any slave trade between British merchants and foreign colonies in 1806 was intended to attack French interests.

Britain 1851 – 1951

10. The candidate assesses how accurate it is to describe Britain as a fully democratic country by 1918 using evidence and arguments such as:

Widening of the Franchise

- In 1867 most skilled working class men in towns got the vote.
- In 1884 many more men in the countryside were given the vote.
- In 1918 most men over 21 and some women over 30 gained the vote. Finally in 1928 men and women over 21 were given the vote.
- Undemocratic anomalies – plural votes and the university constituencies – were not abolished until 1948.

Corruption and Intimidation
• The Secret Ballot (1872) ended open voting.
• The Corrupt and Illegal Practices Act (1883) introduced limits to election expenses.
• The effectiveness of these varied; i.e. where the electorate was small or where a landowner or employer was dominant in an area eg Norwich.

Issues of distribution of seats
• Re-distribution of seats in 1867.
• 1885 Act created single member constituencies with roughly similar number of voters.
• Finally there was another re-distribution of seats in 1918.

Widening membership of House of Commons
• The property qualification to be MP was abolished in 1858.
• Payment for MPs began in 1911, enabling working class members to sit.
• Although the working class electorate increased by 1880s there was no national party to express their interests. The Liberals and Conservatives promoted middle, even upper, class capitalist values.
• The spread of socialist ideas and trade unionism led to the creation of the prototype Labour Party – the LRC – by 1900 thereby offering a wider choice to the electorate, and a party directly linked to the aspirations of the working class.
• As the size of the electorate grew, individual political parties had to make sure their 'message' got across to electorate eg development of National Liberal Federation, Conservative Central Office, Primrose League.

Access to information
• Education – in the later 19th Century there was a great increase in literacy and hence access to information on which to base choice. Also railways spread information nationally and were important to the growth of democracy.

Role of the House of Lords
• From 1911 Lords could only delay bills from the House of Commons for two years rather than veto them. They had no control over money bills.
• In 1949 the two year delaying power of the House of Lords was reduced to only one year but the power of House of Lords (not reformed until 1990s) in law making still continues.
• The voting system is still 'first past the post' in UK. This is arguably undemocratic.

11. The candidate evaluates the extent to which the Liberal Government of 1906 to 1914 introduced social reform due to the social surveys of Booth and Rowntree, using evidence and arguments such as:

The social surveys of Booth and Rowntree
• The reports of Charles Booth and Seebohm Rowntree demonstrated that poverty had causes such as low pay, unemployment, sickness and old age. These were largely outwith the control of the individual.
• The extent of poverty revealed in the surveys was also a shock. Booth's initial survey was confined to the East End of London, but his later volumes covering the rest of London revealed that almost one third of the capital's population lived in poverty. York was a relatively prosperous small town but even there poverty was deep-seated.

Other factors
Municipal socialism
• By the end of the century some Liberal-controlled local authorities had become involved in programmes of social welfare. The shocked reaction to the reports on poverty was a pressure for further reform.

• In Birmingham particularly, but in other large industrial cities, local authorities had taken the lead in providing social welfare schemes. These served as an example for further reforms.

Foreign examples
• Germany had introduced a much admired system of social security. This raised the issue whether Britain was no longer a major European nation.

National efficiency
• By the end of the 19th century Britain was facing serious competition from new industrial nations such as Germany. It was believed that if the health and educational standards of Britain's workers got worse then Britain's position as a strong industrial power would be threatened.

Fears over national security
• The government became alarmed when almost 25% of the volunteers to fight in the Boer War were rejected because they were physically unfit to serve in the armed forces. There was concern whether Britain could survive a war or protect its empire against a far stronger enemy in the future if the nation's 'fighting stock' of young men was so unhealthy.
• Link between national security concerns and national efficiency concerns; financial or economic security.

The rise of the New Liberalism
• New Liberals argued that state intervention was necessary to liberate people from social problems over which they had no control. New Liberal ideas were not important issues in the general election of 1905. Only when 'old liberal' Prime Minister Campbell Bannerman died in 1908 was the door was opened for new 'interventionist' ideas.

Party advantage
• Since 1884 many more working class men had the vote and the Liberals had tended to attract many of those votes. Social reform was a means of appeasing this constituency.

The rise of Labour
• By 1906 the newly formed Labour Party was competing for the same votes. It can be argued that the reforms happened for the very selfish reason of retaining working class votes.

12. The candidates assesses the validity of the statement that the social reforms of the Labour Government failed to deal effectively with the needs of the people, using evidence and arguments such as:

Needs of the people identified by Beveridge as the 5 giants of poverty: Want, Disease, Ignorance, Squalor, Idleness

Want
• 1946 the National Insurance Act: consisted of comprehensive insurance sickness and unemployment benefits and cover for most eventualities.
• It was said to support people from the 'cradle to the grave' which was significant as it meant people had protection against falling into poverty throughout their lives.
• This was very effective as it meant that if the breadwinner of the family was injured then the family was less likely to fall further into the poverty trap, as was common before. However, this act can be criticised for its failure to go far enough.
• Benefits only granted to those who made 156 weekly contributions.
• 1948 the National Assistance Board was set up in order to cover those for whom insurance did not do enough.
• This was important as it acted as a safety net to protect these people.

Disease:
• est. of the NHS in 1948 dealt effectively with the spread of disease
• The NHS was the first comprehensive universal system of health in Britain

- offered vaccination and immunisation against disease, almost
  - totally eradicating some of Britain's most deadly illnesses
- It also offered helpful services such as childcare, the introduction of prescriptions, health visiting and provision for the elderly, providing a safety net across the whole country: everyone, regardless of their financial situation, was entitled to equal opportunities of health care they had previously not experienced
- NHS could be regarded as almost too successful. The demand from the public was overwhelming, as the estimated amount of patients treated by them almost doubled. Introduction of charges for prescriptions, etc.

Education

- Reform started by the wartime government: The 1944 Education Act raised the age at which people could leave school to 15 as part of a drive to create more skilled workers which Britain lacked at the time. Introduction of school milk, etc.
- Labour introduced a two-tiered secondary schooling whereby pupils were split at the age of 11(12 in Scotland) depending on their ability. The pupils who passed the "11+ exam" went to grammar and the rest to secondary moderns.
- Those who went to grammar schools were expected to stay on past the age of 15 and this created a group of people who would take senior jobs in the country thus solving the skills shortages. Whilst this separation of ability in theory meant that children of even poor background could get equal opportunities in life, in practice the system actually created a bigger division between the poor and the rich.
- Labour expanded university education: introduction of grants so all could attend in theory.

Housing

- After the war there was a great shortage of housing as the war had destroyed and damaged thousands of homes; and the slum cleaning programmes of the 1930's had done little to rectify the situation which was leading to a number of other problems for the government.
- Tackling the housing shortage fell upon Bevan's Ministry of Health.
- Labours' target for housing was to build 200,000 new homes a year. 157,000 pre-fabricated homes were built to a good standard, however this number would not suffice and the target was never met.
- Bevan encouraged the building of council houses rather than privately funded construction.
- The New Towns Act of 1946, aimed to target overcrowding in the increasingly built up older cities. By 1950, the government had designed 12 new communities.
- In an attempt to eradicate slums the Town and Country Planning Act provided local communities more power in regards to building developments and new housing.
- By the time Labour left government office in 1951 there was still a huge shortfall in British housing.

Idleness

- Low levels of unemployment post-war so the government had little to do to tackle idleness.
- Increased direct government funding for the universities which led to a 60% increase in student numbers between 1945-46 and 1950-51,which helped to meet the manpower requirements of post-war society. This provided more skilled workers and allowed people from less advantaged backgrounds to pursue a higher education, aiming to keep unemployment rates down.
- Labour government also nationalised 20 percent of industry – the railways, mines, gas and electricity. The government were directly involved with people employed in these huge industries.

- This tackled idleness by the government having control which meant that employees were less likely to lose their job through industries going bankrupt and people were working directly to benefit society.

Britain and Ireland 1900-1985

13. The candidate assesses the validity of the view that the decline of the Nationalist Party was the most significant impact of World War One on Ireland, using evidence and arguments such as:

Decline of Nationalist Party

- Irish Convention failed to reach agreement, which weakened position of Nationalists.
- Led to feeling British could not be trusted and Nationalists could not deliver.
- Three by-elections wins for Sinn Fein gave impression they spoke for people not Nationalists which increased tension between Ireland and Britain politically.
- March 1918 Redmond died which accelerated the decline of the Nationalists. Sinn Fein gained influence and popularity as a result.
- Many moved from the Nationalist Party as they felt Sinn Fein was doing more for Ireland.

Other factors

Irish Attitudes to World War I

- Initially war brought prosperity to Ireland - manufacturing and farming, low unemployment thus improving relations between GB and Ireland.
- Propaganda – powerful Germany invading helpless and small Catholic Belgium so Ireland supported GB.
- Ulster very supportive of Britain to ensure favourable treatment at the end of the war.
- Nationalists and Redmond backed war to get Home Rule, urging Irish men to enlist.
- Press gave support to the war effort.
- Irish Volunteers gave support to help Home Rule be passed after the war.
- Recruitment was successful in the south as almost ¼ million men join up.

Easter Rising

- Rebels saw war as chance to rid Ireland of British by force.
- Felt it was opportunity to gain independence by force as Britain had their troops away fighting the Germans in World War I. This greatly strained relations between Britain and Ireland.
- Britain had to use force to suppress rebellion, such as using the Gunboat, 'Helga' to sail up the River Liffey and fire on the rebels in the GPO, thus distracting GB's attention and resources away from War effort, thus straining relations.
- Strong criticism of Rising initially from the public, politicians, churchmen, as well as press for unnecessary death and destruction. 450 dead, 2500 wounded, cost £2½ million, showing that majority still sided with GB therefore indicating that there was not too much damage to relations between the two countries.
- Initial hostility by majority of Irish people to Rising by small group of rebels, majority of people supported Redmond and the Nationalists Party.
- Strong hostility and criticism by Dubliners to rebels for destruction of city centre.

Changing Attitudes Towards British Rule after 1916

- The secret court martial, execution of leaders over 10 days as well as imprisonment without trial and at least one execution without a trial saw the rebels gain a lot of sympathy from the Irish public, turning them against British rule.
- These political developments meant a growth of sympathy and compassion for rebels who were seen as martyrs and replaced the initial condemnation of the Rising.

- Sinn Fein initially blamed for the Rising saw a subsequent rise in support for them.
- Catholic Church and business community became more sympathetic to the cause of independence.

Anti-Conscription Campaign

- Irish opposed conscription and pushed people in protest to Sinn Fein who openly opposed it.
- Caused the Nationalists to withdraw from Westminster
- Sinn Fein and Nationalists organised campaign e.g. general strike April 23rd.
- Catholic Church, Mayor of Dublin drew up the National Pledge opposing conscription.
- Conscription was not extended to Ireland which Sinn Fein was given credit for.
- Conscription campaign drove Sinn Fein underground where improved their organisation.

Rise of Sinn Fein

- Opposition to war very much a minority in 1914 but supported by Sinn Fein and Arthur Griffith (not powerful at this time), as well as Pearse, Connolly and their supporters and also a section of the Irish Volunteers. This damaged relations with Britain.
- Release of rebel prisoners from Frongoch meant Sinn Fein's struggle against British Rule in Ireland gained momentum.
- Michael Collins was building up IRB and Irish Volunteers when in prison.
- Collins ready to encourage anti-British activity in Ireland on release.
- Collins and De Valera improved Sinn Fein's leadership.
- Opposition to Britain due to martial law, house searches, raids, control of press, arrest of "suspects" without trial, and vigorous implementation of the Defence of the Realm Act
- Hunger striker Thomas Ashe died in 1917. His funeral became a propaganda tool for Sinn Fein.

Entrenchment of Unionism in the North

- Unionists' 'blood sacrifice' on the Western Front – expectation that this would be recognised in any post-war settlement. The rise of Sinn Fein was viewed with increasing alarm, as was the participation of the Catholic Church in wartime politics eg the National Pledge.

14. The candidate evaluates the importance of the divisions in the Republican movement in causing the outbreak of the Irish Civil War, using evidence and arguments such as:

Divisions in Republican Movement

- Signing the Anglo-Irish Treaty of 1921 caused a split in the Republican movement between pro and anti-Treaty factions over whether the Treaty was beneficial to Ireland or not.
- Arthur Griffith supported the treaty; he felt it gave Ireland a voice and equality with England.
- Collins supported treaty; Ireland has elected Government, whoever disobeys it are enemies
- De Valera opposed it and felt it should be resisted even if it meant Civil War.
- Sean MacEntee opposed the treaty as did Liam Lynch and Sinn Fein who wanted an independent Ireland.
- The treaty was accepted by 64 votes to 57 by the Dail Eireann on the 7th of January 1922.
- De Valera voted against the treaty and resigned as President suggesting that the Civil War started due to De Valera's own ambitions rather than due to what the Irish people actually wanted.
- Some of the IRA units supported the treaty, whilst others opposed it.
- Some of the anti-treaty IRA took over some important buildings in Dublin, e.g. Four Courts.

- Division and murder of Sir Henry Wilson (security adviser for the Northern Ireland government) forced Michael Collins to call on the official IRA to attack the "Irregular IRA".

Other Factors

Roles of Collins and De Valera

- Collins claimed Ireland had its own, elected government, so Britain no longer the enemy.
- Collins defended the treaty as he claimed it gave Ireland "freedom to achieve freedom".
- Collins claimed that the elections after the treaty show he has support of the people.
- Collins claims that the new state government cannot give in to the armed minority
- De Valera refused to accept terms of the treaty as they were in "violent conflict with the wishes of the majority of the nation".
- De Valera claimed that treaty meant partition of Ireland and abandonment of sovereignty
- De Valera felt he should have been consulted before the treaty was signed.
- De Valera resigned as President to be replaced by Griffith and Collins became Head of the Irish Free Government
- Collins and De Valera tried to reach a compromise to avoid war but none was reached.

The Anglo Irish Treaty

- People like Collin's and Griffith felt the Anglo Irish Treaty benefited Ireland whereas De Valera and his supporters felt the actual terms of the treaty were detrimental to Ireland.
- Ireland to be "Irish Free State" to govern itself, make its own laws but remain in Empire, which was favoured by the majority of the Irish people. There was only a small minority who felt that this was no the case.
- Governor General to represent King, Britain to remove forces but keep use of naval bases, which caused particular anger amongst those who were strong Republicans.
- Trade issues were relations were settled, which to the majority was regarded as beneficial to the economic well being of Ireland.
- Lloyd George threatened Irish delegation with war if they did not sign, which is what De Valera claimed was the main reason for the Irish Civil War breaking out.
- Collins realised the treaty was his death warrant, De Valera used it as propaganda.

Issue of Partition

- Government of Ireland Act passed, split Ireland in two, 6 counties in North 26 in south, which many in Ireland opposed before the signing of the treaty and was used by opponents of the Treaty as the main problem with the treaty.
- One of the main tings the Republicans wanted was an independent Ireland, but also a complete Ireland, with no partition
- In Northern Ireland Unionists won 40 of 52 seats available, showing that they supported partition, but they always had, as they did not want to be separate from Britain.
- Third of Ulster population were Catholic and wanted to be united to South, and so were unhappy with the treaty.
- Twenty six counties in south had separate parliament in Dublin, which resulted in them being happy with the treaty.
- Council of Ireland set up, to reconcile differences over partition in the future and therefore reduce the risk partition caused to potential violence.
- The IRA refused to recognise the new Parliament in Belfast and resorted to violence as a means of resistance to it.
- Sectarian hatred increased in Ulster, as the summer of 1920 saw 62 Catholics die in reaction to the partitioning of Ireland.

- Ulster Special Constabulary, Special Powers Act, Local Government Emergency Powers Act were passed in the north to suppress Catholics as a result of partition being passed, which increased anger in the south which was predominantly Catholic.
- In the South, the Government of Ireland Act was ignored; Sinn Fein won 124 seats unopposed.

Dominion Status

- Under this agreement Ireland became what is known as a Dominion of the British Empire, which a minority in the south were opposed to, therefore leading to division and subsequently violence between those who accepted this status and those who opposed it.
- Under Dominion Status the new Irish State had to three important things to adhere to.
- The elected representatives of the people were to take an oath of allegiance to the British Crown, which violently opposed by opponents of the Treaty like De Valera.
- A Governor General, which opponents did not like as they saw it as Britain still having an influence in Irish affairs, represented the Crown.
- Appeals in certain legal cases could be taken to the Privy Council in London, which again opponents of the treaty disliked as it meant some important decisions were ultimately still being made in Britain.

15. The candidate evaluates the validity of the statement that the British government policy of Direct Rule was the main obstacle to peace in Northern Ireland between 1968 and 1985, using evidence and arguments such as:

Direct Rule

- A number of reforms had followed on from the Downing Street Declaration, ie on allocation of council housing, investigate the recent cycle of violence and review policing, such as the disbanding of the hated 'B Specials' auxiliaries.
- The British government, now led by Prime Minister Edward Heath, decided to remove control of security from the government of Northern Ireland and appointed a secretary of state for the province leading to resignation of Stormont government. Direct rule imposed.
- Despite attempts to introduce some sort of self-rule, such as the Sunningdale agreement of 1973, which failed in the face of implacable unionist opposition and led to the reintroduction of direct rule. It would last for another 25 years.

Other factors

Religious and communal differences

- The Protestant majority in Northern Ireland belonged to churches that represented the full range of reformed Christianity, while the Catholic minority was united in its membership of a Church that dominated life in the Republic and much of Europe. These religious divisions made it very difficult for both communities to come together.
- These divisions further enhanced by traditions embraced by both communities, such as the 'marching season', which became a flashpoint for sectarian violence. Also differences in sport, language.
- Many Catholic political representatives refused to recognise partition and their views only heightened the nationalist community's sense of alienation and fostered unionist hostility towards the Catholic minority.
- The speeches and actions of unionist and nationalist leaders such as Reverend Ian Paisley and Gerry Adams polarised views in the province, and emphasised the divisions between both communities.

Economic differences

- From 1973, the Common Agricultural Policy changed the decision making environment for food prices and farm economics, and employment in the farming sector continued to decline. Traditionally this sector had been dominated by the unionist community.
- Discrimination against Catholic applicants for employment declined steadily during this period as Catholics in the province began to enjoy the same civil rights enjoyed by the population of the rest of the UK.

Hardening attitudes – the role of terrorism

- Paramilitary groups began to operate on both sides of the sectarian divide, while civil rights marches became increasingly prone to confrontation.
- In late 1969, the more militant 'Provisional' IRA (PIRA) broke away from the so-called 'Official' IRA. PIRA was prepared to pursue unification in defiance of Britain and would use violence to achieve its aims.
- Unionist paramilitaries also organised. The UVF was joined by the Ulster Defence Association, created in 1971.
- Examples of terrorist activity: by the end of 1972 sectarian violence had escalated to such an extent that nearly 500 lives were lost in a single year.
- PIRA prisoners protest at loss of special status prisoners leading to hunger strikes. Second hunger strike in 1981, led by Bobby Sands. Sands was put forward for a vacant Westminster seat and won. Sands and nine other hunger strikers died before the hunger strikes called off in October 1981.
- Sinn Fein won the by-election following Sands' death in June 1983, These electoral successes raised the possibility that Sinn Fein could replace the more moderate SDLP as the political voice of the Catholic minority in Northern Ireland.
- Indiscriminate terrorism meant Eire public opinion turned against PIRA.
- In 1985 the violence of Northern Ireland's paramilitary groups still had more than a decade to run and the sectarian divide remained as wide as it had ever been.

British government policies – Internment

- New Prime Minister Brian Faulkner reintroduced internment i.e. detention of suspects without trial, in 1971 in response to unrest. Policy a disaster, both in its failure to capture any significant members of the PIRA and in its sectarian focus on nationalist rather than loyalist suspects. The reaction was predictable, even if the ferocity of the violence wasn't. Deaths in the final months of 1971 over 150.

The role of the British Army

- The so-called 'Battle of Bogside' in 1969 only ended with the arrival of a small force of British troops at the request of Chichester Clark. An acknowledgement that the govt. of Northern Ireland had lost its grip on the province's security.
- By 1971 policing the province was fast becoming an impossible task, and the British Army adopted increasingly aggressive policies on the ground.
- On 30 January 1972, the army deployed the Parachute Regiment to suppress rioting at a civil rights march in Derry. Thirteen demonstrators were shot and killed by troops, with another victim dying later of wounds. Appalling images of 'Bloody Sunday; led to increased recruitment by Provisional IRA.
- The British Army's various attempts to control the PIRA, such as house-to-house searches and the imposition of a limited curfew, only served to drive more recruits into the ranks of the paramilitaries.

The role of the Irish government.
- Irish government's role in The Anglo-Irish Agreement, signed in November 1985, confirmed that Northern Ireland would remain independent of the Republic as long as that was the will of the majority in the north. Also gave the Republic a say in the running of the province for the first time.
- The agreement also stated that power could not be devolved back to Northern Ireland unless it enshrined the principle of power sharing.

The Crusades, 1071 – 1204

16. The candidate evaluates the importance of peer pressure as a reason for going on crusade, using evidence and argument such as:

Peer pressure
- The pressure put on knights by their families to take the cross was at times severe. Noblemen's wives tended to be keenly aware of the politics at court and had a role in influencing the decisions of some.
- Stephen of Blois had married Adela, daughter of William I of England. It would have been unthinkable for such a notable knight not to go on the Crusade.

Other factors

Religious motives
- It was generally believed that the Remission of Sins offered by Pope Urban was an attractive solution to the dilemma of knights. Salvation was a constant worry for those trained to kill. Urban successfully resolved the need to protect Christianity from the Muslim threat and the general desire to re-establish the pilgrimage routes to the holy lands.
- The promise of remission of current sins was also a great relief to those knights worried about their eternal soul. Tancred's biographer wrote about both his worry over this dilemma and his relief at Urban's suggestion.
- The mass appeal of the People's Crusade shows the power of the belief that they were doing good and helping God.
- Of the leaders of the Princes' Crusade, Raymond of Toulouse, is often held up as an example of a knight riding to the defence of the Holy Lands. His decision to take Tripoli in 1100 casts a shadow over this interpretation of his motives.
- In later Crusades many of the religious aspects of the Crusade are adopted and modified by the growing idea of chivalric codes.

The desire to acquire territory in the Holy Land
- Many of the great magnates on this expedition had intentions to acquire new estates for themselves. The motives of many of the leaders of the Prince's Crusade have been put down to this.
- Bohemend and Baldwin in particular showed little zeal in carrying on with the Crusade once they had acquired Antioch and Edessa respectively.

Seeking of fame and riches
- Some knights did go seeking glory. The Crusade had provided the solution to the problem of knights and their need for salvation. Killing was only wrong if you killed Christians. Urban indicated that the killing of a Muslim was a just act, and the equivalent to prayer or penance.
- Seeking of riches per se was uncommon; land was the real source of wealth and power.

The sense of adventure
- For some, the humdrum existence of 11th century Europe could be replaced by the excitement of the Crusade. Pilgrimages had always been seen as important, and the idea of this as an armed pilgrimage was very appealing. It offered a way out for many serfs from their lives in bondage, or perhaps a chance to see the Holy Lands.

Overpopulation and famine
- Many were forced to leave because of the lack of available farmland in an already overcrowded Europe.
- Several famines have also been suggested as a possible motive. It was popularly believed that the Holy Lands were lands of plenty.

17. The candidate evaluates how important divisions amongst the Crusaders were in bringing about the fall of Jerusalem in 1187, using evidence and arguments such as:

Divisions amongst the Crusaders
- Two factions struggled for power within Baldwin IV's court, those of Guy de Lusignan and Baldwin's close advisor Raymond III of Tripoli. In 1180 Guy married Sibylla, Baldwin's sister. Guy tended to favor an aggressive policy.
- The activities of Reynald of Chatillon helped to destabilize the fragile peace treaty between Baldwin IV and Saladin.
- Divisions amongst Knightly Orders: The Knights Templar, unlike the Hospitallers, were firmly in the camp of the Hawks (warmongers). They wanted nothing more than to carry on with the crusading ideal and rid the Holy Lands of the Muslims. Treaties and compromise were unacceptable to them.

Other factors

The Death of Baldwin IV
- Baldwin IV, despite being physically weak, was an active politician. Even as a young king he was well aware of the different factions at court, and worked hard to maintain a balance of power in his realm.
- Baldwin signed a much needed truce with Saladin in 1180, which allowed supplies to be traded with the Latin Kingdoms.
- In 1183 he was able to prevent Guy from usurping his authority when he had recovered sufficiently from his disease to once again rule directly.
- However. In the latter years of his reign, he struggled to contain the schemes of his sister Sibylla and Guy de Lusignan, and unruly Barons such as Reynald of Chatillon.
- Baldwin died in March 1185, taking his strategy of non-aggression towards Saladin with him. He was replaced for a short time by his nephew, Baldwin V. However a short power struggle after the boy's death in August let Guy de Lusignan assume the throne, abetted by Sibylla.
- His death meant that the factions that he had tried to hold together now became even more disunited. Raymond of Tripoli and Guy hated each other; Jerusalem no longer had a strong ruler to keep it under control.

Importance of Hattin
- King Guy led the armies of Jerusalem to save Count Tiberius's wife as Saladin's forces had surrounded her castle. Tiberius himself had few worries about the safety of his wife. His fortress could have withstood a siege. Saladin's forces lacked the required siege engines to make a successful attack. Additionally, Saladin could not keep his disparate forces in the field for any length of time. Tiberius' advice to Guy was to hold his forces back to protect Jerusalem.
- However, figures such as Reynald had persuaded Guy that to leave the Countess of Tripoli besieged would be un-chivalric and that Guy would lose support if he did not ride out.
- The army could find little water to sustain them in the desert. Their only option was to make for Hattin and the oasis there. This was an obvious trap; Saladin surrounded them with burning brushwood and dry grass. Trapped on the Horns of Hattin, the Christian army were suffering from the sun and lack of water.

- Eventually they were forced to attack before they lacked the strength to do so. The Christian horses were too weak for a prolonged struggle and their infantry were surrounded by Saladin's horse archers and cut off.
- Saladin ordered the slaughter of all members of the militant orders, but Guy and many of his followers were allowed to surrender and enter captivity.
- Without the army to protect the kingdom even the massive fortifications could not stand against Saladin's forces.

The lack of resources of the Christian states
- The Crusaders had sought to redress their military inferiority by constructing powerful fortifications. Without the army to protect the kingdom even the massive fortifications could not withstand Saladin's forces.
- Even the combined armies of the Crusader States were not strong enough to successfully win a war, especially in the long run. It is arguable that it was inevitable for the Crusader States to fall to a united Islamic state.

Unification of Islamic forces under Saladin
- Saladin had managed to successfully unite the Muslims of Syria and Egypt behind his leadership. This effectively surrounded Jerusalem and left them with a very weak military position.
- Saladin successfully used the idea of a religious war against the Christians to hold the separate Islamic groups together.
- Saladin himself had his critics within the Muslim ranks, saying he was more interested in maintaining his position than defeating the Christians. It was seen by many that his stance on the Kingdom of Jerusalem was weak. After Guy assumed the throne and Reynald continued his attacks the pressure on Saladin to respond grew. This encouraged him to act aggressively.

18. The candidate assesses the validity of the view that by the Fourth Crusade of 1204 the crusading ideal was dead, using evidence and arguments such as:

The Fourth Crusade
- The initial inspiration of the Forth Crusade had a strong crusading ideology behind it. Pope Innocent III was a highly effective pope. He had managed to settle the problem of the investiture contest with Germany, and hoped to sort out the issue of the Holy Lands as well. Innocent believed that the inclusion of medieval monarchs had caused the previous two Crusades to fail, unlike the first Crusade that was nominally under the command of Bishop Adhemar. This Crusade would fall under the command of six papal legates. These men would hold true to the ideal of the Crusade and not be bound by earthy greed of politics.
- However, The Fourth Crusade has also been described as the low point of the crusading ideal. Hijacked by the Venetians, the Crusade instead became a tool for their growing political and economic ambitions.
- While attacking Zara, Alexius, son of the deposed emperor of Byzantium, arrived with a new proposal for the Crusaders. He asked them to reinstate his father, who had been imprisoned by his brother, and if they agreed they would be handsomely rewarded. He also promised to return control of the Byzantine Church to Rome. The church was against such an attack on another Christian city, but the prospect of
- wealth and fame led the Crusade to Constantinople.
- When the Crusaders discovered that Alexius and his father could not, or would not, meet the payment as agreed, the Crusaders stormed the city. The murder, looting and rape continued for three days, after which the crusading army had a great thanksgiving ceremony.

- The amount of booty taken from Constantinople was huge: gold, silver, works of art and holy relics were taken back to Europe, mostly to Venice. Most crusaders returned home with their newly acquired wealth. Those that stayed dividing up the land amongst themselves, effectively creating several Latin Crusader States where Byzantium had once stood.

Role of Venice
- By 1123 the city of Venice had come to dominate maritime trade in the Middle East. They made several secret trade agreements with Egypt and North African emirs, as well as enjoying concessions and trade agreements within the Kingdom of Jerusalem. Byzantium however, remained a constant rival for this dominance of trade and in 1183 Venice was cut off from the lucrative trading centres of the empire.
- Venice's participation in the Crusade was only secured when the Pope agreed to pay huge sums of money to Venice for the use of its ships, and supplies as well as half of everything captured during the Crusade on land and sea.
- Venice's leader, the Doge Enrico Dandolo, had sold the Crusaders three times as much supplies and equipment as required for the Crusade. The crusading leader, Boniface of Montferrat, found that he was unable to raise enough money to pay, and the Crusaders were all but imprisoned on an island near Venice. Dandolo's proposal to pay off the Crusaders' debt involved attacking Zara, a Christian city that had once belonged to Venice but was now under the control of the King of Hungary, a Christian monarch. Thus the Crusade had become a tool of the Venetians.
- The Fourth Crusade's intended target, Egypt, was totally unsuitable from a Venetian perspective. Thus when the Pope's representative approached the Venetians in 1201 they agreed to help transport the Crusaders, hoping to divert the Crusade to a less friendly target. The final target for the Fourth Crusade was therefore determined by politics and economics.

Coexistence of Muslim and Crusading states
- Attempts at peace between Muslim and the Crusading states during the reign of Baldwin IV, before his death and the fall of Jerusalem.
- Also other examples, such as the treaty of mutual protection signed between King Alric of Jerusalem and the Emir of Damascus prior to the second crusade.

The corruption of the crusading movement by the Church and nobles
- Popes were willing to use crusades against Christians, such as the Albegensian crusade against the Cathar heretics of Languedoc (Toulouse and southern France) in 1209-1229. The Cathars did not believe in the hierarchy of Rome, all you needed was to be able to read the bible. This is only the first of many such crusades in Europe, seen as diluting the crusading ideal, ie killing Muslims.
- Examples of nobles using the crusade for their own ends are all over the place, from Bohemond and Baldwin in the First Crusade, to arguably Richard in the third. The fourth crusade is littered with examples.

Effects of trade
- Trade links directly into the Fourth Crusade and the influence of Venice.
- Pisa and Genoa both had a lot of influence in events during the Third Crusade, they both had favoured candidates for the vacant throne of Jerusalem for example and used trade rights as a bargaining chip to get what they wanted.

The American Revolution 1763 – 1787

19. The candidate evaluates the validity of the view that disputes over taxation were the main reason for the outbreak of the American Colonists' revolt against British Rule in 1776, using evidence and arguments such as:

Disputes over taxation

Stamp Act

- This first form of taxation on colonies, in 1765, was objected to by colonists because they were not represented in British Parliament which imposed these taxes.
- "No taxation without representation" became familiar protest during this time.
- Act stated that official stamp had to be bought to go on any printed matter, and colonists subsequently refused to pay for this.
- Colonists stated that they already paid financial dues to British through Navigation Acts and other restrictions, and that they had their own militia and did not need to pay for the British Army to protect them.
- However, British said taxation would contribute to costs of Seven Years War and also pay for continued presence of British Army in America to protect colonies.

Townshend Duties

- After Stamp Act was repealed in 1766, these Duties, which were on glass, tea, paper and lead, were imposed in 1767.
- Colonists challenged right of Parliament to impose duties that seemed designed purely to raise revenue.
- However, British insisted that duties be paid in order to maintain costs of acting as Mother Country to protect colonies.

Other factors

Boston Massacre

- Massacre occurred in 1770.
- Although 5 working-class men died, including one black man, reports of 5 middle-class white men dying caused outrage amongst politically-minded colonists.
- Committees of Correspondence meant that news of Massacre spread quickly around 13 colonies.
- Acquittal of British soldiers led many colonists to fear for their personal liberty and believe that they would one day be enslaved by British.
- However Massacre was an incident which animated people mainly in New England area, something which later caused George III to voice his belief that problems in America were "localised".

Punishment of Massachusetts

- Tax remained on tea from 1770 in order to maintain British right to tax colonists.
- Boston Tea Party in December 1773 was expression of some colonists' frustrations at British policy towards them.
- The British response to the Boston Tea Party, in a series of acts starting in March 1774, known to colonists as Intolerable Acts – closing port of Boston, altering constitution of legislature of Massachusetts, billeting British troops in colonial homes, and suspending trial by jury in colony.
- Other colonists acted in sympathy with Massachusetts and showed unity at First Continental Congress in September 1774.
- However, British spoke of punishments as Coercive Acts, which were an attempt to get colonists to see that acts of hostility towards Britain would not be tolerated.

British intransigence

- British policy remained largely unchanged after George III ascended the throne in 1760.
- Britain retained an uncompromising attitude in the face of continued colonist protest and pleas for compromise.
- Re-imposition of the Navigation Acts – after 1763 these were enforced by the Royal Navy after over 40 years of the colonists being able to disregard them during the Whig Ascendancy.

- The Declaratory Act – despite the repeal of the Stamp Act the same year, this stated in 1766 that Britain had the right to maintain a tax on the colonists at all times.
- Repeated speeches in Parliament emphasised the importance of retaining the colonies.
- Dissenters like Burke or Wilkes were ignored.

Rejection of Olive Branch Petition

- George III rejected the colonists' last attempt at compromise.
- 2nd Continental Congress had written appeal to king pledging its allegiance to crown and bitterness towards Parliament, yet appeal fell on deaf ears as George III declared colonists to be in rebellion.
- Many colonists started to consider independence as only means of changing relationship with Britain.
- However, petition was expression of loyalty to George III which masked many colonists' intentions to declare greater autonomy for themselves, regardless of king's reaction.
- George III rejected the Olive Branch petition, possibly as a consequence of increased colonist military activity, e.g. Lexington and Bunker Hill.

Influence of Thomas Paine

- Key British voice for colonists in 1770s was this republican writer.
- Paine had attacked the notion of hierarchical monarchy in debating clubs in London and in revolutionary pamphlets in the 1770s.
- Paine had met Benjamin Franklin in London and he assisted Paine to settle in Philadelphia in October 1774.
- Paine believed he could further cause of American independence, and made republican speeches and met with notable colonists.
- His revolutionary ideas were regarded as too radical for many, including Franklin, who favoured compromise with Britain.
- His views were radical for his time, and people in Britain read his work out of fascination rather than because they agreed with him.
- On 10 January 1776 Paine published 'Common Sense', a propagandist pamphlet in favour of American independence which sold 100,000 copies in the colonies, and more than that in Britain and France.
- During the war, his writings continued to encourage colonists to keep fighting as Britain would one day recognise America's independence.
- The popularity of his work demonstrates the willingness of colonists to expose themselves to his radical views.
- It should be stated that Thomas Paine's primary goal was republicanism, but his was a voice of genuine dissent, reaching the educated middle-class and artisans.

20. The candidate assesses the validity of the view that French intervention changed the whole nature of the American War of Independence, using evidence and arguments such as:

French Intervention

- France entered war on the side of the American colonists and took the conflict to Europe.
- Britain was forced to re-assign its military resources to defend itself and the Empire.
- The French contribution to the colonists' cause took many forms – men, ammunition, training, supplies, uniforms, fighting Britain around the world.
- However, France was not persuaded until February 1778 to make its alliance with America, by which time the Continental Army was already starting to make progress in the war in the colonies.

Dutch and Spanish entry
- When the Dutch and the Spanish entered the war, Britain's navy was stretched even further and it became increasingly difficult to focus on the war in the colonies. European nations now competed for parts of Britain's empire around the world.
- However, the war between Britain and the colonists on land was not directly affected greatly by the Dutch and Spanish involvement.

Armed League of Neutrality
- This grouping of Russia, Sweden and Denmark gave extra cause for concern to Britain, as they were willing to fire on any Royal Navy ships which interfered with their merchant fleets.
- However, the League was not actively involved in the war, merely endeavouring to protect its own shipping.

Control of the sea
- The battle for control of the sea drew massively on the resources of all countries involved and significantly drained Britain's finances.
- However, the war at sea continued after the surrender at Yorktown, and the British recognised the Treaty of Versailles despite regaining control of the sea, suggesting the war on land was more significant on the outcome for the colonists.

World-wide nature of war
- **German mercenaries** – Britain used over 7000 of these in the colonies.
- **Changing views in Britain** – with the increasing European involvement, some Parliamentarians questioned Britain's ability to win a prolonged war.
- **Canadian aspect** – the colonists had appealed unsuccessfully for Canadian support, which meant the British were not distracted by concerns about possible rebellion in Canada.

21. The candidate assesses the extent to which the American Constitution addressed the issues raised by the experience of rule by Britain, using evidence and arguments such as:

The experience of rule by Britain
- As part of the British Empire, colonists had been ruled by the King and the British Parliament, who together made key policy decisions, set laws and taxes, and enforced the law; there were no checks and balances.
- Colonists feared the potentially tyrannical power of a monarch, and designed the Constitution to prevent any such future threat.
- Branches of government were to be predominantly elective, to ensure the participation of the people.

Significance of the Constitution
- When the colonists drew up their Constitution, they built in a separation of powers providing checks and balances within the political system. The Bill of Rights established liberty for individuals in states within a federal union of all states, and set out clear lines of authority between federal government and individual states. This would avoid central government exerting a controlling power over people's lives.
- The hierarchy which existed under rule by Britain was altered by the Constitution, which stated that 'all men are created equal' and that everyone was entitled to 'life, liberty and the pursuit of happiness'. Now people would be asked to ratify many of the stages within the democratic processes at state and national level. However, women and blacks were excluded from the franchise, and in reality only one-fifth of eligible voters turned out for national elections.

Executive: role of President
- Executive power was vested in the elected President, and his Vice-President and Cabinet. The President acted as head of state and Commander-in-Chief but would have no vote in the law-making process, although he could veto legislation. The President would make all key decisions and establish policy. Members of the Executive could be removed from office by the electorate or the other branches of government if it was felt they were not doing their job properly.

Legislature: Congress
- Legislative power lay in the hands of an elected Congress which was divided into two Houses, the Senate and Representatives. Congress passed laws and raised taxes, as well as having responsibility for international trade, war and foreign relations. No one in the legislature could serve in the judiciary or executive without first resigning from the legislature. Congressional elections were held regularly to ensure that Congressmen remained in touch with the people they served.

Judiciary: Supreme Court
- Judicial power was granted to the Supreme Court of the United States. The Supreme Court acted as the highest court of appeal in the country. It also debated the legality of new laws passed by Congress. Supreme Court judges were nominated by the President and their appointment was ratified by Congress after a rigorous checking process. Appointees to the Supreme Court could be removed from their position if they acted improperly.

The French Revolution, to 1799

22. The candidate evaluates the importance of the role of the bourgeoisie in the collapse of royal authority in France in 1789, using evidence and arguments such as:

Role of bourgeoisie
- As part of the Third Estate resented paying the taxation.
- Dominated the Third Estate representatives in the Estates-General.
- Were outside the political process unless they bought a noble title: wanted access to power.
- Very attracted to ideas of a constitutional monarchy as advocated by people like Montesquieu.
- Provided the leadership for the revolution.

Other factors

The economic crisis of 1788/9
- Bad harvests and grain shortages inspired unrest among the peasantry and the urban workers in Paris and in provincial cities throughout France, exerting critical pressures on the Ancien Regime.
- There was less demand for manufactured goods, which led to unemployment increasing amongst the urban workers.
- The nobility were increasingly blamed as peasants started to take political action.
- The economic crisis clearly created an environment in which the Ancien Regime was struggling to survive.

Financial problems of the Ancien Regime
- Because of exemptions the crown was denied adequate income. The privileged orders were an untapped source of revenue but it would require reforms to access i.
- This created resentment amongst the 3rd estate.
- Exacerbated divisions that already existed between the estates.
- Tax-farming meant not all revenues were reaching the government.
- By the 1780s France faced bankruptcy due to heavy expenditure and borrowing to pay for wars.
- Government failed to gain agreement on tax reform.
- This was arguably the biggest threat facing the Ancien Regime. The opposition which this generated not only led to

Calonne's dismissal in 1787 but more importantly to the convocation of the Estates General in 1788. When it met in May 1789 the long-standing divisions between the three estates unleashed forces which culminated in the overthrow of the Ancien Regime.

Influence of the Enlightenment

- The Enlightenment encouraged criticism, and freedom of thought, speech and religion, and was seen as the end of man's self-imposed irrationality at the hands of the Church in particular.
- Ideas of philosophs like Voltaire who attacked religion, Montesquieu who favoured a British system of government and Rousseau who put forward the idea of direct democracy.
- Very much appealed to the bourgeoise, who led the revolution.

The American Revolution

- This war contributed to the financial crisis which came to a head in France post–1786 but for many in France at the time they also represented the practical expression of the enlightened views of the Philosophes in terms of the rights of the individual, no taxation without representation and freedom from tyrannical government. The wars inspired many of the lesser nobility and the bourgeoisie to seek the same freedoms.

The political crisis of 1788/9

- The convocation of the Estates General in August 1788 sharpened divisions between the three estates which came to a head between May and August 1789. The Cahiers des Doleances revealed the depth of dissatisfaction with the existing order, especially among the bourgeoisie and the peasantry. The creation of the National Assembly, the abolition of feudalism and the Declaration of the Rights of Man and the Citizen all contributed to a revolutionary change in French government, society and economy.

Actions of Louis XVI

- Louis was largely under the influence of his wife, Marie Antoinette who, although strong minded, failed to grasp the serious nature of situation and was also unpopular as she was Austrian.
- Louis XVI's handling of the Estates-General contributed towards the start of the Revolution. He wanted to make reform difficult by making the three estates meet separately, in the hope that the First and Second Estates would vote the Third down.
- This backfired: opposition to the King grew, the Third Estate refused to act separately, and many of the clergy changed sides, changing the balance of power.
- Louis allegedly closed the meeting halls, which led to the Tennis Court Oath from members of the Third Estate. He later agreed to a constitution when the Third Estate representatives occupied the Royal tennis courts.
- The King had lost more political ground than if he had just listened to the grievances of the middle classes and the Third Estate from the start.

23. The candidate evaluates the importance of the threat of counter revolution in bringing about the 'terror' in France, using evidence and argument such as:

The threat of counter-revolution

- One of The Convention's major concerns at the start of 1793 was to eliminate counter-revolutionary activity which intensified, particularly in the provinces after Louis' execution At this point the Convention was still controlled by the relatively moderate Girondins.
- The Convention sanctioned a range of counter-revolutionary legislation such as:
  - the creation of the Committee of Public Safety; The Committee of General Security

- Revolutionary tribunals to try opponents of the Republic and impose the death penalty if required and Surveillance Committees established in local areas to identify counter-revolutionary activity.
- Thus, most agree that most of the essential institutions of the Terror were actually in place before the Jacobins – and Robespierre – came to power. The moderates in the Convention had set up the structure of the Terror by the spring of 1793.

Other factors

The outbreak of war

- The war put pressure on the Convention to execute the war against the Republic's émigré and foreign opponents as ruthlessly and as effectively as possible. The nation's resources were mobilized to this end. The early reverses raised alarms about sabotage and possible treason in the new armies.

The threat of invasion

- The initial defeats suffered raised the spectre of invasion.
- External dangers France faced radicalised the revolution. It occasioned a witch hunt for enemies within. The war led to the concept of the 'nation in crisis. This had to be enforced, violently if necessary.
- It was pressure from mass demonstrations in Paris which intimidated the Convention into adopting terror as 'the order of the day' i.e. a method of government control. This was more to do with the exigencies of the foreign and civil wars which were threatening the Republic at this point than with Robespierre's philosophising over the nature of the Republic and the role of terror within it.

Political rivalries

- The Jacobins were one of a number of political groupings contending for power. Other groups included the Girondins.
- The struggle became increasingly bitter with time. Similarly a number of other prominent individuals had sought to control the course of the revolution. Some had already died violently. The Terror was a legitimised means of the Jacobins eliminating their political rivals –'a revolution always consumes its children'.

The role of Robespierre

- Robespierre believed that the 'general will' of the sovereign people both created and sanctioned policy-making within the nation. The will of the people could only prevail within a Republic. Any individual who sought to oppose this was, by implication, guilty of treason against the nation itself. In such circumstances death – the ultimate weapon of Terror – was entirely appropriate. Hence Robespierre's belief that 'terror is virtue' – that to create and maintain a 'virtuous' nation which enshrined the revolutionary principles of liberty and equality, it was necessary to violently expunge any counter-revolutionary activity.
- Robespierre became a member of the Committee of Public Safety in July 1793 and came to control its operations. Until his own execution in July 1794, the Committee became the main instrument for the application of terror in defence of Robespierre's ideal of a 'Republic of Virtue'. During this period Robespierre sanctioned the use of terror against:
  - the monarchy and émigré opponents of the Republic e.g. Marie Antoinette executed
  - provincial counter-revolutionaries particularly in the Vendee
  - Hebertists, whose anti-Christian stance Robespierre found both distasteful and dangerous
  - Dantonists who challenged the authority of Robespierre and who were therefore (since Robespierre's government represented the 'general will') guilty of treason.

- With the imposition of the infamous Law of 22nd Prairial (June 1794), Robespierre was given virtually unlimited powers to eliminate opponents of his Republic of Virtue and during the period of the Great Terror in June and July 1794, over 1500 were executed.
- Had Robespierre lived beyond Thermidor there is no doubt the death toll would have risen even higher. However, while Robespierre must bear responsibility for the intensification of the Terror during 1793-1794, the use of terror as an instrument of state policy was by no means confined to Robespierre.

Religious and regional differences.
- The uprising in the Vendee was supported by priests and former nobles. It also secured British support. It was brutally suppressed. Many women and children were drowned in the Loire at Nantes.
- There were also demands in the south for greater autonomy.
- Under the Civil Constitution of the Clergy, priests had to swear an oath of loyalty to the state. Many refused and became leaders of resistance.

24. The candidate assesses the extent to which the peasantry gained most from the revolution by 1799, using evidence and arguments such as:

The peasantry
- In contrast to the Catholic Church and the nobility the position of the peasantry was in many ways strengthened by the Revolution. The ending of feudalism in August 1789 removed many of the legal and financial burdens which had formed the basis of peasant grievances in the Cahiers des Doleances presented to the Estates-General in 1789.
- The revolutionary land settlement, instigated by the nationalisation of church lands in November 1789, had transferred land from the nobility and the clergy to the peasantry to their obvious advantage. It should be noted, however, that not all peasants benefited equally from this. Only the well-off peasants could afford to purchase the Church lands which had been seized by the National Assembly.

The impact on other sections of Society

The impact of the Revolution on the bourgeoisie
- The Revolution instigated a fundamental shift in political and economic power from the First and Second Estates to the bourgeoisie.
- The ending of feudalism in August 1789 heralded profound social and economic change (e.g. facilitating the development of capitalism) whilst the Declaration of the Rights of Man and the Citizen later in the month did the same for political life. In both cases the main beneficiaries were the bourgeoisie.
- Successive constitutions and legislative reforms throughout the1790s favoured the bourgeoisie above all other social groups by emphasising the notion of a property-owning democracy with voting rights framed within property qualifications, whilst the ending of trade restrictions and monopolies favoured an expanding business and merchant class.
- France had moved from a position of privileged estates to one where increasingly merit was what counted. It was the educated Bourgeoisie who were best placed to benefit from this profound change in French society.

The urban workers
- At key points throughout the Revolution overt demonstrations of discontent by the urban masses- particularly in Paris-impacted on key events as successive regimes framed policy with an eye to appeasing the mob. However, any modest gains by the urban poor were short-lived. A decade of almost continuous wars in the 1790s had created shortages and inflation which hit the urban poor particularly hard.
- The passing of the Chapelier Law in May 1791, by a bourgeois-dominated National Assembly protecting the interests of industrialists, effectively banned the formation of trade unions and thereafter the Revolution brought few tangible economic or political gains for urban workers.

The impact of the Revolution on the First Estate
- The Catholic Church was a key pillar of the Ancien Regime. The Upper Clergy (usually drawn from the ranks of the traditional nobility) enjoyed considerable wealth and status based on a raft of privileges and tax exemptions. These privileges and exemptions were swept away by the Revolution and the position of the Catholic Church within France by 1799 was far less assured than it had been under the Ancien Regime.
- The Civil Constitution of the Clergy (July 1790) polarised attitudes towards the place of the Catholic Church within French society and promoted conflict between opposing factions through the rest of the period to 1799. In November 1789 Church lands were nationalised, stripping the Church of much of its wealth. The net result of all of this was that the Church never regained its primacy within the French state and can be seen to have lost far more than it gained.

The impact of the Revolution on the Second Estate
- The aristocracy had enjoyed similar privileges and tax exemptions to those of the Catholic Church under the Ancien Regime. Advancement in the key positions of the State, the Army and, indeed the Church, depended more often on birth than merit. The traditional nobility monopolised these key positions and sought at all times to defend its favoured position. Again, the Revolution swept away aristocratic privilege even more completely than that of the clergy.
- The ending of feudalism in August 1789 marked the prelude to a decade when the status of the nobility in France effectively collapsed. In 1790 outward displays of 'nobility' such as titles and coats of arms were forbidden by law and in 1797, after election results suggested a pro-royalist resurgence, the Convention imposed alien status on nobles and stripped them of French citizenship.
- The Revolution brought in a regime where careers were open to talent regardless of birth or inheritance and the traditional aristocracy simply ceased to exist. Having said that, some nobles simply transformed themselves into untitled landlords in the countryside and continued to exercise significant economic and political power.

Germany 1815 – 1939

25. The candidate assesses the validity of the view that by 1850 political nationalism had made little progress in Germany, using evidence and arguments such as:

Opponents of nationalism
- One-fifth of the population of the Austrian empire were German; the Austrian Emperor feared nationalism would encourage them to break away and join Germany; this would leave Austria weaker and cause other national groups in the Empire to demand their independence.
- In 1815 Metternich became worried about the growth of liberal and nationalist student societies.
- In 1819 Carlsbad Decrees banned student societies and censored newspapers.
- The following year the power of the Diet was increased so that soldiers could be ordered to stop the spread of new ideas in any of the German States.

- The particularism of the various German states – autonomous and parochial in many ways.
- Popular apathy – most Germans had little desire to see a united Germany.
- France and Russia feared that a strong, united Germany would be a political, economic and military rival to them.

Supporters of nationalism
- Liberal nationalists – a united Germany should have a Liberal constitution that would guarantee the rights of citizens.
- Cultural nationalists – unity was more important than individual rights and that what mattered was the preservation of German identity and culture.
- Economic nationalists – unity would remove the trade barriers between states and this would allow economic growth and prosperity.
- To encourage trade Prussia formed a customs union in 1818 that by the 1830s was called the Zollverein; the Zollverein helped nationalist ideas to spread.
- Nationalist ideas were spread by philosophers, historians, poets and dramatists who influenced the literate middle classes and especially the students: Jahn and the burschenschaten movement; Wartburg in 1817; Hamburg in 1832; Young Germany in 1833; the Rhine Movement in 1840.
- Fichte described 'Germany' as the Fatherland where all people spoke the same language and sang the same songs.
- German poets and authors, such as the Grimm brothers, and composers such as Beethoven, encouraged feelings of national pride in the German states.
- In 1830 anti-French feelings promoted 'the watch on the Rhine' and nationalist festivals such as Hambach (1832) also encouraged nationalist feelings.
- Liberal nationalists – a united Germany should have a Liberal constitution that would guarantee the rights of citizens.
- Cultural nationalists – unity was more important than individual rights and that what mattered was the preservation of German identity and culture.
- Economic nationalists – unity would remove the trade barriers between states and this would allow economic growth and prosperity.
- To encourage trade Prussia formed a customs union in 1818 that by the 1830s was called the Zollverein; the Zollverein helped nationalist ideas to spread.
- Nationalist ideas were spread by philosophers, historians, poets and dramatists who influenced the literate middle classes and especially the students: Jahn and the burschenschaten movement; Wartburg in 1817; Hamburg in 1832; Young Germany in 1833; the Rhine Movement in 1840.
- Fichte described 'Germany' as the Fatherland where all people spoke the same language and sang the same songs.
- German poets and authors, such as the Grimm brothers, and composers such as Beethoven, encouraged feelings of national pride in the German states.
- In 1830 anti-French feelings promoted 'the watch on the Rhine' and nationalist festivals such as Hambach (1832) also encouraged nationalist feelings.

Attitudes of peasants
- Golo Mann wrote that most Germans 'seldom looked up from the plough'. He doubted the influence of artists and intellectuals whom most Germans knew little or nothing about; nationalism attracted mainly the educated/business/middle classes.
- But by the late 1840s peasants were demanding that remaining feudal dues should be cancelled by their German princes.

Political turmoil in the 1840s
- Trade depression, unemployment and high food prices because of bad harvests led to revolutions throughout Europe.
- In the German Confederation nationalists and liberals saw their chance; the rulers of the small states fled; elections were held to local assemblies and then to a national convention to create a united Germany; this convention or parliament met at Frankfurt.

The Frankfurt Parliament, divisions
- This was the first serious attempt to challenge Austria's political power in Germany and Austrian opposition to the liberals and nationalists.
- Failure of the Frankfurt Parliament – lack of clear aims and no armed force to enforce its decisions.
- Nationalists could not agree on the size of a new Germany - should it include Austria and the Hapsburg lands and Prussia's Polish possessions?
- Should it be governed by a King or be a republic or a mixture of both?
- The Protestants of the North distrusted the Southern Catholics.

The collapse of the revolution in Germany, 1848-1849
- Frankfurt Parliament failed to satisfy the needs of the starving workers who had helped create the revolution.
- Parliament had to rely on the Prussian army to put down a workers revolt.
- Self-interest of German rulers led to opposition to the actions at Frankfurt.
- Frederick William, King of Prussia, tried to take advantage of the defeat of the 1848 revolution to increase Prussian power to exclude Austria from the Confederation – the Erfurt Parliament.
- Austria was still too strong in 1850 and was able to force Prussia to back down; at Olmutz it was agreed to return to the Constitution of 1815.

26. The candidate evaluates how important the attitude of foreign states was to German unification being achieved in 1871, using evidence and arguments such as:

Attitude of foreign states
- Role of Napoleon Bonaparte and France pre-1815-stimulated German nationalism.
- Attitude of Denmark towards Schleswig-Holstein.
- Attitude Russia toward Austria after Austrian failure to intervene over Crimea.
- Attitude of Italian states in Austro-Prussian War of 1866 considered.

Other factors

Actions of Napoleon III
- Meeting at Biarritz secured French border while Prussia fought Austria.
- Napoleon III hoped for long war between Austria and Prussia.
- Napoleon III instrumental in ensuing armistice.
- Napoleon III and role over Hohenzollern candidature.

The role of Bismarck
- Bismarck's aim was to increase the power of Prussia by whatever means necessary.
- Bismarck and his 'realpolitik'/diplomacy in the '3 wars' against Denmark, Austria and France.
- Bismarck took the initiative, as opposed to Austria, in the war against Denmark; his 'solution' to the Schleswig-Holstein question.

- Bismarck's skilful manipulation of events leading up to the war with Austria in 1866 plus his establishment of friendships with potential allies of Austria beforehand.
- Bismarck's wisdom in the Treaty of Prague, 1866.
- Bismarck's manipulation of the Ems Telegram to instigate a war with France in 1870.
- Bismarck's exploitation of the weaknesses of European statesmen/rulers e.g. Napoleon III; mistakes made by Bismarck's adversaries.
- Bismarck's skill in isolating his intended targets (diplomatically).
- Arguments about the role of Bismarck:
  - 'Bismarck did not fashion German unity alone. He exploited powerful forces which already existed...' (Williamson)
  - '...it was he (Bismarck) who created the conditions which rendered possible the creation of a Great Germany.' (Hitler)
  - 'Bismarck's admirers often exaggerate the extent of the obstacles in his path.' (Medlicott)

Prussian military strength
- Significance of military reforms of Moltke and Roon – creation of modern powerful army which Bismarck used.
- Increase in army conscription time from 2 to 3 years.
- Introduction of breech loading guns like needle guns.
- Introduction of better systems of communication and new battle tactics.

Prussian economic strength
- Growth in Prussian economic power – development of railways, transport links, roads, for example; importance of the Rhineland and the Saarland to Prussian economic development. Able to finance and equip Prussian army.
- The Zollverein – the Prussian-dominated free-trade area; the significance to German political unification- the 'mighty lever' of German unification.
- The Nationalverein – aim was the creation of a united Germany; composed of intelligent and economically important section of German society – businessmen; identified Prussia as leader of a united Germany.
- Railway system facilitated swift mobilization of Prussian army to borders with Austria and France

Decline of Austria
- The 1848 revolutions in German states – importance of Frankfurt Parliament/decisions taken regarding a unified Germany; Prussia was a potential leader; Austria was excluded from Germany ('kleindeutschland').
- The decline in Austrian power and influence – economically and militarily – during the 1850s particularly.
- Distraction to Austria of commitments in Italy.

27. The candidates assesses the accuracy of the view that 'Propaganda was crucial to the maintenance of power by the Nazis', using evidence and arguments such as:

Propaganda
- Use of Nuremburg Rallies
- Use of Radio
- Cult of the Leader: the Hitler myth
- Use of the Cinema: Triumph of the Will, the Eternal Jew, etc
- Role of Goebbels

Other factors

Success of Economic policies
- Nazi economic policy – attempted to deal with economic ills affecting Germany, especially unemployment.
- Nazis began a massive programme of public works; work of Hjalmar Schacht.

- Nazi policy towards farming e.g. Reich Food Estate – details of various policies.
- Goring's policy of 'guns before butter'. Popular once foreign policy triumphs appeared to justify it.

Social policies
- Creation of the *volksgemeinschaft* (national community).
- Nazi youth policy.
- Nazi education policy.
- Nazi policy towards the Jews-first isolate, then persecute and finally destroy.
- Nazi family policy – Kinder, Kirche, Kuche.
- Kraft durch Freude programme.
- A Concordat with the Catholic Church was reached; a Reichsbishop was appointed as head of the Protestant churches.

Success of foreign policy
- Nazi success in foreign policy attracted support among Germans; Rearmament, Rhineland, Anschluss.
- *'Much of Hitler's popularity after he came to power rested on his achievements in foreign policy'.* (Welch)

Establishment of totalitarian state
- Political parties outlawed; non-Nazi members of the civil service were dismissed.
- Nazis never quite able to silence opposition to the regime.
- Speed of takeover of power and ruthlessness of the regime made opposition largely ineffective.
- Anti-Nazi judges were dismissed and replaced with those favourable to the Nazis.
- Acts Hostile to the National Community (1935) – all-embracing law which allowed the Nazis to persecute opponents in a 'legal' way.

Fear and state terrorism
- The use of fear/terror through the Nazi police state; role of the Gestapo.
- Concentration camps set up; the use of the SS.

Crushing of opposition
- Opponents liable to severe penalties, as were their families.
- Opponents never able to establish a single organisation to channel their resistance – role of the Gestapo, paid informers.
- Opposition lacked cohesion and a national leader; also lacked armed supporters.
- Lack of cooperation between socialists and communists – role of Stalin considered.

Italy 1815 – 1939

28. The candidate assesses the extent to which the idea of nationalism was established in Italy before 1850 using evidence and arguments such as:

Supporters of nationalism

Educated middle class
- Risorgimento saw 'patriotic literature' from novelists and poets including Pellico, and Leopardi. These inspired the educated middle class.
- Gioberti, Balbo and Mazzini promoted their ideas for a national state, this inspired nationalism amongst the middle classes.

Liberals
- Some liberals and business classes were keen to develop an economic state. Napoleon Bonaparte had built roads and encouraged closer trading. One system of weights, measures and currency appealed.

Popular sentiment

- French revolutionary ideals had inspired popular sentiment for a national Italian state.
- There was a growing desire for the creation of a national state amongst students; many joined Mazzini's 'Young Italy'.
- Operas by Verdi and Rossini inspired growing feelings of patriotism.
- The use of Tuscan as a 'national' language by Alfieri and Manzoni spread ideas of nationalism.
- Membership of secret societies such as the Carbonari grew. Members were willing to revolt and die for their beliefs which included desire for a national state.

Opponents

Austria

- Resentment against Austria and its restoration of influence in the Italian peninsula and there use of spies and censorship, helped increase support for the nationalist cause. However, any progress made by nationalists was firmly crushed by the Austrian army. Strength of the Quadrilateral. Austrians never left Italian soil. Carbonari revolts in Kingdom of Naples 1820 – 1821, Piedmont 1821, Modena and the Papal States 1831 all crushed by Austrian army. During 1848 – 1849 revolutions, Austrian army defeated Charles Albert twice – Custoza and Modena, retook Lombardy and destroyed the Republic of St Mark.

Italian princes and rulers

- Individual rulers were opposed to nationalism and used censorship, police and spies as well as the Austrian army, to crush revolts 1820 -1821, 1830 and 1848 – 1849.

Attitude of the peasants

- The mass of the population were illiterate and indifferent to politics and nationalist ideas. They did revolt during bad times as can be seen in 1848 – but there revolts were due to bad harvests and bad economic times and were not inspired by feelings of nationalism.

Position of the Papacy

- Pope Pius IX. Nationalist movement had high hopes of New Pope Pius IX, initially thought of as a liberal and sympathetic to nationalist cause. Hopes dashed when Pope Pius IX denounced the nationalist movement during 1848 – 49 revolutions.

Failures of 1848 – 1849 revolutions

- These showed that nationalist leaders would not work together, nor did they seek foreign help thus hindering progress. Charles Albert's 'Italia farad a se' declared that Italy would do it alone – she did not. Lombardy and Venetia suspected Charles Albert's motives and were reluctant to work with him. Venetians put more faith in Manin.
- All progress was hampered when Pope Pius IX denounced nationalism.
- Charles Albert hated Mazzini and would not support the Roman Republic.
- Austrian military might based on the Quadrilateral defeated Charles Albert twice – at Custoza and Modena, retook Lombardy and destroyed the Republic of St Mark.
- The French crushed the Roman Republic.

29. The candidate evaluates the extent to which the unification of Italy in 1870 was the result of foreign intervention, using evidence and arguments such as:

Foreign Intervention

Actions of Britain

- Britain was involved in diplomacy over the Duchies. British naval presence helped Garibaldi. Britain refused a joint naval blockade with France to stop Garibaldi crossing Strait of Messina – crucial for Garibaldi's success.
- Britain was first power to officially recognise the Kingdom of Italy.

Prussia

- The Italians made a secret agreement to help Prussia in the war against Austria in 1866.
- The Prussian war against France gave Italians chance to take Rome in 1870.

Attitudes and actions of Napoleon III

- Napoleon III met Cavour at Plombieres. The result was a formal treaty, January 1859. Napoleon promised 200,000 men to fight for Piedmont if Austria attacked.
- War of Liberation 1859: French victories gained Lombardy for Piedmont.
- Napoleon accepted Duchies/Romagna uniting with Piedmont.
- Secretly, Napoleon accepted Cavour's invasion of Papal States to stop Garibaldi reaching Rome, allowing the Piedmontese to defeat the Papal Army and take the Marches/Umbria. In 1866 Austria handed Venetia to France who gave it to Italy.

Other factors

Decline of Austria

- Austria had successfully regained control of Northern Italian states after the failure of the 1848/49 revolutions; however, she faced financial difficulties maintaining forces in the Quadrilateral.
- Austria lost prestige amongst European Powers after her failure to get involved in Crimean war.
- Austria faced difficulties with the growing economic and military power of Prussia. Napoleon III was keen to emulate his uncle and key to this was a campaign against Austria, now relatively isolated in Europe.
- Austria was defeated at Magenta and Solferino by the French and handed over Lombardy. This war virtually excluded Austria from events in 'Italy' as the 'Italians' forced the pace of change. Events in the Duchies/Romagna were outside Austrian control. Austria was defeated by Prussia in 1866 and handed Venetia to France to give to Italy.

Rise of Piedmont

- Development economically, politically and militarily.

Role of Victor Emmanuel

- King of Piedmont retained the Statuto – Piedmont became the focus for Italian nationalism. He appointed Cavour and made anti-Austrian speeches to parliament to antagonise the Austrians.
- He took Piedmont to war – Crimean, war of Liberation, invasion of the Papal States and war against Austria 1866.
- He became Italy's first king and his forces took Rome in 1870.

Cavour

- Modernised Piedmont, set her on international stage; diplomacy with Napoleon III at Plombieres resulted in the secret treaty of 1859. Cavour provoked Austria into the 1859 war. His agents stirred up trouble in the Duchies/Romagna. He organised plebiscites after more negotiations with the British and Napoleon III.
- He organised the invasion of Papal States following a secret agreement with Napoleon III. Following this Victor Emmanuel met Garibaldi at Teano – union of north and south – the Kingdom of Italy was proclaimed. Cavour ensured it was a limited constitutional monarchy led by Piedmont.

Role of Garibaldi

- He was a committed nationalist and championed idea of united Italy. He led the Garabaldini volunteers in the 1859-60 war against Austria. His military expedition resulted in Sicily and Naples being taken.

- Mazzini wanted to make liberated Southern Italy a republic. The populace acclaimed Garibaldi as ruler, but Garibaldi himself remained loyal to Victor Emmanuel. After meeting the king at Teano, near Naples, he relinquished his conquests to Sardinia. Shortly afterward (1861) Victor Emmanuel was proclaimed king of a united Italy.
- In 1862, Garibaldi led a volunteer corps against Rome, but the king, fearing international intervention, sent an Italian army that defeated Garibaldi at Aspromonte. Garibaldi was given a pardon.

30. The candidate evaluates how important propaganda was in maintaining Fascist power in Italy between 1922 and 1939, using evidence and arguments such as:

Propaganda
- Press, radio and cinema were all controlled.
- Mussolini was highly promoted as a 'saviour' sent by God to help Italy.
- Mussolini portrayed as heir to Caesar, world statesman, supreme patriot, a great thinker who worked 20 hours a day, a man of action, incorruptible.

Other factors

Fear and intimidation
- Mussolini favoured complete State authority with everything under his direct control. All Italians were expected to obey Mussolini and his Fascist Party.
- The squadristi were organised into the MVSN Milizia Voluntaria per la Sicurezza Nazionale the armed local Fascist militia (Blackshirts). They terrorised the cities and provinces causing fear with tactics such as force-feeding with toads and castor oil.
- After 1925-6 around 10,000 non-fascists/opposition leaders were jailed by special tribunals.
- The Secret police, OVRA was established in 1927 and was led by Arturo Bocchini. Tactics included abduction and torture of opponents. 4000 people were arrested by the OVRA and sent to prison.
- Penal colonies were established on remote Mediterranean islands such as Ponza and Lipari. Conditions for those sentenced to these prisons were primitive with little chance of escape.
- Opponents were exiled internally or driven into exile abroad.
- The death penalty was restored under Mussolini for serious offences but by 1940 only ten people had been sentenced to death.

Establishment of the fascist state
- Nov/Dec 1922 Mussolini was given emergency powers. Nationalists merged with PNF 1923. Mussolini created MSVN (fascist militia) – gave him support if the army turned against him – and Fascist Grand Council – a rival Cabinet. These two bodies made Mussolini's position stronger and opposition within PNF weaker. The establishment of a dictatorship began:
  - 1926 – opposition parties were banned. A one party state was created
  - 1928 – universal suffrage abolished
  - 1929 – all Fascist Parliament elected.

Crushing of opposition
- Liberals had divided into four factions so were weakened.
- The Left had divided into three – original PSI, reformist PSU and Communists – they failed to work together against fascists.
- Pope forced Sturzo to resign and so PPI (Catholic Popular Party) was weakened and it split.
- Acerbo Law passed. 1924 elections – fascists won 66% of the vote.

- Opposition parties failed to take advantage of the Matteotti crisis. By walking out of the Chamber of Deputies (Aventine Secession) they gave up the chance to overthrow Mussolini; they remained divided – the Pope refused to sanction an alliance between PPI and the socialists. The King chose not to dismiss Mussolini.
- Communists and socialists did set up organisations in exile but did not work together. Communist cells in northern cities did produce some anti-fascist leaflets but they suffered frequent raids by OVRA.
- PPI opposition floundered with the closer relationship between Church and State (Lateran Pacts).

Social controls
- Workers were controlled through 22 corporations, set up in 1934; overseen by National Council of Corporations, chaired by Mussolini.
- Corporations provided accident, health and unemployment insurance for workers, but forbade strikes and lock-outs.
- There were some illegal strikes in 1930s and anti-fascist demonstrations in 1933 but these were limited.
- The majority of Italians got on with their own lives conforming as long as all was going well. Middle classes/elites supported fascism as it protected them from communism.
- Youth knew no alternative to fascism, were educated as fascists and this strengthened the regime. Youth movements provided sporting opportunities, competitions, rallies, camps, parades and propaganda lectures – 60% membership in the north.

Foreign policy
- Mussolini was initially extremely popular, as evidenced by huge crowds who turned out to hear him speak.
- Foreign policy successes in the 1920s, such as the Corfu Incident, made him extremely popular. He was also able to mobilise public opinion very successfully for the invasion of Abyssinia.
- Mussolini's role in the Munich Conference of 1938 was his last great foreign policy triumph.
- As Mussolini got more closely involved with Hitler his popularity lessened. His intervention in Spain proved a huge drain on Italy's resources. The invasion of Albania was a fiasco. The Fascist Grand Council removed him in 1943.

Relations with the Papacy
- Lateran treaties/Concordat with Papacy enabled acceptance of regime by the Catholic majority.
- Many Catholics supported Mussolini's promotion of 'family values'.

Economic and social policies.
- Fascists tried to develop the Italian economy in a series of propaganda-backed initiatives eg the 'Battle for Grain'. While superficially successful, they did tend to divert resources from other areas.
- Development of transport infrastructure, with building of autostrade and redevelopment of major railway terminals eg Milan.
- One major success was the crushing of organized crime. Most Mafia leaders were in prison by 1939.
- Dopolavoro had 3.8 million members by 1939. Gave education and skills training; sports provision, day-trips, holidays, financial assistance and cheap rail fares. This diverted attention from social/economic problems and was the fascist state's most popular institution.

Russia 1881 – 1921

31. The candidate evaluates the extent to which Bloody Sunday was responsible for the 1905 Revolution in Russia using evidence and arguments such as:

Bloody Sunday
- 22nd Jan 1905 Father Gapon, an Orthodox priest attempted to lead a peaceful March of workers and their families to the Winter Palace to deliver a petition asking the Tsar to improve the conditions of the workers.
- Marchers were fired on and killed by troops.
- Many of the people saw this as a brutal massacre by the Tsar and his troops.
- Bloody Sunday greatly damaged the traditional image of the Tsar as the "Little Father", the Guardian of the Russian people.
- Reaction to Bloody Sunday was strong and was nationwide with disorder strikes in urban areas, terrorism against government officials and landlords, much of which was organised by the SR's.
- The situation was made worse by the defeat to Japan in 1905.
- There was the assassination of government minister Plehve.

Other Factors

Discontent of Working Class
- At the start of the 1900's there was industrial recession which caused a lot of hardship for the working class.
- The working class complaints were long hours, low pay, poor conditions, the desire for a constitutional government and an end to the war with Japan.
- There was a wave of strikes in Jan 1905 with nearly half a million people on strike (10 times the number in the previous decade).
- In October there were two and half million people on strike as well as demonstrations carried out.
- Soviets were speaking for the workers and expressing political demands.

Discontent with Repressive Government and its policies
- There was discontent amongst various factions in Russian society.
- The middle class and some of the gentry were unhappy with the government at the time.
- The middle class were aggrieved at having no participation in government, and angry at the incompetence of the government during the war with Japan.
- There was propaganda from middle class groups, Zemstva called for change, the Radical Union of Unions was formed to combine professional groups.
- Students rioted, and carried out assassinations.
- The gentry tried to convince the Tsar to make minor concessions.
- Political groups did not really play a role although they encouraged peasant unrest, and strikes in the urban areas.
- The Mensheviks had influence in the soviets and the Bolsheviks were involved in the Moscow Rising.
- Russification: The National minorities were aggrieved at the lack of respect for their culture language and religion, and the imposition of the Russian language.
- The National minorities harboured a great desire for independence or at least greater autonomy and began to assert themselves, such as Georgia which declared its independence.

Economic problems
- Worsening economic conditions such as famines in 1897, 1898 and 1901 had led to shortage and distress in the countryside. Urban workers conditions and pay also dreadful.
- Economic recession between 1899 and 1903 had also led to growing unemployment throughout the Empire.

Discontent amongst the Peasants
- The peasants had several grievances such as Redemption payments, high taxes, Land Hunger and poverty.

- There was a wave of unrest in 1902 and 1903, which had gradually increased by 1905. There were various protests like timber cutting, seizure of lords' land, labour and rent strikes, attacks on landlord's grain stocks, landlords states seized and divided up.
- There were claims that peasants should boycott paying taxes, redemption payments and refuse to be conscripted to the army.

War with Japan
- The war with Japan was a failure and humiliation for the country and moreover this was compounded by the heavy losses suffered by the Russian army.
- The war was initially to distract the public from domestic troubles by rallying patriotism.
- The incompetence of the government during the war made social unrest worse rather than dampening it.
- Troops suffered from low morale after the defeat and were complained about poor pay and conditions.
- There were some sporadic but uncoordinated revolts although nothing too major.
- There were mutinies by troops waiting to return from the war and on the Trans-Siberian Railway.
- In June there was the Potemkin mutiny although the planned general mutiny did not follow.
- Generally though most of the troops remained loyal (unlike 1917).

32. The candidate evaluates the extent to which working class discontent caused the outbreak of the February revolution, using evidence and arguments such as:

Working Class discontent
- The growing working class worked and lived in poor conditions, with long hours and poor wages as well as overcrowded accommodation.
- Due to their poor working and living conditions the industrial working class were receptive to the new socialist ideas that were around.
- The working class began to organize a series of strikes and demonstrations in 1917. Many of the working class were starving as grain was being given to the soldiers and much of it was not reaching the cities as the trains were requisitioned for the use of the army.
- There was a lack of food made worse by the transport problems and the loss of agricultural land to the Germans and as a result in the cities there were long queues and bread riots culminating in International Women's Day protest in Petrograd.

Other Factors

Peasant discontent
- Peasant discontent over the land issue did not abate during the war years. When order began to break down, land seizures by peasants became common.
- The war put extra strains on the peasantry with requisitioning of horses and conscription of men. This hit output.
- The horror of Russia's huge casualties was felt most among the peasants.

Impact of the First World War
Military defeat
- The war did not go well for the Russian armed forces and they suffered many defeats. Russia also lost control of Poland in 1915, which was a severe blow to Russian pride.
- The Russian army lacked vital resources, including adequate medical care, and this led to high fatality and casualty rates. There were claims of defeats caused by incompetent officers who refused to cooperate with each other as well as communication difficulties. This led to low morale and desertions; the Tsar began to lose control and support of the armed forces. The generals forced his abdication at Pskov.

Economic problems

- The war was costing 17 million roubles a day and Russia had to get loans from Britain and France. Economic problems such as heavy taxes, high inflation and price rises meant that many were living in poverty.
- The people had expected the war to be won by Christmas 1914 so they were war weary by 1917 and suffering from grief, anxiety and low morale. They wanted the war to end but they knew the Tsar would not agree to that and they became so unhappy and frustrated they protested and went on strike which led to the February Revolution as the army sympathised with them and consequently sided with them against the Tsarist system.
- War exacerbated existing economic problems and showed the frailty of the Russian economy in dealing with a modern, industrial conflict.

Inherent weaknesses of Autocracy

- Concentration of power in the hands of one person: their character mattered.
- Great difficulties ruling such a vast Empire with its varied nationalities.
- Difficulties in managing change, especially political change demanded by economic developments.

Role of Tsar Nicholas II

- The Tsar was seen as a weak ruler as he was so easily influenced by the Tsarina, Rasputin and his Ministers. At times the Tsar appeared to be more interested in his family than in issues facing Russia.
- He was stubborn as he ignored advice and warnings from Rodzyanko and he failed to understand the severity of events in February 1917.
- In September 1915 the Tsar took personal control of the armed forces, which left him personally responsible for any defeats.
- By February 1917 the Tsar had lost control of the armed forces as well as the support and loyalty of the Russian people, which contributed to the February 1917 revolution.

Role of Tsarina Alexandra

- In September 1915 the Tsar left the Tsarina in charge, which was not welcomed in Russia as she was German.
- Her relationship with Rasputin was viewed with suspicion.
- His disreputable behaviour tainted the royal family.
- His increasing political role led to opposition from within the ruling elite.

Political problems

- The propaganda of the Revolutionary parties helped undermine the loyalty to the regime amongst the soldiers and workers. Not a huge reason, but contributory.
- Revolutionary Parties frightened the government in to repressive measures which encouraged revolution in 1917.
- Failure to allow growing middle-class a meaningful political voice and role in decision making.

Bourgeoisie discontent

- There was a growth of the middle class and they were becoming increasingly critical of the Tsarist regime: the Duma's had not given them the access to political power that they had wanted. This put into stark relief by the way in which the Tsar sqa and the elite ran the war.
- The development of the professions, commerce and industry resulted in a growing desire for change and modernization of the Russian political system.
- Spread of education meant people were becomingly more politically aware and encouraged spread of propaganda.

33. The candidate evaluates whether the role of Trotsky was the main reason why the Reds won the Civil War, using evidence and arguments such as:

Role of Trotsky

- Trotsky had a completely free hand in military matters.
- HQ was heavily armed train, which he used to travel around the country.
- He supervised the formation of the Red Army, which became a formidable fighting force of three million men.
- He recruited ex-Tsarist army officers and used political commissars to watch over them, thus ensuring experienced officers but no political recalcitrance.
- He used conscription to gain troops and would shoot any deserters.
- Trotsky helped provide an army with great belief in what it was fighting for, which the whites did not have.

Other Factors

Organisation of the Red Army

- The Red Army was better organized than the White army and better equipped and therefore able to crush any opposition from the White forces.
- Use of ex-officers from old Imperial Army
- Reintroduction of rank and discipline
- Role of Commissars

Terror (Cheka)

- The Cheka was set up to eradicate any opposition to the Reds.
- There was no need for proof of guilt for punishment to be exacted.
- There was persecution of individual people who opposed the Reds as well as whole groups of people, which helped to reduce opposition due to fear, or simply eradicate opposition.
- The Cheka group carried out severe repression.
- Some of the first victims of the Cheka were leaders of other political parties.
- 140 000 were executed by 1922 when Lenin was happy that all opposition had been suppressed.

Disunity among Whites

- The Whites were an uncoordinated series of groups whose morale was low.
- The Whites were a collection of socialists, liberals, moderates etc who all wanted different things and often fought amongst themselves due to their political differences. All of the Whites shared a hatred of Communism but other than this they lacked a common purpose.
- No White leader of any measure emerged to unite and lead the White forces whereas the Reds had Trotsky and Lenin.

Unity of the Reds

- Unified political leadership
- Unity of land controlled
- Co-ordinated military action

Superior Red resources

- Once the Reds had established defence of their lines they were able to repel and exhaust the attacks by the Whites until they scattered or surrendered.
- By having all of their land together it was easier for the Reds to defend.
- With the major industrial centres in their land (Moscow and Petrograd) the Reds had access to factories to supply weapons etc and swiftly due to their control of the railways.
- Control of the Railways meant they could transport troops supplies quickly and efficiently and in large numbers to the critical areas of defence or attack.
- The decisive battles between the Reds and Whites were near railheads.

- The Reds were in control of a concentrated area of western Russia, which they could successfully defend due to the maintenance of their communication and supply lines.
- Having the two major cities of Moscow and Petrograd in their possession meant that the Reds had the hold of the industrial centres of Russia as well as the administrative centres.
- Having the two major cities gave the Reds munitions and supplies that the Whites were unable to therefore obtain.

Foreign Intervention
- The Bolsheviks were able to claim that the foreign "invaders" were imperialists who were trying to overthrow the revolution and invade Russia.
- The Reds were able to stand as Champions of the Russian nation from foreign invasion.
- The help received by the Whites from foreign powers was not as great as was hoped for.
- The Foreign Powers did not provide many men due to the First World War just finishing and their help was restricted to money and arms.

Propaganda
- Whites were unable to take advantage of the brutality of the Reds to win support as they often carried out similar atrocities.
- The Whites were unable to present themselves as a better alternative to the Reds due to their brutality.
- The Reds kept pointing out that all of the land that the peasants had seized in the 1917 Revolution would be lost if the Whites won. This fear prevented the peasants from supporting the Whites.

Leadership of Lenin
- Introduction of War Communism.
- By forcing the peasants to sell their grain to the Reds for a fixed price the Reds were able to ensure that their troops were well supplied with and well fed.
- The Whites troops were not as well supplied and fed as the Reds troops.
- Skilled delegation and ruthlessness.

USA 1918 – 1968

34. The candidate evaluates the extent of divisions within the black community were the main obstacle to achieving civil rights before 1941, using evidence and arguments such as:

Divisions in the black community
- Booker T Washington, accomodationist philosophy, regarded as an 'Uncle Tom' by many.
- In contrast W E B De Bois founded the NAACP – a national organization whose main aim was to oppose discrimination through legal action. 1919 he launched a campaign against lynching, but it failed to attract most black people and was dominated by white people and well off black people.
- Marcus Garvey and Black Pride – he founded the UNIA (Universal Negro Improvement Association) which aimed to get blacks to 'take Africa, organise it, develop it, arm it, and make it the defender of Negroes the world over'.

Other factors

Activities of the Ku Klux Klan
- Racist organization formed in 1860s to prevent former slaves achieving equal rights. Suppressed by 1872, but in the 1920s there was a resurgence.
- Methods horrific: included beatings, torture and lynching.
- Roosevelt refused to support a federal bill to outlaw lynching in his New Deal in 1930s - feared loss of Democrat support in South.
- Activities took place at night – men in white robes, guns, torches, burning crosses.

- The 'second' Klan grew most rapidly in urbanizing cities which had high growth rates between 1910 and 1930, such as Detroit, Memphis, Daytona, Atlanta, Dallas, and Houston.
- Klan membership in Alabama dropped to less than 6,000 by 1930. Small independent units continued to be active in places like Birmingham, where in the late 1940s; members launched a reign of terror by bombing the homes of upwardly mobile African Americans.
- However, their activities in the 1940s led to continued migration of black Americans from the South to the North.

Legal impediments
- 'Jim Crow Laws' – separate education, transport, toilets etc – passed in Southern states after the Civil War.
- 'Separate but Equal' Supreme Court Decision 1896, when Homer Plessey tested their legality.
- Attitudes of Presidents e.g. Wilson 'Segregation is not humiliating and is a benefit for you black gentlemen'.

Lack of political influence
- 1890s: loopholes in the interpretation of the 15th Amendment were exploited so that states could impose voting qualifications.
- 1898 case of Mississippi v Williams – voters must understand the American Constitution.
- Grandfather Clause: impediment to black people voting.
- Most black people in the South were sharecroppers they did not own land and some states identified ownership of property as a voting qualification.
- Therefore black people could not vote, particularly in the South, and could not elect anyone who would oppose the Jim Crow Laws.

Popular prejudice
- After the institution of slavery the status of Africans was stigmatized, and this stigma was the basis for the anti-African racism that persisted.
- The relocation of millions of African Americans from their roots in the Southern states to the industrial centers of the North after World War I, particularly in cities such as Boston, Chicago, and New York (Harlem). In northern cities, racial tensions exploded, most violently in Chicago, and lynching -mob-directed hangings, usually racially motivated - increased dramatically in the 1920s.

35. The candidate assesses the effectiveness of the New Deal in solving with America's problems in the 1930s, using evidence and arguments such as:

The New Deal: Aims
- Context of the victory of Roosevelt in 1932 presidential election after the inadequate response of Hoover and the Republicans to the Great Depression: that followed the Wall Street Crash. The New Deal is associated with Roosevelt and the Democrats who took a more interventionist approach to dealing with the economy than the Republicans. The New Deal aimed to provide relief for the unemployed: aid recovery of the economy and reform to create a fairer society.

The First New Deal 1933-34
- Launch of 'Alphabet Agencies' giving relief and recovery in first 100 days of Roosevelt presidency: e.g. Federal Emergency Relief Administration [FERA], Tennessee Valley Authority [TVA], Public Works Administration [PWA] providing relief and work.
- Economy Act sought to balance the budget.
- Economic prudence by cutting wages of state employees by 15% and spending savings on relief programmes.
- Ending unpopular prohibition to raise revenue and cheer people up!

The Second New Deal 1935-1937
- Reform to improve living and working conditions for many Americans through acts such as:
- National Labour Relations Act ("Wagner Act") [1935]; protecting rights of workers to collectively bargain with employers
- Banking Act, (1935) established the Federal Bank Deposit Insurance Corporation, that insured deposits up to $5,000, and later, $10,000
- WPA [Works Progress Administration] (1935) launched programme of public works across America. By 1938 it provided employment for 3 million men [and some women].
- Rural electrification [1936] provided loans to electrify rural areas of America
- Social Security Act [1935] providing a state pension scheme for the old, widows, as well as help for the disabled and poor children.

Power of the Federal Government
- New Deal increased role of the Federal Government in American society and in particular the economy.
- Role of Government in strengthening the power of organised labour.
- Government role as regulator between business, labour and agriculture was confirmed by its increased intervention.
- Challenges to this in the Supreme Court.
- Opposition from State governments, especially in the South, employers groups forming Liberty League opposed to the New Deal.

Economic effects
- Debate on the economic effects in terms of relief and recovery: they certainly helped in terms of providing basic relief.
- Roosevelt's first term in office saw one of the fastest periods of GDP growth in US history. However downturn in 1937–38 raised questions about just how successful the policies were.
- Although it never reached the heights of before the Depression the New Deal did see a couple of positive results economically. Between 1933 to 1939 GDP increased by 60% from $55 billion to $85 billion;; the amount of consumer products bought increased by 40% while private investment in industry increased by 5 times in just six years.
- However, unemployment continued to be a problem, never running at less than 14% of the working population.
- The importance of rearmament in reducing unemployment and revitalizing the American economy was considerable, particularly after the mini-slump of 1937.

Confidence building
- Confidence building measures such as checking banks in 1933 to ensure they were well run and credit worthy. [Emergency Banking Act], and only allowing 'sound' banks to reopen.
- By end of 1933 many small banks had closed or were merged.
- Most depositors regained much of their money.
- Role of Roosevelt and his 'fire side chats': over 30 from March 1933.
- Roosevelt declared that "the only thing we have to fear is fear itself" and his "fireside chats" on the radio did a great deal to help restore the nation's confidence.

36. The candidate assesses how far the Civil Rights movement met the needs of black Americans up to 1968, using evidence and arguments such as:

Aims of Civil Rights movement
- Were mainly pacifist and intended to bring civil rights and equality in law to all non-white Americans.

- More radical segregationist aims of Black Radical Movements.

Role of NAACP
- Work of NAACP in the Brown v Topeka Board of Education, 1954.
- Work of NAACP in the Montgomery Bus Boycott, 1955.

Role of Congress of Racial Equality [CORE]
- Organised sit-ins during 1961 and freedom rides.
- Helped organize march on Washington.
- Instrumental in setting up Freedom Schools in Mississippi.

Role of SCLC and Martin Luther King
- Emergence of Martin Luther King and the SCLC.
- Little Rock, Arkansas – desegregation following national publicity.
- Non-violent protest as exemplified by Sit-ins and Freedom Rides.
- Birmingham, Alabama 1963: use of water cannon: Reaction of Kennedy.
- March on Washington, August 1963 - massive publicity.
- Martin Luther King believed that the Civil Rights Act of 1964 'gave Negroes some part of their rightful dignity, but without the vote it was dignity without strength'.
- March 1965, King led a march from Selma to Birmingham, Alabama, to publicise the way in which the authorities made it difficult for black Americans to vote easily.

Changes in Federal Policy
- Use of executive orders: Truman used them to appoint black appointments, order equality of treatment in the armed services: Kennedy signed 1962 executive order outlawing racial discrimination in public housing, etc.
- Eisenhower sent in army troops and National Guardsmen to protect them protect nine African-American students enrolled in a Central High School: Kennedy sent troops to Oxford, Mississippi to protect black student: James Meredith.
- Johnson and the 1964 Civil Rights Act banning racial discrimination in any public place, Voting Rights Act of 1965: by end of 1965 over 250,000 Blacks newly registered to vote, Affirmative Action, etc.

Social, Economic and Political changes
- Civil Rights Acts of 1964 and 1965 irrelevant to the cities of the North.
- Economic issues more important in the North.
- Watts riots and the split in the Civil Rights movement.
- King and the failure in Chicago.
- Urban poverty and de facto segregation still common in urban centres – failure of King's campaign to attack poverty.

Rise of black radical movements
- Stokely Carmichael and Black Power.
- Malcolm X publicised the increasing urban problems within the ghettos of America.
- The Black Panthers were involved in self-help schemes throughout poor cities.
- Kerner commission 1968 recognised US society still divided.

Appeasement and the Road to War, to 1939

37. The candidate assesses the effectiveness of military threat and force in pursuing Fascist governments foreign policies from 1933, using evidence and arguments such as:

Fascist strategies: use of Military threat and force
- Italy's naval ambitions in the Mediterranean – 'Mare Nostrum'.
- Italian invasion of Abyssinia – provocation, methods, and relatively poor performance against very poorly equipped enemy.

- German remilitarisation of Rhineland – Hitler's gamble and timing, his generals' opposition, lack of Allied resistance.
- Spanish Civil War – aid to Nationalists, testing weapons and tactics, aerial bombing of Guernica.
- Anschluss – attempted coup 1934; relations with Schuschnigg; invasion itself relatively botched militarily; popularity of Anschluss in Austria.
- Czechoslovakia – threats of 1938; invasion of March 1939.
- Italian invasion of Albania – relatively easy annexation of a client state.
- Poland – escalating demands; provocation, invasion.
- The extent to which it was the threat of military force which was used rather than military force itself – e.g. Czechoslovakia in 1938; and the extent to which military force itself was effective and/or relied on an element of bluff – eg Rhineland.

German Rearmament
- Open German rearmament from 1935.
- The speed and scale of rearmament, including conscription.
- The emphasis on air power and the growing threat from the air.
- By 1939, Hitler had an army of nearly 1 million men, over 8,000 aircraft and 95 warships.

Military agreements, pacts and alliances
- The German-Polish Non-Aggression Pact between Nazi Germany and Poland signed on January 26, 1934 – normalized relations between Poland and Germany, and promised peace for 10 years. Germany gained respectability and calmed international fears.
- Rome-Berlin axis – treaty of friendship signed between Italy and Germany on 25 October 1936.
- Pact of Steel an agreement between Italy and Germany signed on May 22, 1939 for immediate aid and military support in the event of war.
- Anti-Comintern Pact between Nazi-Germany and Japan on November 25th, 1936. The pact directed against the Communist International (Comintern) but was specifically directed against the Soviet Union. In 1937 Italy joined the Pact Munich Agreement – negotiations led to Hitler gaining Sudetenland and weakening Czechoslovakia.
- Nazi Soviet Non-Aggression Pact August 1939 – Both Hitler and Stalin bought time for themselves. For Hitler it seemed war in Europe over Poland unlikely. Poland was doomed. Britain had lost the possibility of alliance with Russia.

Fascist diplomacy as a means of achieving aims:
- Aims can be generally accepted as destruction of Versailles, the weakening of democracies, the expansion of fascist powers and countering communism.
- Diplomacy and the protestation of 'peaceful' intentions and 'reasonable' demands.
- Appeals to sense of international equality and fairness and the righting of past wrongs e.g. Versailles.
- Withdrawal from League and Disarmament Conference.
- Anglo German Naval Treaty 1935 - Germany allowed to expand navy. Versailles ignored in favour of bi-lateral agreements. A gain for Germany.
- Prior to Remilitarisation of Rhineland Hitler made offer of 25 year peace promise. Diplomacy used to distract and delay reaction to Nazi action.

Fascist strategies: Economic
- Use of economic influence and pressure, e.g. on south-eastern European states.
- Aid supplied to Franco (Spain) was tactically important to Hitler. Not only for testing weapons but also access to Spanish minerals.

38. The candidate assesses the validity of the view that British foreign policy was a complete failure in containing the spread of fascist aggression up to March 1938, using evidence and arguments such as:

British Aims
- Britain's foremost aim was to preserve peace. This was this achieved.
- Conflicts that did occur (Abyssinia, Spain) were on the periphery of Europe/the Mediterranean.

Abyssinia
- Mussolini's plans for a new Roman Empire in the Adriatic, the Mediterranean and North Africa were a blow to British foreign policy in hoping to convert Mussolini into an ally.
- Stresa Front (1935) initially seemed successful.
- Hoare-Laval Pact – public revulsion to Franco-British connivance at Italian aggression led to Hoare's resignation.
- Imposition of limited sanctions on Italy alienated Mussolini, thereby driving him closer to Hitler, yet failing to save Abyssinia.

Rhineland
- Hitler was successful in remilitarising Rhineland – more as a result of bluff, clever timing and French/British weakness than German military strength. But Britain and France had known about Hitler's plans earlier and did not plan to take action.
- Hitler was successful in remilitarising Rhineland. He could now secure his western frontier against attack and turn his attention eastwards.

Naval Agreement
- The Anglo German Naval Agreement (1935). This successfully limited German naval strength to 35% of British.
- The Anglo German Naval Agreement (1935). Britain accepted that Versailles would no longer contain Germany. Britain bowed to inevitable, but Germany had successfully revised Versailles.
- Although successful in 'managing' German Naval expansion, Hitler was successful in reintroducing conscription and rearming and by the late 1930s Britain's potential enemies were rearming at a faster rate.
- The growth of the Luftwaffe was a serious reverse for Britain.

Anschluss
- Anschluss took place bloodlessly. Austrians largely welcomed it. No conflict arose from this revision of a treaty that had already been revised many times.
- Anschluss – although Britain claimed it was not a vital British interest Churchill argued it was. Either way, Britain could have done little to prevent it.

Non-intervention: Spain
- Spain – the Non Intervention Committee played a part in preventing the escalation of a civil war into a wider European War.
- Spain – Britain's failure to enforce the Non Intervention Committee gave out signals of weakness to Hitler who used the SCW as a dress rehearsal for major conflict.

39. The candidate evaluates the extent to which the outbreak of war in September 1939 was brought about by the failures of British diplomacy and relations with the Soviet Union after Munich, using evidence and arguments such as:

British diplomacy and relations with the Soviet Union
- Stalin knew that Hitler's ultimate aim was to attack Russia.
- Lord Halifax, the British Foreign Secretary was invited by Stalin to go to Russia to discuss an alliance against Germany.

- Britain refused as they feared Russian Communism, and they believed that the Russian army was too weak to be of any use against Hitler.
- In August 1939, with war in Poland looming, the British and French eventually sent a military mission to discuss an alliance with Russia. Owing to travel difficulties it took five days to reach Leningrad.
- The Russians asked if they could send troops into Poland if Hitler invaded. The British refused, knowing that the Poles would not want this. The talks broke down.
- This merely confirmed Stalin's suspicions regarding the British. He felt they could not be trusted, especially after the Munich agreement, and they would leave Russia to fight Germany alone. This led directly to opening talks with the Nazis who seemed to be taking the Russians seriously by sending Foreign Minister von Ribbentrop and offering peace and land.

Importance of Nazi-Soviet Pact
- Pact – diplomatic, economic, military co-operation; division of Poland.
- Unexpected – Hitler and Stalin's motives.
- Put an end to British-French talks with Russia on guarantees to Poland.
- Hitler was freed from the threat of Soviet intervention and war on two fronts.
- But, given Hitler's consistent, long-term foreign policy aims on the destruction of the Versailles settlement and lebensraum in the east, the Nazi-Soviet Pact could be seen more as a factor influencing the timing of the outbreak of war rather than as one of its underlying causes.
- Hitler's long-term aims for destruction of the Soviet state and conquest of Russian resources - lebensraum.
  - Hitler's need for new territory and resources to sustain Germany's militarised economy.
  - Hitler's belief that British and French were 'worms' who would not turn from previous policy of appeasement and avoidance of war at all costs.
  - Hitler's belief that the longer war was delayed the more the balance of military and economic advantage would shift against Germany.

British abandonment of the policy of Appeasement
- Events in Bohemia and Moravia consolidated growing concerns in Britain.
- Czechoslovakia did not concern most people until the middle of September 1938, when they began to object to a small democratic state being bullied. However, most press and population went along with it, although level of popular opposition often underestimated.
- German annexation of Memel [largely German population, but in Lithuania] further showed Hitler's bad faith.
- Actions convinced British government of growing German threat in south-eastern Europe.
- Guarantees to Poland and promised action in the event of threats to Polish independence.

The position of France
- France had signed an agreement with Czechoslovakia offering support if the country was attacked. However, Hitler could all but guarantee that in 1938, French would do nothing as their foreign policy was closely tied to the British.
- French military, and particularly their airforce, allowed to decline in years after 1919.
- After Munich, French more aggressive towards dictators and in events of 1939 were keen on a military alliance with the Soviet Union, however despite different emphasis on tactics were tied to the British and their actions.

The occupation of Bohemia and the collapse of Czechoslovakia
- British and French realisation, after Hitler's breaking of Munich Agreement and invasion of Czechoslovakia in March 1939, that Hitler's word was worthless and that his aims went beyond the incorporation of ex-German territories and ethnic Germans within the Reich.
- Promises of support to Poland and Rumania.
- British public acceptance that all attempts to maintain peace had been exhausted.
- Prime Minister Chamberlain felt betrayed by the Nazi seizure of Czechoslovakia, realised his policy of appeasement towards Hitler had failed, and began to take a much harder line against the Nazis.

Developing crisis over Poland
- Hitler's long-term aims for the destruction of Versailles, including regaining of Danzig and Polish Corridor.
- British and French decision to stick to their guarantees to Poland.

Invasion of Poland
- On 1 September 1939, Hitler and the Nazis faked a Polish attack on a minor German radio station in order to justify a German invasion of Poland. An hour later Hitler declared war on Poland stating one of his reasons for the invasion was because of "the attack by regular Polish troops on the Gleiwitz transmitter."
- France and Britain had a defensive pact with Poland. This forced France and Britain to declare war on Germany, which they did on September 3.

The Cold War 1945 – 1989

40. The candidate assesses the accuracy of the statement that the Soviet Union effectively controlled Eastern Europe in the years up to 1961, using evidence and arguments such as:

The international context
- 1955 – emergence of Nikita Khrushchev as leader on death of Stalin. He encouraged criticism of Stalin and seemed to offer hope for greater political and economic freedom across the Eastern European satellite states.
- Speech to 20th Party Congress, Feb 1956: Khrushchev attacked Stalin for promoting a cult of personality and for his use of purges and persecution to reinforce his dictatorship. Policy of de-Stalinisation.
- Development of policy of peaceful co-existence to appeal to the West.
- Development of policy of different roads to Socialism to appeal to satellite states in Eastern Europe who were becoming restless.

Military and ideological factors
- Buffer zone could not be broken up as provided military defence for Soviet Union.
- Use of force and Red Army to enforce control in late 40s and early 50s.
- Need to ensure success of Communism hence policy.

Domestic pressures
- Intention to stop any further suffering of Soviet Union in aftermath of WW2 made leadership very touchy to change.
- Some economic freedoms were allowed, but at the expense of political freedoms.
- Need to stop spread of demands for change.

Demands for change and reaction: Poland (1956)
- Riots sparked off by economic grievances developed into demands for political change in Poland.
- On the death of Stalinist leader Boleslaw Bierut in 1956 he was replaced by Wladyslaw Gromulka, a former victim of Stalinism which initially worried the Soviets.

- Poles announced their own road to Socialism and introduced extensive reforms.
- Release of political prisoners (and Cardinal Wyszynski, Archbishop of Warsaw); collective farms broken up into private holdings; private shops allowed to open, greater freedom to factory managers.
- Relatively free elections held in 1957 which returned a Communist majority of 18.
- No Soviet intervention despite concerns.
- Gromulka pushed change only so far. Poland remained in the Warsaw Pact as a part of the important 'buffer zone'. Political freedoms were very limited indeed. Poland was a loyal supporter of the Soviet Union until the 1980s and the emergence of the Solidarity movement.

Demands for change and reaction: Hungary (1956)

- Hungarians had similar complaints: lack of political freedom, economic problems and poor standard of living.
- Encouraged by Polish success, criticism of the Stalinist regime of Mátyás Rákosi grew and he was removed by Khrushchev.
- Popular upsurge of support for change in Budapest led to a new Hungarian government led by Imre Nagy, who promised genuine reform and change.
- Nagy government planned multi-party elections, political freedoms, the withdrawal of Hungary from the Warsaw Pact and demands for the withdrawal of Soviet forces.
- Nagy went too far. The Soviet Union could not see this challenge to the political supremacy of the Communist Party and the breakup of their carefully constructed buffer zone. They intervened and crushed the rising brutally.
- Successful intervention, but lingering resentment from mass of Hungarian people, through some economic flexibility allowed the new regime of Janos Kadar to improve economic performance and living standards.

Demands for change and reaction: Berlin (1961)

- Problem of Berlin – a divided city in a divided nation.
- Lack of formal boundaries in Berlin allowed East Berliners and East Germans to freely enter the West which they did owing to the lack of political freedom, economic development and poor living standards in the East.
- Many of those fleeing (2.8 million between 1949 and 1961) were skilled and young, just the people the communist East needed to retain. This was embarrassing for the East as it showed that Communism was not the superior system it was claimed to be.
- Concerns of Ulbricht and Khrushchev: attempts to encourage the Western forces to leave Berlin by bluster and threat from 1958 failed.
- Kennedy of America spoke about not letting the Communists drive them out of Berlin. Resultant increase in tension could not be allowed to continue.
- Building of barriers: barbed wire then stone in August 1961 to stem the flood from East to West.
- Success in that it reduced the threat of war and the exodus to the West from the East to a trickle.
- Frustration of many in East Germany. Propaganda gift for the US and allies.

41. The candidate evaluates the extent to which difficulties faced by the US military was the reason why the US lost the war in Vietnam, using evidence and arguments such as:

Difficulties faced by the US military

- Difficulty of using Superpower force in a Third World country.
- US Soldiers brave, but a minority did not believe in the war.
- Difficulties dealing with the conditions and knowing which Vietnamese were the enemy led to stress and confusion.

- Many saw war in purely military terms: failure to win 'hearts and minds' of local population.
- Short commissions for officers and rotation of troops led to loss of expertise in the field.

Other factors

Failure of military methods

- Mass bombing had no real effect according to the Jason Study by MIT in 1966, owing to the agricultural nature of North Vietnam and the widespread jungle cover.
- Use of defoliants, although widespread, had limited effect militarily.
- 'Search and destroy' missions became 'Search and avoid' missions for many American troops.

Public opposition in America

- Public opposition supported by the press was probably the main reason for withdrawal. Vietnam a media war, images showed the public the brutality of war e.g. South Viet police chief executing a Viet Cong in Saigon during the Tet Offensive of '68. Such images damaged American claims to be the 'good guys'. Extent of the opposition is debated. Probably a minority in '65, growing by the time of crucial Tet offensive in '68. Oct 1969 largest anti-war protest in US History. Protestors in every major city in America. Opposition of Black power groups. Protest could be violent: May 1970 protest at Kent State University, Ohio led to four students being shot. Unpopularity of the draft. On the other hand, there was pressure for escalation from 'hawks' in America as well.
- USA was a democracy: public pressure and perception mattered. Nixon noted extent of opposition: withdrawal of 60,000 troops in 1969, policy of Vietnamisation. Economic cost of the war: US deficit of $1.6 billion in 1965 increased to $25.3 billion in 1968. Tax increases unpopular. Congress only got involved in limiting money and action in late 60s and early 70s. Divisions within administrations: e.g. LBJ had Rusk advising to continue the struggle in South-East Asia, compared to Senator Fulbright arguing for de-escalation.

North Vietnamese strengths

- A hard peasant life bred determined soldiers. Viet Cong enlisted for years unlike American troops who signed up for a year. Belief in their cause of Communism also a factor. Great determination: eg the Ho Chi Minh trail was kept open despite American bombers continually bombing it. Viet Cong knew the jungle, survived in atrocious conditions, developed effective tactics and were more effective in winning the 'hearts and minds' of civilians than the Americans.
- Military objectives were realistic: General Giap aimed to break the will of the American Government.
- Support of Chinese and Soviet aid from 1965 of importance.

South Vietnamese weaknesses

- Corruption and decay of South Vietnamese government, especially in Saigon.
- Lack of political and social cohesion in South Vietnam led to divisions and turmoil which filtered through to their armed forces.
- Divisions between Catholic ruling elite and Buddhist population.

International isolation of the U.S.A.

- Widespread criticism of American conduct of war internationally. A propaganda gift for the Soviet Union.
- Although some 'allied' help from nations like Australia, most main US allies, like Britain, pointedly stayed out of the war.

42. The candidate evaluates the validity of the view that the economic weakness of the Soviet Union led to the end of the Cold War, using evidence and arguments such as:

Soviet Economic weakness
- The Soviet economy was at breaking point by the late 1980s.
- Commitments to the arms race meant the Soviet economy was hugely unbalanced.
- Propping up allied regimes was also causing a drain on resources.
- Consumer goods and housing were neglected as a result.

Other factors

Role of President Mikhail Gorbachev
- Gorbachev saw that the USSR could not afford a new arms race. Gorbachev implemented policies of Perestroika and Glasnost which aimed to reform the Soviet economy and liberalise its political system.
- Gorbachev worked to improve relations with the USA. He took ideology out of his foreign policy, as exemplified by arms agreements to allow the USSR to concentrate on internal matters: Intermediate Nuclear Forces Treaty, Dec 1987, Nuclear Weapons Reduction Treaty, 1989.
- Gorbachev told leaders of the satellite East European states in March 1989 that the Soviet army would no longer help them to stay in power.

Role of President Ronald Reagan
- Unlike many in the US administration Reagan actively sought to challenge Soviet weakness and strengthen the west in order to defeat Communism. In 1983 he denounced the Soviet Union as an 'Evil Empire.'
- Programme of improving US armed forces, including nuclear weapons and he proposed a Star Wars missile shield to challenge the belief in MAD (SDI). He was very charming when he met Gorbachev and visited Soviet Union.

Western economic strength
- Allowed America to embark on the Star Wars weapons programme.
- Perception of the affluent West through television and consumer goods undermined Communist claims of the superiority of their economic system.

Withdrawal of the Soviet Union from Afghanistan
- Symptom of the problems of Soviet Union.
- Intervention in Dec 1979: conflict with the Mujaheddin. Russian army morale crumbled when over 20,000 Soviet soldiers died, as did support at home.
- The conflict showed the weaknesses of the Soviet economy. War led to a slump in living standards for ordinary Russians.
- Russians began to question the actions of their own government. Gorbachev withdrew troops in 1988.

Failure of Communism in Eastern Europe
- Strong Polish identity and history of hostility with Russia. By 1970s, Poland in economic slump. Emergence of opposition around Gdansk in 1980: industrial workers strike led by Lech Walesa, who argued for the creation of an independent trade union. Solidarity grew to nine million members in a matter of months. Movement suppressed in 1981 by General Jaruzelski's government.
- Multiparty elections in Poland, after Soviet troops left, victory for Solidarity.
- Czechoslovakia, political prisoners released in November 1989 and by the end of the month, the communist government had gone. No Soviet intervention.
- Opening of the Berlin Wall: division of Germany finally came to an end.
- Soviet domination ended.
- Perestroika and Glasnost and end of Communist rule in USSR.

HIGHER HISTORY PAPER 2
2013

SPECIAL TOPIC 1: THE WARS OF INDEPENDENCE, 1286–1329

1. The candidate makes a judgement on how fully Source A illustrates the succession problem in Scotland, in terms of:

Points from the source which show the candidate has interpreted the significant views:
- John Balliol's success would both maintain and even increase Comyn power.
- Bruce's who were determined to stake their claim to power
- before Maid's death in September 1290, Bruce had tried to increase his territorial power.
- Bruce put forward the case that he was the rightful successor to Alexander II.

Points from recall which support and develop those in the source:
- Two rival noble dynasties saw an opportunity to seize power, Robert Bruce (grandfather of the future King Robert I) and John Balliol (ally of the powerful Comyn family).
- The two main claimants were descendants through the daughters of David the Earl of Huntingdon had valid claims as descendant of David I of Scotland.

Points from recall which offer a wider contextualisation such as:
- The tragic death of Alexander III, 18th March, 1286.
- Alexander's children had all died before him; Alexander, David and Margaret.
- After the Maid's death, the marriage Treaty of Birgham, between Edward (son of King Edward) and Margaret (Maid of Norway) was now null and void.
- There was a real fear of Civil War, particularly amongst factions from Bruce.
- The Guardians compromised the Independence of Scotland by inviting Edward's mediation.
- The Guardians negotiated a specific treaty (of Birgham) protecting Margaret's rule as Queen of Scots.
- Edward's aim to establish Feudal Overlordship at Norham, 1291.
- Bishop Fraser was sympathetic to the Balliol claim.
- The Bruce family wrote to make their claim to Edward, known as the 'Appeal of the seven Earls'.
- Edward's decision to make John Balliol, King of Scots, November 1292.
- The Bruce family did not accept the decision.
- The Bruce family paid homage to Edward I in 1296.
- Any other relevant points.

2. The candidate makes a judgement on the extent to which **Sources B** and **C** agree about the subjugation of Scotland by Edward I, in terms of:

Overall: **Source B** and **Source C** basically agree that Edward I invaded Scotland with significant forces, attacked the town of Berwick, slaughtering the Scots inside. The English also fought a pitched battle at Dunbar, besieging the Scottish held castle, but the Scots were also defeated by nobles disloyal to King John, such as the Bruce dynasty.

Developed through detail:

Source B

- The King of England, being strongly stirred up, marched in person on Scotland with a large force.

- Upon the town of Berwick he put to the sword some 7500 souls.

- On 27 April, was fought the battle of Dunbar, where many Scottish nobles fell wounded in defeat.

- Bruce's party, were generally considered traitors to their king and country.

Source C

- For Edward the campaign to Scotland was carried out from the outset by using the full force of England's experienced army.

- He made a swift example of the town of Berwick, slaughtering over 7,000 inhabitants.

- In the ensuing battle at Dunbar on 27 April the Scots were defeated resoundingly.

- Scottish nobles who preferred to side with the English King, included the Bruce's.

3. The candidate makes a judgement on how useful Source D is as evidence of the growth of Scottish resistance to King Edward, 1296–1297 in terms of:

Points from the source which show the candidate has interpreted the significant views:
- Origin: It was written in the Yorkshire Priory of Guisborough, in England, about 1300. It is well informed about some parts of Scotland in the 1290's.
- Possible purpose: A biased appraisal of the pitched battle at Stirling, based on the English account of the battle of Stirling Bridge in 1297.
- Content:
  1. We are ready for the fight, to free our kingdom.
  2. There was not a more suitable place to put the English into the hands of the Scots.
  3. Cressingham was cut down by Scots pikemen and cut into pieces.

Points from recall which support and develop those in the source:
- Resistance to the English grew in the South West, and in the North East.
- William Wallace and Andrew Murray brought leadership to Scottish resistance.
- Scottish guerrilla tactics in their early resistance had moved towards a pitched battle at Stirling, under the combined leadership.

Points from recall which offer a wider contextualisation such as:
- Rebellions began in the spring of 1297.
- The Nobles Bruce and Steward started an armed revolt against Edward at Irvine.
- Andrew Murray took castles at Inverness, Elgin and Aberdeen.
- Murray had removed all English garrisons north of Dundee.
- William Wallace present at killing of Sir William Heselrig, the English Sheriff of Lanark.
- Scottish victory at the Battle of Stirling Bridge, 11th September, 1297.
- Wallace and Murray appointed Guardians.
- Wallace invaded the North of England, around Carlisle and Newcastle.
- Any other relevant points.

4. The candidate makes a judgement on how far **Source E** illustrates Robert Bruce's abilities as a military leader in terms of:

Points from the source which show the candidate has interpreted the significant views:
- Scots rejoice in their victory at Bannockburn, under the leadership of Robert Bruce.
- Bruce defeated Sir Henry de Bohun by striking him on the head with an axe.
- Robert Bruce marshalled his forces who numbered about forty thousand men and were well armed with axes and lances.
- Split his forces into three divisions, advancing in thick-set hedge, which could not easily be broken.

Points from recall which support and develop those in the source:
- Vital military victories under Bruce's leadership, such as Loudon Hill, Old Byland.
- 1307 Victory at Glen Trool.
- Military victory at the Battle of the Pass of Brander 1308
- Leadership of Bruce in other battles, such as, the Battle of Inverurie, 1308.
- Bruce gained support and trained his men during his military campaign 1307–1314.
- Bruce used tactics such as siege, guerrilla warfare and schiltrons.

Points from recall which offer a wider contextualisation such as:
- Fought a military campaign to defeat first, his Scottish enemies, before his campaign against the English.
- Defeated the Comyn/Balliol factions in the Scottish Civil War.
- The 'Herschip of Buchan 1308'.
- Bruce used the loyalty of nobles to extend his military campaign in the South eg Galloway.
- Bruce's repeated invasions into Northern England 1309, 1312, 1315, 1316, 1318 & 1327.
- Forced Edward II to withdraw from Scotland 1311.
- Recovery of English held castles in Scotland eg Linlithgow, Edinburgh & Roxburgh.
- Stirling Castle besieged and captured in 1314.
- In 1315 launched a war in Ireland under his brother Edward, later again under Bruce.
- In 1318 Berwick was recovered from the English, last outpost.
- Robert's invasion of 1327 was a further pressure on the Isabella/Mortimer guardianship (Edward III).
- Any other relevant points.

SPECIAL TOPIC 2: THE AGE OF REFORMATION, 1542–1603

1. The candidate makes a judgement on how fully Source A explains the reasons for the Reformation of 1560, in terms of:

Points from the source which show the candidate has interpreted the significant views:
- In December 1557 Protestant nobles sent ambitious requests for reform to Mary of Guise.
- Protestant nobles asked to be allowed to host Protestant sermons on their estates; and they also wanted prayers in the vernacular to be used in parish churches.
- The return of John Knox to Scotland and his inflammatory sermon at Perth triggered a full-scale riot.
- Mary of Guise mishandled the situation in 1559, uniting most of the political nation against her.

Points from recall which support and develop those in the source:

• The Lords of the Congregation were encouraged by the prospect of support from the English after Elizabeth became Queen in 1558.
• John Knox's return was pivotal in advancing the Protestant cause. In 1545 he was with the Protestant rebels at St Andrew's Castle and in 1546, involved in the assassination of Cardinal Beaton.
• In Perth religious houses were attacked and religious objects were destroyed and in the early spring of 1559, Perth and Dundee announced they were Protestant.

Points from recall which offer a wider contextualisation such as:

• Protestant ideas had been coming into Scotland for some time.
• English Bibles and books critical of the Catholic Church were distributed in Scotland following the Reformation in England.
• The Catholic Church failed to make sufficient reform to satisfy its critics.
• Increased numbers of the nobility opted for the new faith.
• The Lords of the Congregation had increasing support and took up arms against Mary of Guise.
• The weaknesses of the Catholic Church – decline and corruption; pluralism had not been addressed. Minors being given top positions in church – crown and nobility taking much of churches' revenues; Monarchs placed their offspring in important positions in the Church.
• The 'Beggar's Summons' was nailed to friaries demonstrating anger at the Church's domination and wealth and demanded the flitting of the Friars.
• Mary of Guise's religious attitude and pro-France stance meant she asked the French for help it pushed many Scots into supporting the Lords of the Congregation.
• Mary of Guise's prosecution of reformers was unpopular.
• Any other relevant factors.

2. The candidate makes a judgement on the extent to which **Sources B** and **C** agree about the events which brought Mary's marriage to Darnley to an end, in terms of:

Overall Comparison: **Sources B** and **C** describe the explosion and reaction to Darnley's murder, plus the attendance of the Queen and Bothwell at the masque in Holyrood. However, **Source B** describes the Queen's feeling that she was a target, whereas **Source C** shows that she was accused of the murder.

Source B	Source C
• The house in which the King was lodged was in instant blown in the air … it must have been done by force of gunpowder and appears to have been a mine.	• The Lords of the Council concluded that the Old Provost's 'Prebendaries' Chambers had been blown into the air by the force of the powder.
• It is not yet known who carried out this deed and in what manner.	• In the aftermath of Darnley's death there was much speculation as to who was implicated in the murder and how exactly it was carried out.

Source B (continued)

• Queen believed that she was the intended victim.

• Mary did not stay the night at Kirk o' Field by chance – 'by reason of some masque in the abbey (of Holyrood)'.

Source C (continued)

• The Queen herself was accused of the murder of Darnley.

• Mary returned to Holyrood around midnight, Bothwell was in attendance on her, and conspicuously dressed in a masquing costume.

3. The candidate makes a judgement on how useful **Source D** is as evidence of the efforts of the Kirk to maintain its independence, in terms of:

Points from the source which show the candidate has interpreted the significant views:

Origin: The source, articles from The Second Book of Discipline written in 1578, was central to the development of Presbyteries through which the Kirk would be virtually independent of secular government.

Possible Purpose: To set out the views of a Presbyterian Kirk and to establish the relationship between church and state.

Content

• Kings and princes have supreme power over their subjects in civil law.
• Christ alone is 'Lord and Master' of the Kirk.
• Christ will 'command and rule in his Kirk, through his Spirit and word' and through the service of 'the ministry of men'.

Points from recall which support and develop those in the source:

• The *Second Book of Discipline* (1578) set out the vision of a Presbyterian Kirk. The views expressed were consistent with Andrew Melville's – in that he protected the rights of the Kirk from the King and Government.
• The *Second Book of Discipline* led to the development of regular meetings of ministers from 10 to 20 parishes to discuss doctrine which developed into the Presbyteries.
• A Presbyterian system could make the Kirk almost entirely independent of the King and his nobles.

Points from recall which offer a wider contextualisation:

• By 1581 plans were in place for 13 Presbyteries with responsibility for Kirk matters such as: visiting parishes; the appointment of ministers; responsibility for disciplinary matters; and the selection of representatives for future General Assemblies.
• At parish level, Kirk Sessions had consisted of elders and deacons who were elected annually until the *Second Book of Discipline* developed the idea of 'once an elder, always an elder'.
• From 1560, Kirk Sessions exercised the right to fine, imprison and excommunicate offenders against their authority in moral matters.
• The *Second Book of Discipline* (1578) established a vision of a Presbyterian Kirk but the 'Black Acts' (1584) subsequently stated the supremacy of the monarch in all matters.
• The Golden Act (1592) recognised the recovery of Presbyterian influence within the Kirk but it did not reduce the power of the monarch.
• Any other relevant factors.

4. The candidate makes a judgement on how far **Source E** explains the cultural impact of the Reformation on Scotland to 1603, in terms of:

Points from the source which show the candidate has interpreted the significant views:

- Former Catholics were required to dispose of all religious objects which in the past might have provided a sense of comfort.
- Abolition of Christmas and Easter reflected fear of Catholic custom.
- Declared Monday to be a day of rest for all servants.
- Abolition of saints' days and respect for Sabbath understandable, but harsh on working population.

Points from recall which support and develop those in the source:

- The observance of Catholic festivals and the performance of plays were actively discouraged.
- Kirk Sessions were preoccupied with keeping wedding and other celebrations under control.
- The interiors of most parish Kirks were plain and whitewashed few reminders of Catholic styles of decoration. However, some altars and treasured objects from the pre-Reformation period remained in some places.
- The Kirk decided to remove all organs from places of worship. However, there is evidence that in some areas music during services survived.

Points from recall which offer a wider contextualisation:

- At the beginning of 1560, Scotland was a Catholic country with a Protestant minority. By 1603, it was a Protestant country with a tiny Catholic minority.
- The only Protestant bibles available to lowland Scots were in English. However, through time the English language became more familiar as English bibles were used in church.
- Great emphasis was laid upon attendance at both daily and Sunday services.
- There were no significant playwrights in Scotland as in England (William Shakespeare and Ben Johnson). Courtiers rather than priests and monks were responsible for producing poetry and verse and many of these followed James VI to England. Prose writers tended to write in English rather than Latin or Scots – this also applied to sermons.
- The aim of a school in every parish was not achieved but some advances were made and Scotland's parish school network was more secure with more than half of the 800 schools recorded in Scotland sited in or next to kirks.
- Overall, literacy rates improved.
- Increased persecution of witchcraft in line with the view of James VI.
- The catechism was used by ministers, school masters and elders to teach the principles of Protestantism to young Scots. Young people would be examined on their knowledge during the Sunday afternoon service.
- Any other relevant factors.

SPECIAL TOPIC 3: THE TREATY OF UNION, 1689-1740

1. The candidate makes a judgement on how fully **Source A** explains the reasons for worsening relations with England after 1690 in terms of:

Points from the source which show the candidate has interpreted the significant views:

- England has ruined Scotland by giving land and pensions as bribes.
- Offices in Scottish government given to those who will comply with English wishes.
- Scotland appears to the rest of the world to be a conquered province.

- English court has bribed Scots so that the English are now masters of us at our own cost.

Points from recall which support and develop those in the source:

- King William and English ministers did seek to gain advantage over Scottish interests, eg over Darien Scheme.
- Successive appointments to posts in Scottish government did go to those who were subservient to English command.

Points from recall which offer a wider contextualisation such as:

- The "Ill" Years.
- Navigation Acts.
- Effect of English wars.
- English military intervention with Scottish trade.
- Lack of English investment in the Darien Scheme.
- Dutch withdrawal from Darien.
- Limits of the Darien Scheme.
- William's hand in the Darien failure.
- The cost of Darien.
- Act of Settlement enacting the Hanoverian succession.
- Act of Security proclaiming Scottish independence in terms of trade, law and religion and asserting Scotland's right to choose its monarch.
- Act Anent Peace and War stating future monarchs could not declare war on Scotland's behalf without parliamentary consent.
- Wool Act, Wine Act; Scotland would continue to trade when England was at war.
- Aliens Act; Scots to be treated as Aliens in England if Hanoverian succession not accepted in Scotland.
- Jacobite opposition to William, assassination plot.
- Scottish parliamentary opposition to the Anglican church.
- English Bill of Rights.
- Claim of Right, Articles of Grievance.
- Scots Act of Settlement.
- Opposition to William in the Highlands, Glencoe Massacre.
- Covenanters' objections to monarchical interference in church affairs.
- Other relevant factors.

2. The candidate makes a judgement on the extent to which **Sources B** and **C** agree about attitudes in Scotland towards union, in terms of:

Overall **Source B** and **Source C** agree that many in Scotland were against union and the nature of this oppositon; they differ in their views as to how many people in Scotland understood the issues involved.

Source B	Source C
• In November, a flood of Addresses to parliament from Royal Burghs, etc.	• 90-plus Addresses streamed into parliament from beginning of November.
• Addresses opposed to union, none in favour.	• Addresses reveal widespread public opposition to union.
• Addresses said union was "contrary to honour and independence".	• Addresses defended Scotland's honour and independent sovereignty.
• Addresses showed widespread literacy and awareness of issues.	• Signatures made on behalf of illiterate who were not fully aware of issues.

3. The candidate makes a judgement on how useful **Source D** is as evidence of the passage of the union through the Scottish parliament in terms of:

Points from the source which show the candidate has interpreted the significant views:
- Origin: Daniel Defoe observed Scottish parliamentary proceedings first-hand.
- Possible purpose: To show the influence of the Equivalent on Scottish MPs voting for union.
- Content: – the Equivalent compensated Darien investors.
    – the Equivalent took the edge off opposition to union.
    – Squadrone Volante could now be persuaded to vote for the Union.

Points from recall which support and develop those in the source:
- English spies informed English government of proceedings in parliament.
- Financial payments to Scots were a feature of the debate period.
- The Equivalent was a major factor in swaying many towards union.
- The Equivalent: £398,085.10s to cover the taking on of English debt.
- Bribery of Scottish ministers/politicians through £20,000 issued to Earl of Glasgow by English government to distribute as "arrears in pay".
- Promise of favours, pensions, military patronage, high-ranking positions and cash ensured government majorities; threats of loss of civil list pension.

Points from recall which offer a wider contextualisation such as:
- Act of Security for the Kirk also turned many in favour of union.
- Political management of Court party better than Country party.
- Court members consistently voted through all Articles of the Treaty.
- Role of Hamilton as an erratic and divisive leader of Country party.
- Hamilton may have been bribed by the Court party.
- Hamilton refused to participate in planned walkout of parliament.
- Failed armed rising proved opponents of union were unwilling to engage in violence.
- Hamilton divided opponents of union and obstructed arguments against union.
- Divisions amongst opponents.
- Squadrone Volante's hold on balance of power was crucial.
- Economic assurances, incentive of free trade with England and English colonies.
- Payment made to wool industry as well as payment of Scottish public debt.
- Last minute concessions by Godolphin on tax issues, eg salt, liquor.
- Incentives for Scottish nobles regarding retained privileges, seats in House of Lords.
- Rights of burghs and Royal Burghs to remain.
- Legal protection, Scottish law and courts to remain.
- Future stability within one kingdom secured; peace secured by being in Great Britain.
- Military argument; threat of English invasion as forces moved north in late 1706.
- English and Scottish parliaments in agreement over union for first time.
- Security of liberty and stability under one parliament.
- Any other relevant points.

4. The candidate makes a judgement on how far **Source E** explains the causes of the Jacobite Rising of 1715 in terms of:

Points from the source which show the candidate has interpreted the significant views:
- Patriotic Scots wishing to free Scotland from English domination moved to the Jacobite cause.
- James promised to restore Scotland to its ancient free and independent state.
- Union was a mistake because Scotland was dominated by English priorities.
- Union was a mistake because Scotland was heavily taxed, with worse to come.

Points from recall which support and develop those in the source:
- Areas with Jacobite MPs did indeed provide troops in 1715, such as Fife, Perthshire, the North-East, Lanarkshire and Linlithgow.
- Jacobites had come to lead national sentiment after the Union.

Points from recall which offer a wider contextualisation such as:
- Desire for restoration of Stuart dynasty.
- Failure of French-sponsored 1708 rebellion.
- Influence of Jacobite literature and music within Scottish culture generated support for movements against union and for armed rebellion.
- Jacobite support with ulterior motives, eg Lowlanders hoping to court royal favour should there be a return of the Stuart dynasty.
- Resentment towards George I and Hanoverian Succession.
- Leadership of the Earl of Mar who had lost political office under George I.
- Weakness of Scottish defences made Jacobite success appear more likely.
- Strength of the Episcopalian Church, especially in North-east.
- Assumed support of the French.
- 1713 – motion to repeal Act of Union defeated, leading to greater determination of those who believed in armed rebellion.
- Scottish industries such as linen, wool and paper struggling in the post-1707 period.
- Resentment at withholding of payment of the Equivalent.
- Political resentment of consequences of union such as House of Lords becoming court of appeal for Scottish cases in 1712.
- Resentment towards Parliament's 1711 banning Scottish peers with English titles.
- Treaty did exert strong Anglicising influence which many Jacobites resented.
- Guarantees which preserved the Presbyterian Church raised objections from Jacobites.
- Any other relevant points.

SPECIAL TOPIC 4: MIGRATION AND EMPIRE, 1830–1939

1. The candidate makes a judgement on how fully **Source A** explains the reasons for the migration of Scots in terms of:

Points from the source which show the candidate has interpreted the significant views:
- Incessant rain had made it impossible for the population of the west coast to harvest the peat on which they depended for domestic fuel.
- The crofts to which the mass of Highlanders had been driven as a result of earlier clearances had long since proved incapable of providing adequately for their occupants.
- Crofting families survived on a diet consisting largely of potatoes and when that crop failed as it did regularly – hunger became more severe.
- Landlords, did not feel very pressing responsibility for the Highlanders fate and simply organised still more evictions in order to create still more sheep farms.

Points from recall which support and develop those in the source:
- Highland Clearances – relevant details about poverty and hardship.
- Harsh employment conditions on the land.
- Pressures on small farmers of poor quality soil and harsh weather conditions.
- The Highland Problem: over-crowding, sub division of land into crofts with each successive generation leading to insufficient land/food to support families.
- Pressure from landlords wishing to 'improve' their land by creating sheep farms.

Points from recall which offer a wider contextualisation such as:
Push factors:
- Landlords looked to improve their land not only with sheep farms but also deer forests grouse moors.
- 'Balmoralism' and the tourist income potential after the Highlands became fashionable with Royal approval also created pressure for change in Highlands.
- Lack of real opportunities encouraged emigration from the Highlands of Scotland.
- Failure of the kelp and herring industries.
- Effects of the Agricultural Revolution on farming and employment.
- Effects of Industrial Revolution on craftsmen.

Pull factors
- Bitterness rarely the sole reason for emigration.
- Better prospects abroad both for self and next generation. Not all were driven out of Scotland – many left willingly.
- Hope, ambition and adventure stronger than despair and resignation.
- Improvement in life expected through emigration.
- Letters from relatives already emigrants.
- Voluntary migrants from a strong, urban economy in Scotland.
- Emigration Agencies actively working to attract emigrants – New Zealand and Australian authorities work was widespread, offering free passages and other inducements.
- Promises of free/cheap land abroad, especially in Canada.
- Discovery of gold in Australia.
- Use of free and assisted passages by many territories encouraged both agricultural and urban workers to leave Scotland.
- Government schemes to assist emigration eg Highland and Islands Emigration Society.
- Transport Revolution meant that travel times greatly reduced by steam ship – an important factor when migrants had to consider loss of wages while en route.
- Steam ships.
- Migration to Canada seen by many urban industrial workers as a 'back door' to USA at a time when it was harder to gain direct entry to the USA.
- Attractions of a new life, possibly in a city (including UK cities) – employment, better wages, easier work, chances of marriage partner, entertainment.
- Any other relevant points.

2. The candidate makes a judgment on the extent to which **Sources B** and **C** agree about the experience of Irish immigrants in Scotland in terms of:

Overall: **Source B** and **Source C** agree that the experience of Irish immigrants in Scotland was negative with both **Source B** and **Source C** complaining about the problems caused by the Irish immigrants in terms of maintaining Scottish identity and limiting numbers of immigrants, pressure on poor rates, competition for jobs and also lowering wages rates and moral standards.

Developed through detail:

Source B	*Source C*
• Let us redouble our efforts not to keep Scotland for the Scotch, for that is impossible; but to keep Scotland – Scotch!.	• Irish immigration that washes over us each year should be restricted.
• They have swallowed up our rapidly increasing Poor Rates.	• interferes …in their dependence on adequate funds within the poor rates.
• By their great numbers they have…deprived thousands of the working people of Scotland of that employment which legitimately belonged to them.	• We have no doubt that the work of this parish could be done, and the harvest got in, without the competition from Irish labourers.
• By their great numbers they have lessened wages.	• Irish labourers whose presence forces down the wages to be earned from this work.

3. The candidate makes a judgment on how useful **Source D** is as evidence about the contribution of Scots to the economic growth and development of the Empire in terms of:

Points from source which show the candidate has interpreted the significant views:
Origin: Laing's letter is an eyewitness primary source from someone working on the railways in Canada thereby contributing towards the economic growth and development of the Empire.
Possible purpose: The purpose of the letter is to inform Laing's sister about his wellbeing, his work and to comment on the contribution of Scots to the development of the railways in Canada.
Content:
- We have 86 locomotive engines to keep in repair and 400 miles of rails to keep in good repair so that the produce of this land can reach the ports and then across the world.
- Our foremen are nearly all Scots.
- Without these men there would be no railway, no prosperity and no trade in this part of the world.

Points from recall which support and develop those in the source:
- Scots very important to the development of the Transatlantic Canadian Pacific Railway.
- Strong support for the railway came from Sir John A. MacDonald, the first Prime Minister of Canada, born in Glasgow in 1815.
- Scots were important in the financing and engineering of the project. Scots, George Stephen at the Bank of Montreal and John Rose in London helped finance it. Another Scot, Sandford Fleming, was the railway's main engineer.

Points from recall which offer a wider contextualisation such as:
- By the 1920s it has been calculated that one quarter of Canada's business leaders were born in Scotland, with another twenty-five percent having Scottish-born fathers.
- The Hudson's Bay Company recruited heavily in the Western and Northern Isles of Scotland.
- Scots brought new ideas on how to farm to Canada such as crop rotation.
- Scots were very important in the development of trade in furs and timber as well as agriculture in Canada.

The impact of Scots on other parts of Empire.

Australasia

- Scots were important in the development of farming in Australia.
- Scotland was also a significant investor in developing agriculture in Australia eg huge sheep runs in New South Wales and Victoria.
- Scots also helped the sugar and wine industries in Australia.
- Samuel McWilliam planted his first vines at Corowa in New South Wales in 1877.
- Scots involved developing Australian trade, mining, manufacturing, shipping, engineering and finance.
- Robert McCracken from Ayrshire developed brewing in Melbourne.
- Robert Campbell from Greenock played such an important role in developing Australian trade that he was known as 'The father of Australian Commerce'.
- Melbourne Iron works was founded by John Buncle from Edinburgh.
- The Commercial Banking Company of Sydney was founded in 1834 by an Aberdonian.
- Scots dominated many shipping firms in Australia.
- Scottish involvement in the development of education in Australia.
- Schools that were set up and run by Scots were important as they produced many of the political, economic, military and educational leaders of the future.
- Scots founded New Zealand's paper-making industry and were important engineers and shipbuilders.
- Peter and David Duncan, originally from Forfar, developed a successful business in Agricultural implements in Christchurch.
- Scots were skilled farmers and influenced the development of New Zealand through sheep and mixed farming.

India

- Scots had become involved in trading with India before 1830. They were involved with the East India Company.
- After 1830 Scots were of great importance in extending British influence into India eg James Andrew Broun-Ramsay, 1st Marquess of Dalhousie. Dalhousie was made Governor-General of India in 1848. He served until 1856.
- Dalhousie developed a plan to build railway lines to connect the main regions of India as well as build a telegraph communication system.
- Dalhousie encouraged a national postal service and the development of schools, roads and irrigation.
- Any other relevant factors.

4. The candidate makes a judgment on how far **Source E** illustrates the social and cultural impact of immigrants on Scotland, in terms of:

Points from the source which show the candidate has interpreted the significant views:

- The Italians in Scotland quickly became committed to the catering trade and brought new consumer delights to the working class – ice-cream parlours and fish and chip shops.
- They were a huge attraction for young people who wanted somewhere to meet, support from temperance groups.
- These cafes attracted support from temperance groups who saw the ice cream parlours as a real and attractive alternative to the alcoholic temptations of the public house.
- Limited assimilation or integration with native Scots – most worked in family run businesses, kept close ties with their homeland, hoped to return there some day and marriages were kept within the Italian family network.

Points from recall which support and develop those in the source:

- Italian families contributed to the growing leisure industry. In 1903 there were 89 cafés in Glasgow, growing to 336 by 1905.
- Italian families settled in many towns on the coast and in the main towns. The Nardini family developed what was to become the largest café in Britain.
- Small sea side towns also had their own Italian cafés.
- Not only cafés – In the late 1920s the College of Italian Hairdressers was set up in Glasgow.

Points from recall which offer a wider contextualisation such as:

- Jews settled in central Glasgow, typically setting up small businesses.
- Cigarette making was a common job for the Jewish immigrants to Scotland.
- Jewish tailors helped produce affordable, quality clothing.
- Lithuanian immigrants were largely employed in the coal industry.
- Lithuanians were much fewer in numbers than Irish immigrants and not perceived as a threat to Scottish way of life by native Scots.
- Most Lithuanians returned to Eastern Europe during First World War.
- The immigrant Irish had a positive economic effect on Scotland.
- Irish labourers were prepared to tackle the hardest of jobs.
- The immigrant Irish contributed to the building of roads, canals and railways across Scotland.
- Impact of Irish reflected in existence of separate Catholic schools across most major urban centres in Scotland.
- Effect of migration on Scottish sporting life – Edinburgh Hibernian was founded in 1875 by Irishmen living in the Cowgate area of Edinburgh. Glasgow Celtic was founded in 1887 by Brother Walfrid, a Catholic priest. a Catholic team in Dundee called Dundee Harp also existed for a short time.
- Dundee United was founded in 1909 and was originally called Dundee Hibernian.
- Existence of Protestant Orange Lodge order.
- Irish immigrants and their descendants were important in the Scottish Trade Union movement and the development of the Labour Party in Scotland.
- By the 1890s, both Catholic and Protestant Irish were gaining apprenticeships and beginning to move up the social ladder.
- The Irish community produced important political leaders like John Wheatley and James Connolly.
- Any other relevant factors.

SPECIAL TOPIC 5: SCOTLAND AND THE IMPACT OF THE GREAT WAR, 1914-1928

1. The candidate makes a judgement on how fully **Source A** describes the involvement of Scots on the Western Front in terms of:

Points from the source which show the candidate has interpreted the significant views:

- His unit was relieved, after holding their own against German counter-attack but their replacements lost one of the trenches that they had taken.
- They got the trench back before coming out of the trenches with only about 70 or 80 men surviving, out of the 1100 original.
- Sir John French came along just as they were leaving their old billets and praised their efforts.
- French explained that he chose Cameron highlanders as his bodyguard as they never gave up.

Points from recall which support and develop those in the source:

- Detail on Queens Own Cameron Highlanders – recruitment drive led by Colonel D W Cameron of Lochiel. Camerons' involvement at Loos, the Somme and Arras.
- Development of detail regarding trench warfare – attacks followed by enemy counter attacks, gain and loss of trenches with limited movement of trench lines.
- Detail on the battle of Loos which saw the 'blooding' of Kitchener's New Army divisions including Scots.
- Scots units involved in the Loos and Somme offensives with high casualty rates.
- Scots units tended to be seen as 'shock' impact attack formations.
- Controversy regarding role of Commander –in – Chief, Sir John French, known to care about the welfare of his troops and failure to co-operate with the French.
- Sir John French replaced by Haig, December 1915.
- Role of Haig at Loos – 'unfavourable ground', use of gas, problem with reserves.
- Detail on losses at Loos – 20,598 names on the memorial at Loos – one third are Scottish.

Points from recall which offer a wider contextualisation such as:

- Details relating to recruitment – volunteering to go to the front.
- Scots in action – 'shock' troops – 'ladies from hell'.
- Conditions facing the Scots.
- 3 Scottish divisions 9th, 15th [Scottish] and 51st [Highland] took part in the Battle of the Somme, as well as numerous Scottish battalions in other units.
- Scottish losses at the Somme – 16th (McCrae's Battalion) Royal Scots lost 12 officers and 573 soldiers, 51st Highland Division suffered 3,500 casualties.
- Somme success – the 51st [Highland] Division launched a successful attack at Beaumont Hamel with relatively few casualties in November 1918.
- Role of Haig at the Somme.
- Attitude of the survivors: losses were replaced and the Scottish units carried on though grousing and criticisms became more common.
- Scots involvement at Arras.
- Any other relevant points.

2. The candidate makes a judgement on the extent to which **Sources B** and **C** agree about recruitment and conscription in Scotland, in terms of:

Overall: **Source B** and **Source C** agree that Scots volunteered in great numbers at the outbreak of war and that recruitment fell as the war progressed. Both also agree that the National Registration Act did not work. **Source B** however shows newspaper support for the introduction of conscription whilst **Source C** mentions the anti-conscription rallies taking place in 1915.

Developed through detail:

Source B	*Source C*
• Scots responded in great numbers... indeed by December 1914 25% of the labour force of Western Scotland had signed up.	• 20,000 recruits in Edinburgh by end of August and in Glasgow over the first weekend of the war six thousand men enlisted.
• It was being reported throughout the press from as early as October that the numbers enlisting were falling slightly.	• The number of volunteers began to fall off in 1915.

Source B (continued)

- The *Glasgow Herald* reported in December 1914 that if voluntarism did not work then conscription was the only alternative. The Daily Record ran similar articles promoting support for conscription.

- Despite the National Registration Act recruitment levels fell to around 80,000 per month by January 1916 and conscription became a reality.

Source C (continued)

- There were increasing concerns that compulsory military service would be introduced and anti-conscription rallies had been held in Glasgow since the end of 1915, one meeting being addressed by committed anti-war protesters Sylvia Pankhurst and John MacLean.

- The national registration scheme proved to be cumbersome and unworkable and recruitment continued to fall.

3. The candidate makes a judgement on how useful **Source D** is as evidence of the economic difficulties faced by Scotland in terms of:

Points from the source which shows the candidate has interpreted the significant views:
Origin:

- Contemporary source from accounts by the men who worked on the fishing fleets and the women whose job it was to gut the herring the fishermen caught.

Possible purpose:

- To explain the adverse changes the war brought to the fishing industry.

Content

- Price of a barrel of herring had been the same throughout the war but, after an initial rise at the end of the war it began to go down.
- Fuel, gear and wage costs had risen so much that the fishermen could not pay the gutters so they went on strike.
- Those involved in the fishing industry including fish merchants had lost markets in Germany and Russia during the war.

Points from recall developing those in the source:

- The collapse of foreign markets for herring greatly affected the industry - European countries started to compete strongly with Scottish fleets and in 1920 the government removed the guaranteed price for the herring. The price of herring dropped dramatically; it was no longer profitable; and for twenty years the industry went into a steep decline.

Points from recall relating to other industries:

- **Agriculture** – competition came after the war from cheap foreign imports of food like refrigerated meat from Argentina, frozen lamb and tinned fruit from Australia and New Zealand.
- **Jute** – During the war Dundee's jute industry boomed as demand for sack cloth rose but after the war the industry faced direct competition from Calcutta in world markets. Price of goods collapsed resulting in mass unemployment, deep social misery and discontent especially in Dundee and several firms went into liquidation.
- **Iron and Steel** – Demand for iron decreased during the war years. Demand for steel increased during the war as it was needed for the shipbuilding industry. But other countries increased their steel making during the war years and Scots manufacturers could not compete. As a result the iron and steel industries were severely affected by the downturn in demand from 1921 onwards.

- **Shipbuilding** – the immediate impact of war on Clydeside shipyards was very positive and profits were good. However, after the war a return to competitive tendering alongwith the decline in the demand for steel and for ships, foreign competition, labour disputes and a shortage of manpower and materials all led to problems and shipbuilding went into decline.
- Any other relevant points.

4. The candidate makes a judgement on how far **Source E** explains the strength of support for Unionism in Scotland in terms of:

Points from the source which show the candidate has interpreted the significant views:
- Both the Glasgow Herald and the Scotsman were Unionist and many local newspapers had also abandoned Liberalism.
- The Unionists considered giving financial support to local newspapers to bolster the party's message.
- There was a rightward shift of Presbyterian leadership in the 1920s favourable to the Conservatives.
- The enfranchisement of women has also been seen as favourable to the Unionists/ Conservatives as the women enfranchised in 1918 were older, over thirty, and reasonably well off.

Points from recall which support and develop those in the source:
- Mainstream popular newspapers all strongly pro-union. Examples of Glasgow Bulletin, launched in 1915 and Sunday Post, begun in 1914.
- Examples of local Liberal newspapers in places like Dundee and Aberdeen being taken over by their Unionist rivals.
- Protestantism played an important part in the party's working-class appeal projected through the endorsement and promotion of well-known Church of Scotland members.
- Presbyterian churches attacked the 'Irish menace' and, since the bulk of Irish Catholics were Labour Party voters, the political impact was to encourage support for Unionism.
- Female friendly in terms of candidates and elected MPs. First Scottish female MP was the Duchess of Atholl, a Tory.

Points from recall which offer a wider contextualisation such as:
- There was desire for social changes after the horrors of the war but also a sense that the suffering was UK wide, not unique to Scotland so no great desire to break the union.
- Support for conservatives/Scottish Unionists was high particularly amongst the middle classes who saw their future as being part of union. The Independent Labour Party was seen as a threat to the middle classes resulting in the Scottish Unionists achieving a majority of Scottish seats in 1924.
- The Scottish unionist/conservative party built up its working class support by emphasising the connection between the Union, the Empire, and the fate of local industry.
- The party's promise of 'unity across the classes' was promoted as a reason to support Unionism.
- The Conservatives were one of the big political winners from the war. Conservative/Scottish unionist message of patriotism and the return to pre-war certainties was just the message that the electorate wanted to hear; the war had been 'worth it', but now life could get back to 'normal'.
- Instances of radicalism after the war (eg events of January 1919 George Square) led to some fears that the union would be forcibly broken up. Conservative party seen as the barrier to this and the more reliable party in resisting the socialist threat.
- There were fears of 'Bolshevism' in Scotland fuelled by increase in communism eg McLean and others. The Scottish unionists/conservatives were seen as the barrier against the 'red menace' which threatened the 'British' way of life.

- The war years showed that support for Scottish Home Rule continued but post war patriotic support for UK union left little room for nationalist sympathies or support.
- The war undermined Scottish Liberalism. The Liberals were the big losers from the war. Though many had opposed the war in 1914 however as the party of government they had taken the decision to go to war and faced blame for the handling of it.
- Economic troubles in 1920s saw Scotland suffering more than many parts of England due to her reliance on old industries. Despair and hopelessness as the economy crashed in 1920 following the collapse of the short-term restocking boom and employment insecurity in the cities – periodic slumps due to the trade cycle. But this did not lead to desire to break the union.
- Scottish legal system also had strong links with the Conservatives.
- Scottish Unionist Party was well organised and resourced across Scottish constituencies.
- Any other relevant points.

HIGHER HISTORY PAPER 1
2014

1. Each question is marked out of 20.

2. In Paper 1 candidates will be rewarded according to:

(a) **Knowledge and Understanding – 6 marks are allocated for** the relevant knowledge they use to address the question. Marks will be awarded for each accurate, full point they make; these points may be further developed, as in the following example, relating to the effectiveness of the Liberal Reforms:

Old age pensions (*0 marks for stating this*) **were given to all people over 70** (*1 mark*)**; married couples received 7/6 and single people 5s** (*a second mark for knowledge*)**. This provision was not enough to live on, but old people were able to help pay their families if they lived with them** (*no further mark for knowledge, but an argument which would receive credit under the category Argument and Evaluation*)**.

(b) **Argument/Evaluation – 10 marks are allocated for** the quality of thought revealed in their answers by the arguments and evaluation demonstrated. This should be taken as including the extent to which the candidate:

- gives an answer which is relevant to the question and relates explicitly to the question's terms;
- argues a case;
- makes the various distinctions required by the question;
- responds to all the elements in the question, and to any isolated factor in particular;
- explains, analyses, debates and assesses rather than simply describes or narrates;
- answers with clarity and fluency and in language appropriate to historical writing at this level.

(c) **Structure – 4 marks are allocated for** the appropriateness of the organisation of the answer, according to the degree to which the response

- establishes the context of the question and the relevant factors to be considered in the introduction
- responds to the question in the form of a balanced conclusion based on the evidence and arguments deployed.

3. The following descriptions provide additional guidance on the marks awarded to essays displaying various characteristics. Many essays will exhibit some, but not all, of the features listed; others will be stronger in one area than another.

KNOWLEDGE – Up to 6 marks can be awarded if:
These are for substantive points and points further developed which are relevant and accurate.

STRUCTURE – Up to 4 marks can be awarded if:
The introduction clearly sets the issue in its wider context, indicates relevant factors and demonstrates a solid line of argument.
The conclusion is balanced, summarising the arguments and coming to an overall judgement directly related to the question.

ARGUMENT – Up to 10 marks can be awarded if:
The evidence is integrated into a sustained analysis.
The argument is sustained and balanced, with some awareness of alternative interpretations and/or historical debate.

HISTORICAL STUDY: BRITISH HISTORY

Church, State and Feudal Society

1. The candidate assesses the validity of the view that the landed class was the most important feature of feudal society. Using evidence and arguments such as:

The role of the landed classes

- Barons and other powerful magnates received land from the feudal overlords. These lands offered rights and privileges that in turn led to wealth and a comfortable lifestyle.
- These privileges usually gave the barons judicial control and the right to bear arms, build castles and hold tournaments. This often supplemented their income.
- Barons enjoyed a relatively leisured life, with pastimes such as hunting and hawking.
- The main drawback for the landed classes was the requirement to provide military service. This was occasionally dangerous, even fatal. Many circumvented this by providing substitutes or making excuses for non-appearance.

The role of the peasant classes

- Peasants played an important part of feudal society, beyond the need for a productive class working in agriculture. It was expected that peasants would run their own day-to-day lives without the need for the feudal lord's presence. Local reeves and bailiffs, appointed by the peasants or the lord himself, would act in his stead.
- Villeins had to organise themselves through the local manor court. The court dealt with sharing the land, fined those that broke the rules, and even brought murderers to trial.
- The feudal term of villein or serf indicated a peasant who was not free to leave his home farm or village. They were bought and sold along with the land and were expected to work at least 3 days a week in the lord's lands without recompense and hand over the best of their produce in exchange for the rent of their farmland.
- Peasants, or villeins, tended to work hard, mostly in the agricultural sector. All the work had to be done by hand and this resulted in long hours of backbreaking work.
- Improvements in agricultural equipment and the use of ploughs drawn by horses instead of oxen sped up the work and reduced the hours required in the field.
- While work was hard the manor court ensured that everyone had a fair share of the good land to grow their crops. During bad times there were systems in place to share out food so that no one in the village went hungry
- Not all peasants received the same amount of good farming land, and often it was the case that land was rotated amongst the peasants. This dissuaded them from attempts to improve the land; many did not put in the extra effort when next year their neighbour would reap the benefit.
- Accommodation was often very poor, especially for the lower strata of peasant society. Many peasants lived in poorly constructed one-bedroom dwellings, which they shared with their animals. A single hearth provided all the heat, lighting and cooking facilities.
- Firewood was at a premium; peasants were forced to pay a penny to their lord for the right to pick up fallen wood for the fires.
- Food was basic and, in times of famine, starvation was a real threat. As the 12th century progressed famine became rare in England, since the manor system pulled in isolated communities and helped create more viable villages throughout the kingdom.
- Archaeological evidence points to homes occupied by small nuclear families, some with upper rooms that indicate a level of privacy previously thought impossible. Evidence of

leisure activities included cards, chess pieces, musical instruments and even football.

Social divisions

- Social stratification was relatively rigid, though it was possible for landowners to rise through the ranks of the nobility, through ability or exceptional service.
- Some peasants famously left behind their humble beginnings, proving that social mobility was possible in the 13th and 14th centuries. William of Wykeham became bishop of Winchester but such rises outside the church were rare.

The changing role of knights – the development of chivalry

- The medieval knightly class was adept at the art of war, trained in fighting in armour, with horses, lances, swords and shields. Knights were taught to excel in the arms, to show courage, to be gallant and loyal. As time went by, the idea developed that they had a duty to protect the weaker members of society and women in particular. This ideal did not always extend beyond their own class.
- Christianity had a modifying influence on the classical concept of heroism and virtue. The Truce of God in the 10th century was one such example, with limits placed on knights to protect and honour the weaker members of society and also help the church maintain peace. At the same time the church became more tolerant of war in the defence of faith, espousing theories of the just war.

Any other relevant factors.

2. The candidate assesses the extent to which the power of the Church declined by the end of the fourteenth century, using evidence and arguments such as:

Evidence of decline of Papal power/successes for monarchs

Background: The Great Schism

- Europe became divided between the two popes; allegiance divided along political lines, and local clergy followed the lead of their kings. Scotland and England supported different popes.
- The entire affair tarnished the reputation of the Papacy. People now condemned the political manoeuvring of the cardinals and the popes. Local bishops now looked to the secular kings of their area, rather than the Papacy, for guidance.
- While at Avignon the Papacy appeared to be more powerful than ever, but it was also seen as the tool of the French monarchy. The growing concern of the church in worldly matters, the increased taxation and pressure on kings meant that many questioned the autocratic nature of the Papacy and the Church.

The Investiture Contest

- Henry I had many disputes with Archbishop Anselm of Canterbury over the choice of different bishops in his realm. Henry II argued with Becket over the trials of criminal clerics and the proper position of the Church within England.
- William the Lion had the same issue when he tried to have his candidate for Bishop of St Andrews replace the Pope's choice. King David I used the monasteries to support his leadership and bring areas of the countryside under his law.
- In practice the king's hold over the English or Scottish Churches tended to remain unbroken. Even after the murder of Becket, Henry retained the right to appoint bishops. The Scottish Church remained free of control from the Archbishop of York thanks to the Papal Bull of 1192.
- Kings allowed the taxation of the Church by the Papacy, but in England the royal government appointed most of the collectors and they kept the majority of the proceeds.

- The effects of excommunication and interdict were blunted through overuse. The Scottish Church never carried out the excommunication of Robert Bruce, and the years of interdict in England seemed to have had little obvious impact.

Other factors

- Long term abuses by the clergy, heavy taxation and the lavish lifestyles of the higher clergy and the papal court increasingly brought the Papacy into disrepute. Monarchs could use this to challenge the Papacy.
- The political struggles of the Papal Court to hold onto their Italian provinces, even open warfare in the Italian peninsula with the Holy Roman Emperor, further weakened the moral authority of the Papacy

Evidence of successes for the Church/restriction of monarchical power

- The simple fact that it was the Church that crowned the kings led to the idea that the king was dependent on God for his role, and thus in a way subservient to the Church. Popes could apply religious sanctions against kings, through excommunication and interdicts. This was often used to bring political pressure against an opponent, as seen during the reign of King John in England and Robert Bruce in Scotland. The threat of such political powers was one way in which the Church could enforce its will during the battle between itself and the state.
- The Church's importance within the feudal structure remained. Kings needed the literacy and numeracy skills of the clergy in order to help administer their realms; therefore the clergy could hold high office in government.
- The wealth of the Church came mostly from large grants of land by nobles and especially kings. Thus the Church became an integral part of the feudal structure, holding lands in both Scotland and England and being subject to military duties. The Regular Church was also politically important.
- The development of canon law, along with papal lawyers, helped to focus the arguments for papal authority. Christ was 'Lord of the World', and the Pope as his vicar was the dispenser of his power. Thus he passed that power to the kings when the Church crowned them. The improving education of the population of Europe helped the Church to train their priests in canon law and develop a Christendom-wide structure.

Any other relevant factors

3. The candidate evaluates the importance of the need to develop the economy in David I's and Henry II's attempts to centralise royal power in Scotland and England, using arguments such as:

The effects of foreign influence

- David I spent considerable time in the English court and saw the benefits of the feudal system for increasing the power and authority of the monarchy. His introduction of feudalism allowed him to increase the number of loyal barons and create a new feudal court.

The need to develop the economy

- In England the issue of revenue became apparent during the civil war between Stephen and Matilda.
- Sheriffs had become increasingly lax in paying their taxes. Sheriffs kept the taxes collected in their region for themselves, or only a small amount found its way into the royal treasury.
- Prior to David I, revenue in Scotland was mostly limited to the incomes from royal demesnes.
- The lack of royal burghs limited international trade and early medieval Scottish kings lacked the financial resources to tackle the Mormaers directly without the Community of the Realm backing them.

Other factors

Law and order

- When Henry came to power England had suffered from a lack of central control during the civil war period. It was necessary to restore law and order, and a strong monarch was required to restore royal power
- When David came to power in Scotland he introduced knights who were loyal to him. He faced considerable opposition within the Scottish kingdom. He was now able to rely upon a feudal host that was, in theory at least, loyal to him and able to exercise royal control/law and order
- Throughout England and Scotland the justice system was liable to change depending on which lord held sway over that part of the land. Money often bought justice and archaic trial by ordeal or combat was still common.
- Royal justice was usually reserved for more serious crimes. Issues of land, an important aspect of justice, were often poorly judged or unfairly settled.

The growth of the nobility

- In both England and Scotland the power of the monarchies was threatened by the growth in power of the nobility.
- During the time of the civil war in England the barons had increased in stature and political importance due to both sides vying for their support. As a result barons built castles without royal permission, increased the numbers of knights beyond limits agreed by their charters, acquired land illegally and many hired large armies of Flemish mercenaries.
- The Mormaers in Scotland were semi-independent and held almost autonomous power over large parts of Scotland. The Earls of Moray had a long tradition of independence, even going so far as to usurp the crown during the reign of Macbeth. The common army of Scotland was summoned by the Mormaers not the king, and was directly under their control.

The cost of warfare

- Throughout the 12th Century kings were finding it increasingly more expensive to raise the costs to build castles or raise feudal armies.
- Constant warfare during the period of civil war in England drained the treasury.

Any other relevant factors

The Century of Revolutions 1603 -1702

4. The candidate evaluates the significance of economic issues within a wider context of factors causing the challenge to the authority of James I in England, using evidence and arguments such as:

Economic issues

- James had been accustomed to having financial power in Scotland, and wanted to exist equally independently of the English Parliament in order to avoid owing them favours in return for money granted. He re-imposed anachronistic laws, drawn from meticulous searching through the statute books, which could raise revenue for him in unpopular but legal ways. Devices such as monopolies and wardships were used, and having angered MPs with these, he proceeded to offend the aristocracy by selling honours and titles to the 'nouveau riche', thereby devaluing seats in the House of Lords.
- The English Parliament openly defied the king's economic policy by declaring his increases in customs duties to be illegal in 1611, despite James's victory in the courts the year before to have them declared legal.

Other factors

The difficulties of ruling both countries

- The practicalities of ruling both Scotland and England were a problem to James, which led him to suggest a closer union. He claimed he felt like an animal with two heads.
- As a Scot, James faced prejudice from some English people, exacerbated by the retinue he brought south with him.
- By the time he left for London, Scotland was more peaceful than it had been for a long time; James even boasted he could rule it "with his pen", whereas his predecessors had had to rule it with the sword.

The Divine Right of Kings

- Divine Right was a notion repulsive to the English Parliament, yet James attempted to assert this as a traditional Stuart belief as he had been trying to do in Scotland. Those in the House of Commons opposed this, many seeing Divine Right as a Scottish concept which made James an unsuitable monarch for England. This belief was James' riposte to attempts by the Presbyterian Church to assert its independence of the crown.

Political issues

- The difference between the relationships King James had with the English Parliament and the one he had with the Scottish Parliament created difficulties. The Scots Parliament had not been encouraged to formulate policy and James antagonised English MPs so accustomed by refuting their right to do so.
- The king's defeat in the Goodwin Case gave the English Parliament a sense that they could continue to challenge him over many issues. In response, the king's imprisonment of outspoken MPs was his attempt to devalue the freedom of speech traditionally given to English MPs.

Religious issues

- James had grown up developing an antipathy towards Presbyterianism, feeling that the power of the bishops underlined his own position as head of the church. Puritanism was growing in England and demands for church reform south of the border were growing. The king sensed that religious change was a popular policy with many MPs, and took a stance against this at the Hampton Court Conference of 1604, during which the only concession he made to Puritans was the publication of an English translation of the Bible.
- James had supported the maintenance of an Episcopalian church in Scotland and was determined to do likewise in England.
- He infuriated English MPs further by relaxing the Recusancy Laws, which led many to charge him with favouritism towards Catholicism, particularly against the background of the Gunpowder Plot of 1605.
- The English Parliament was horrified that the king allowed Prince Charles to marry a Roman Catholic French princess.

Any other relevant factors

5. The candidate evaluates the importance of political issues as a cause of the English Civil War within a wide context of factors, using evidence and arguments such as:

Political issues

- Charles I offended Parliament with his belief in Divine Right. He curtailed Parliamentary freedom of speech. Parliament forced the king to sign the Petition of Right in 1628 but, although this reduced the king's powers, in 1629 Charles I dissolved Parliament because it criticised his levying of tonnage and poundage. Between 1629 and 1640 he ruled without Parliament in what became known as the Eleven Years' Tyranny. Archbishop Laud and Thomas

Wentworth, the Earl of Stafford, encouraged Charles I during this period to become more absolute.

- Charles I abused the Court of Star Chamber, using it as an instrument for enforcing royal policy, which caused Parliamentary resentment. The king authorised Laud's use of the Court of High Commission to persecute Puritans opposing his religious policies. Wentworth was the king's chief minister who used the Council of the North to enforce his ruthless 'thorough' policies, putting down rebellions and influencing the justice system. In 1633 Wentworth was made Lord Deputy of Ireland. There he generated more money for the Crown and made the Irish subservient to the king.

Other factors

Legacy of James VII/I

- James had antagonised MPs between 1603 and 1625 with his own attempts to exist financially independent of Parliament, his assertion of Divine Right and curtailing of freedom of speech, his rejection of Puritan demands for church reform, his relaxed approach to Roman Catholicism, and his abuse of the justice system.

The character of Charles I

- Charles was vain, stubborn and loyal to subordinates (up till a crisis). He abandoned Laud and particularly Stafford, his strongest supporter. His attempt to rule without Parliament suggests that he was not given to compromise.

Religious issues

- The Archbishop of Canterbury, William Laud, Charles I's appointment, wanted to stamp out Puritanism and enforce the authority and discipline of the Church. Laud's High Church policies were detested by all Puritans, including many MPs. Charles I authorised Laud's punishment of Puritan preachers in the Court of High Commission and censorship of printed criticism of the High Church. 20,000 Puritans fled England to America in 10 years.
- In 1637 Laud imposed the Prayer Book in Scotland, causing thousands to sign the National Covenant pledging to defend Presbyterianism. Charles I allowed his queen, Henrietta Maria, to celebrate Mass publicly at court which infuriated Puritans in Parliament.

Economic/financial issues

- Charles I resorted to anachronistic methods of raising revenue, such as forced loans, forest laws and the distraint of knighthood, which provoked outrage amongst MPs. Parliament only voted to grant tonnage and poundage to Charles I for one year, but he raised it without Parliament's consent for several years. The king used the Court of Star Chamber to impose heavy fines on those accused of committing crimes against royal policy. The king sold monopolies to companies rather than individuals. In 1634 Charles I imposed Ship Money on coastal towns and in 1635 extended the tax inland. Parliament opposed this, as there was no guarantee that it would always be used for ship-building.

The impact of events in Scotland and Ireland

- In Ireland the threat of a Catholic rebellion alarmed many English MPs who feared that, if successful, Catholic troops from Ireland would be used to quell unrest in England.
- The Bishops' Wars with Scotland triggered a financial crisis for the monarchy and handed the initiative to Parliament. Charles was not willing to concede their demands in 1642 and this was the spark that led to civil war in England.

Charles' actions after 1640

- Charles entry into the Commons to arrest Puritan MPs was a disaster. As well as failing to catch them, it convinced Parliament that conflict was inevitable.

- The king left for the north, joined by two-thirds of the Lords and one-third of the Commons: by leaving the capital, he conceded his loss of authority and may have actually encouraged Parliament to raise the stakes.

The actions of Parliament after 1640

- MPs took advantage of the request of Charles I for the funding of the Bishops' Wars and demanded the abolition of prerogative courts and Ship Money. The House of Commons introduced the Triennial Act and demanded the impeachment of Wentworth and Laud. Throughout 1640 and 1641 Puritan MPs and the High Church were in bitter dispute over proposed reforms of the Church of England.
- By March 1642 Parliament had formed an army to which the king responded by raising his standard at Nottingham.

Any other relevant factors

6. The candidate evaluates the validity of the view that Cromwell's dominance was the main reason for the failure to find an alternative form of government, 1649-1658, using evidence and arguments such as:

Cromwell's dominance

- Cromwell dominated politics and was in a unique position to influence the direction of the country. However, he was a contrary character, who espoused democratic principles but acted in a dictatorial manner, as he knew an elected government would contain his enemies and could lead to independence for Scotland and Ireland. His roots were in Parliament but his rise to the rank of general during the Civil War meant that he favoured the military during the Interregnum.
- He was naturally conservative, but many of his policies were ahead of their time, such as relief for the poor and the insane during the Barebones Parliament. Cromwell was a Puritan but passed progressive reforms, such as civil marriages, which horrified many.
- He was heavily preoccupied with foreign matters early on in the Interregnum, relied heavily on the Army, ignored Parliamentary concerns and suffered from the absence of a monarch to act as a check on his actions such as passing unpopular legislation.

Other factors

Legacy of Civil War

- The Civil War was deeply divisive of society, and caused lasting bitterness, as well as causing high casualties and destruction of property. Royalist exiles intrigued for a return to power, while parliament's supporters feared plots everywhere. This engendered an atmosphere of suspicion and mistrust which intensified tension and made compromise more difficult.
- All of the pre-Civil War problems such as religious, political, legal and economic issues, plus additional foreign policy issues, meant that Cromwell was always going to encounter difficulties.

The effects of execution of the king

- After the execution of Charles I in 1649, the Council of State abolished the monarchy and declared a Republic, or Commonwealth. Previously problems could be tackled by monarch and Parliament. However, now there was no check on Parliamentary power.
- Royalists accused Cromwell of regicide and refused to acknowledge his authority.
- In Scotland, Charles II was crowned king and some of his supporters wanted him to ascend the throne in England also. Without a king, Cromwell ruled on his own for two different periods during the Interregnum, drawing comparisons with Charles I's eleven year tyranny.

The role of the Army

- Army extremists pushed for greater martial authority.
- Army officers formed the Council of State with the Rump Parliament. Extremists in the army opposed too great an involvement of Parliament in governing the country.
- The creation of a military dictatorship from 1653 drew comparisons with the Stuart monarchs' martial law, as did the formation of the first Protectorate in September 1654 and the drawing up of military districts under the governance of major-generals during the second Protectorate from October 1656.
- Parliamentarians resented the influence of the Army on constitutional affairs throughout the Interregnum.

The role of Parliament

- The Rump Parliament consisted of MPs who had failed to avert Civil War in 1642 and who now had to address the same problems in 1649. Puritans amongst them were keen on church reform and viewed this as their priority. Parliament was opposed to the role of the Army, and wanted to have a greater say in drawing up the constitution.
- Quarrels between MPs and army officers were a feature of the Interregnum. Parliament stood in the way of toleration and thus prevented religious wounds healing.

Unpopular legislation

- The Treason Law and Censorship Law were introduced in 1649. In 1650 the Oath of Allegiance was imposed for all men over 18. He abolished the High Court in 1654 which caused a backlog of 23,000 cases.
- The Barebones Parliament consisted of many well-intentioned but inexperienced figures who proved incapable of using power effectively; it was accused of introducing too many reforms in too short a space of time. The constitution was drawn up solely by army officers which drew further criticism. Roman Catholics and Anglicans were excluded from voting by the First Protectorate, which also introduced strict Moral Codes that curtailed popular forms of entertainment and enforced the Sabbath.
- The Commission of Triers and Committee of Ejectors, who oversaw the appointment of clergymen and schoolmasters, proved unpopular with the church.
- A 10% land tax was resented by the aristocracy. Taxation in general increased to fund wars with Spain.
- Cromwell's approval of his son Richard as his successor led many to feel that Cromwell viewed himself as a monarchical figure.

Foreign policy

- Faced with possible invasion, Cromwell was forced to fight several battles to control Scotland.
- He had to put down rebellions in Ireland by Royalists and Catholics brutally, which caused further resentment and hostility.
- War was waged on Holland to enforce the Navigation Acts. In the mid-1650s war with Spain caused increased taxes.
- Distractions caused by foreign affairs may have led to social issues such as coal shortages in the winter of 1652-3 not being addressed appropriately and therefore increasing instability in England.

Any other relevant factors

The Atlantic Slave Trade

7. The candidate evaluates the significance of religious factors in the development of the slave trade, using evidence and arguments such as:

Religious factors

- The Church of England had links to slavery through the United Society for the Propagation of the Gospel missionary organisations which had plantations and owned slaves. The Church of England supported the laws not to educate enslaved Africans. Some bible passages such as the Curse of Ham from Genesis were used to justify slavery. Other bible passages such as Exodus were banned in British colonies because they could be interpreted as being anti-slavery.
- Many believed that Africans benefited from slavery as they became 'Christian'. This would result in the spread of 'civilization'. This however did not necessarily mean that they would be treated as equals.
- Some clergy tried to push the idea that it was possible to be a 'good slave and a Christian' and pointed to St Paul's epistles, which called for slaves to 'obey their masters'.
- However very little missionary work actually took place during the early years. Religion got in the way of a moneymaking venture by taking Africans away from their work. It also taught them potentially subversive ideas and made it hard to justify the cruel mistreatment of fellow Christians.

Other factors

Racist attitudes

- The unequal relationship that was created as a consequence of the enslavement of Africans was justified by the ideology of racism – the mistaken belief that Africans were inferior to Europeans.
- Entrenched racism among members of the merchant and landowning classes meant that enslaving African captives was accepted by colonists.
- Many Europeans claimed that African captives would suffer if slave trade was abolished eg criminals and prisoners of war would be butchered and executed at home.
- Many colonists believed that slaves were fortunate to be provided with homes, protection and employment, in the care of enlightened Europeans rather than African despots.

The labour shortage

- Huge profits made from the trade in tropical crops created a demand for labour to work on plantations in the colonies. Crops such as sugar cane required a large labour force to plant, look after, harvest and process crop in harsh conditions. There was a high death rate among native populations due to lack of resistance to diseases brought by Europeans and ill-treatment at the hands of colonists created labour shortage in the West Indies.

The failure of alternative sources

- Few colonists were willing to work on plantations as manual labour. There was a limit to the number of British criminals who could be sent as forced labour. Some Britons, particularly Scots, sold themselves as indentured servants, but numbers were limited.

The legal position

- The legal status of slaves as property was long established. It took a series of court cases from the 1770s that dealt with the rights of former slaves within the British Isles to challenge the legality of slavery and the slave trade eg Granville Sharp's resolute campaign to prove the illegality of slavery in England that culminated in Lord Mansfield's decision in the Somerset case.

Military factors

- The Seven Years War was chiefly an imperial war fought between Britain, France and Spain and many of the most important battles of the Seven Years War were fought at sea to win control of valuable overseas colonies. Britain emerged from the war as the leading European imperial power, having made large territorial gains in North America and the Caribbean, as well as India. Slave labour was necessary to exploit these gains.

Importance of slave trade to British economy

- Financial, commercial, legal and insurance institutions emerged to support the activities of the slave traders. Slave traders became bankers and many new businesses were financed by profits made from slave trading.

Any other relevant factors

8. The candidate evaluates the validity of the view that financial considerations were the most important factor in the treatment of slaves, using evidence and arguments such as:

Financial considerations

- In essence, the slave trade and the institution of slavery were commercially based. Most participants entered the trade or owned or worked the plantations as a means of income. Financial considerations were usually paramount.
- The debate over 'loose' or 'tight' pack on board slave ships had little to do with humanitarianism. In loose pack, slaves were treated better and had better conditions, but the prime motivation was the transport of as many slaves as possible to the auctions in the West Indies, alive.
- To extract as much work from slaves as possible on the plantations, slaves were often beaten or worse.
- As slaves were property, bought and paid for, they were valuable. On the other hand, they were cheap enough to work, or beat, to death. This was known as 'wastage'.
- The British Caribbean islands were particularly cursed by a culture of absentee owners; estates were managed by overseers whose main interest was to amass profits in order to gain a foothold in the plantation economy.
- Owners and overseers were aware of the risks to their own health from a lengthy stay in the West Indies and often were concerned to make as much money as quickly as possible in order to return to Britain and enjoy their wealth.

Other factors

Religious concerns

- Slave traders/owners were able to point to the existence of slavery in the Bible, and use this as a justification for the institution.
- Traders/owners claimed that slaves were being exposed to Christianity. Enslavement was therefore good for them, as it gave them the chance of eternal salvation.
- Some participants were religious and moderated their treatment of slaves accordingly.

Humanitarian concerns

- Humanitarian concerns had little impact on the treatment of slaves in Africa or on the Middle Passage. Participants were not in daily close contact with slaves and did not get to know them personally.
- The West Indian plantations, on the other hand, were often small communities. Where members of the owner's family were present, bonds of affection grew between slaves and free. Where such personal ties did not exist, there was less moderation of the brutalities of slavery.

The fear of revolt

- Both on slave ships and plantations there was a constant fear of a slave revolt. On ships, security was paramount, as crews were heavily outnumbered by their cargoes. This meant that slaves were kept under decks for long periods. It also meant that they were usually shackled for the whole passage.
- On plantations, there was fear of slave resistance, both overt and otherwise. Draconian legal codes were enacted by island assemblies (dominated by planters) covering the treatment/punishment of runaways as well as those who resisted openly.

Racism and prejudice

- There was ignorance of African culture and achievements. Africans were regarded by some Europeans as almost another species. This was used as an excuse for extreme brutality.

Any other relevant factors

9. The candidate assesses the extent of the impact of the slave trade on West African Society, using evidence and arguments such as:

Development of slave based states and economies

- Africans could become slaves as punishment for a crime, as payment for a family debt, or most commonly of all, by being captured as prisoners of war. With the arrival of European and American ships offering trading goods in exchange for captives, Africans had an added incentive to enslave each other, often by abducting unfortunate victims.
- Some societies preyed on others to obtain captives in exchange for European firearms, in the belief that if they did not acquire firearms in this way to protect themselves, they would be attacked and captured by their rivals and enemies who did possess such weapons. This led to the growth of states such as Dahomey whose raison d'etre was the slave trade.

Destruction of society

- Rich and powerful Africans were able to demand a variety of consumer goods and in some places even gold for captives, who may have been acquired through warfare or by other means, initially without massive disruption to African societies.
- By the end of 17th century European demand for African captives, particularly for the sugar plantations in the Americas, became so great that they could only be acquired through initiating raiding and warfare; large areas of Africa were devastated and societies disintegrated.
- It is estimated that around 10 million people were transported from Africa over the eighteenth century. This was a huge drain on the most productive and economically active sections of the population and this led to economic dislocation and falls in production of food and other goods.

Slave sellers and European 'factories' on West African Coast

- Europeans seldom ventured inland to capture the millions of people who were transported from Africa as captives. In the areas where slavery was not practised, such as among the Xhosa people of southern Africa, European slave ship captains were unable to buy African captives.
- Development of European 'factories' on coast to control the slave trade.

Development of foreign colonies

- West Africa was impoverished by its relationship with Europe while the human and other resources that were taken from Africa contributed to the economic development and wealth of Europe and the European colonies in the New World. The transatlantic trade also created the conditions for the subsequent colonial conquest of Africa by the European powers.

Role played by African societies in continuing the trade

- African slave sellers grew wealthy by selling African captives to European traders on the coast. They were able to deal on equal terms with European traders who built 'factories' on the West African coast to house captives before selling them onto the slave ship captains who in turn transported the captives to the colonies of the New World.
- On the African side, the slave trade was generally the business of rulers or wealthy and powerful merchants, concerned with their own selfish or narrow interests, rather

than those of the continent. At that time, there was no concept of being African – identity and loyalty were based on kinship or membership of a specific kingdom or society, rather than to the African continent.
- States based on slavery, particularly Dahomey, grew in power and influence.

Any other relevant factors

Britain 1851-1951

10. The candidate evaluates the validity of the view that Britain became more democratic between 1851 and 1928 due to the effects of industrialisation and urbanisation, using evidence and arguments such as:

The effects of industrialisation and urbanisation
- Urbanisation and growing class identity within an industrial workforce and the spread of socialist ideas led to demands for greater voice for the working classes. Also the growth of the Labour party offered a greater choice.
- Demographic change, including rapid urbanisation, sparked demands for redistribution of seats.
- The growing economic power of middle class wealth-creators led to pressure for a greater political voice.
- Basic education, the development of new cheap, popular newspapers and the spread of railways helped to create an awareness of national issues.
- After 1860 the fear of the 'revolutionary mob' had declined. Skilled working men in cities were more educated and respectable. That was an argument for extending the vote in 1867.

Other factors

Changing political attitudes
- Political reform was no longer seen as a threat. In the USA and in Europe struggles were taking place for liberty and a greater political say for 'the people'. Britain tended to support these moves abroad, making it logical for this to happen in Britain too.
- The growing influence of the Liberal Party in challenging older vested interests. The Liberal Party opposed the power of the old land owning aristocracy eg the secret ballot to assist working class electorate to use their 'political voice' to promote social reforms.
- Politicians combined acceptance of changes which they suspected were unavoidable while ensuring that their own party political interests would be protected.
- The death of former PM Palmerston represented the changing tone of politics as the reactionary ideas of early 19th century gave way to new ideologies.
- The veto of the unelected chamber was removed partly as result of the 1910 elections fought on the issue of 'peers v people' and the financing of social reform to help the poor, especially in urban areas.

Party advantage
- In 1867 the Conservative Party became the government after 20 years out of power. To an extent the Reform Act could be seen as 'stealing the Liberal's clothes' to gain support.
- The Corrupt and Illegal Practices Act of 1883 limited the amount of spending on elections; the Liberals believed the advantage held by wealthier Conservative opponents would be reduced.
- By placing the reforms of 1883 and 1884 close to the next election, the Liberals hoped to gain advantage from grateful new voters in towns more fairly represented after the redistribution of seats.

Popular attempts to gain the franchise
- The 1867 Reform Act was passed amongst considerable popular agitations; before them the Reform League and Reform Union had been active.

Pressure groups
- The Suffragists and Suffragettes were influential in gaining the franchise for women.

The effects of the First World War
- The war necessitated more political change. Many men still had no vote but were conscripted to fight from 1916. As further reform for males was being considered, fears of a revival of the militant women's campaign, combined with a realisation of the importance of women's war work led to the Reform Act of 1918 which gave votes to more men and some women.

The effects of examples of developments abroad
- In a number of foreign countries there was a wider franchise than in Britain; in others women could also vote. Neither development had threatened the established social order.

Any other relevant factors

11. The candidate evaluates how significant the militant Suffragette campaign was in helping women achieve the vote, using evidence and arguments such as:

The militant Suffragette campaign up to 1914
- Emmeline Pankhurst formed the Women's Social and Political Union (WSPU) in 1903. WSPU adopted the motto 'Deeds Not Words'. The new strategy gained publicity with noisy heckling of politicians. Newspapers immediately took notice. The Suffragettes had achieved their first objective – publicity. Violent protest followed eg window smashing campaign and arson attacks aimed to provoke insurance company pressure on the Government. The prisons filled with Suffragettes.
- Women used starvation as a political weapon to embarrass the government. In response the government introduced the Prisoner's Temporary Discharge for Ill Health Act – the Cat and Mouse Act.
- The actions of the Suffragettes mobilised opinion for and against. It can be argued that were it not for the Suffragette campaign, the Liberal Government would not even have discussed women's suffrage before World War One. But for opponents the militant campaign provided an excellent example of why women could not be trusted with the vote.

Other factors

The part played by women in the war effort, 1914-18
- Britain declared war on Germany on 4 August 1914 and two days later the NUWSS suspended its political campaigning for the vote. Undoubtedly the sight of women 'doing their bit' for the war effort gained respect and balanced the negative publicity of the earlier Suffragette campaign. A WSPU pro-war propaganda campaign encouraged men to join the armed forces and women to demand 'the right to serve'.
- Women's war work was important to Britain's eventual victory. Over 700,000 women were employed making munitions.
- The creation of a wartime coalition also opened the door to change.
- The traditional explanation for the granting of the vote to some women in 1918 has been that women's valuable work for the war effort radically changed male ideas about their role in society and that the vote in 1918 was almost a 'thank you' for their efforts. But the women who were given the vote were 'respectable' ladies, 30 or over, not the younger women who worked long hours and risked their lives in munitions factories.

- Another argument about the 1918 act is that it only happened because politicians grew anxious to enfranchise more men who had fought in the war but lost their residency qualification to vote and women could be 'added on' to legislation that was happening anyway.
- The war acted more as a catalyst but the tide was flowing towards female franchise before it started.

The women's suffrage campaigns

- The NUWSS believed in moderate, 'peaceful' tactics to win the vote such as meetings, pamphlets, petitions and parliamentary bills. Membership remained relatively low at about 6,000 until around 1909 but grew to 53,000 by 1914 as women angered by the Suffragettes' campaign found a new home.

Changing attitudes to women in society

- The campaigns for women's suffrage could also be seen within the context of societies' changing attitudes towards women in the late 19th and early 20th centuries. For example, in the words of Martin Pugh, 'their participation in local government made women's exclusion from national elections increasingly untenable.' Millicent Fawcett, a leader of the NUWSS, had argued that wider social changes were vital factors in the winning of the right to vote.

The example of other countries

- Women were able to vote in other countries such as New Zealand, and in some American states.

Any other relevant factors

12. The candidate evaluates the importance of the fears over national security as a reason why the Liberal Government introduced social welfare reforms 1906-14, using evidence and arguments such as:

Fears over national security

- The government became alarmed when almost 25% of the volunteers to fight in the Boer War were rejected because they were physically unfit to serve in the armed forces. There was concern whether Britain could survive a war or protect its empire against a far stronger enemy in the future if the nation's 'fighting stock' of young men was so unhealthy.
- Link between national security concerns and national efficiency concerns; financial or economic security

Other factors

Concerns over poverty – the social surveys of Booth and Rowntree

- The reports of Charles Booth and Seebohm Rowntree demonstrated that poverty had causes such as low pay, unemployment, sickness and old age. These were largely out with the control of the individual.
- The extent of poverty revealed in the surveys was also a shock. Booth's initial survey was confined to the East End of London, but his later volumes covering the rest of London revealed that almost one third of the capital's population lived in poverty. York was a relatively prosperous small town but even there poverty was deep-seated.

Municipal socialism

- By the end of the century some Liberal-controlled local authorities had become involved in programmes of social welfare. The shocked reaction to the reports on poverty was a pressure for further reform.
- In Birmingham particularly, but in other large industrial cities, local authorities had taken the lead in providing social welfare schemes. These served as an example for further reforms.

Foreign examples

- Germany had introduced a much admired system of social security. This raised the issue whether Britain was no longer a major European nation.

National efficiency

- By the end of the 19th century Britain was facing serious competition from new industrial nations such as Germany. It was believed that if the health and educational standards of Britain's workers got worse then Britain's position as a strong industrial power would be threatened.

The rise of the New Liberalism

- New Liberals argued that state intervention was necessary to liberate people from social problems over which they had no control. New Liberal ideas were not important issues in the general election of 1905. Only when 'old liberal' Prime Minister Campbell Bannerman died in 1908 was the door opened for new 'interventionist' ideas.

Party advantage

- Since 1884 many more working class men had the vote and the Liberals had tended to attract many of those votes. Social reform was a means of appeasing this constituency.

The rise of Labour

- By 1906 the newly formed Labour Party was competing for the same votes. It can be argued that the reforms happened for the very selfish reason of retaining working class votes.

Any other relevant factors

Britain and Ireland 1900–1985

13. The candidate evaluates the importance of Unionist and Nationalist responses to the Home Rule Bill in increasing tension in Ireland up to 1914, using evidence such as:

Unionist and Nationalist responses to the Home Rule Bill

- The roles of Carson and Craig: Sir Edward Carson's theatrical political performances caught the public imagination and brought the case of the Unionists to the nation. At the signing of the Solemn League and Covenant in Belfast at Town Hall, to the world's press, 250,000 Ulstermen pledged themselves to use 'all means necessary' to defeat Home Rule.
- Setting up of the UVF.
- Curragh Mutiny: British officers stationed in Ireland declared they would not use force against the Unionists.
- The Irish Volunteer Force (IVF) was set up as a reaction. Members from the Gaelic League, the Gaelic Athletic Association, Sinn Fein and the IRB all joined hoping to use the IVF for their own purposes. By May 1914 it had 80,000 members.
- In 1913, a third private army was set up, the Irish Citizen Army, under the leadership of James Connolly, a socialist. It had two clear aims – to gain independence for Ireland and set up a socialist republic, for working class of all religions to join up with to improve their lives.

Other factors

The British Position over Ireland – the effects of the 1910 elections

- After 1910 the Liberals needed the help of the Irish Nationalists to run the country as they would not have a majority otherwise; they passed the third reform bill. In 1908 Campbell-Bannerman had been replaced as Prime Minister by Asquith, who in 1909 had declared that he was a supporter of Home Rule.
- With the support of John Redmond, leader of the Nationalists, a Bill was passed to reduce the power of the

House of Lords, which was dominated by Conservatives, from being able to block a Bill to only being able to hold up the passing of a Bill for two years. As a result the Home Rule Bill for Ireland, which was previously blocked by the House of Lords, could now be passed.

The Irish Cultural Revival and Re-emergence of Irish Republicanism
- In 1884 the Gaelic Athletic Association was set up 'for the preservation and cultivation of our national pastimes'. Games like Gaelic football and hurling became very popular. In 1883 the Gaelic League was also set up whose aim it was to revive, and preserve the Irish language and Gaelic literature.
- Sinn Fein (Ourselves Alone) was founded by Arthur Griffith in 1904 to boycott all things British and to press for the Irish to set up their own parliament in Ireland, which Griffith thought would cause the British Government to collapse. The IRB was revived with Thomas Clarke recruiting young men in Dublin for the movement. Both these groups wanted an Ireland separate from Britain and both willing to use force.

Redmond and Home Rule
- Redmond claimed that the Home Rule Bill would lead to greater unity and strength in the Union, ending suspicion and disaffection in Ireland, and between Britain and Ireland. It would show Britain was willing to treat Ireland equally, as part of the empire. Redmond's Party was consistently strong throughout southern Ireland, where there was strong support for Home Rule.

Distinctive economic and religious features of the Northern Counties
- Ulster was mainly Protestant and feared that a government led by Dublin would see the imposition of laws on Northern Ireland based on Catholic faith; this they were opposed to.
- Ulster people were worried they would lose the economic benefits they enjoyed from being part of the British Empire, such as the linen industry and the shipbuilding industry.

Any other relevant factors

14. The candidate evaluates the significance of IRA tactics and policies as an obstacle to peace in Ireland up to the Anglo-Irish Treaty using evidence such as:

IRA tactics and policies
- The IRA campaign used guerrilla tactics against a militarily stronger foe eg attacks on agencies of law and order, RIC, magistrates and police barracks, ambush, assassination, the disappearance of opponents, the sabotage of enemy communications and the intimidation of local communities into not supporting the British forces, attacks on British troops and G-men (detectives concentrating on IRA atrocities), the attempted assassination of Lord French (Viceroy). British forces found these increasingly frustrating to contend with, and this ramped up the violence and bitterness on both sides.

Other factors

The legacy of the First World War – 1918 election, and the growth of Sinn Fein
- The aftermath of the Easter Rising, and the anti-conscription campaign, led to a decline in support for the Nationalist Party and a huge growth in support for Sinn Fein (Sinn Fein membership reached 112,000). In the 1918 General Election Sinn Fein won 73 seats, compared to winning none in 1910, 34 were in prison, one had been deported, two were ill and seven were absent on Sinn Fein business, so there was only 25 present when they held their first public meeting in January 1919. This meant control of the nationalist movement

largely moved to the IRB and the IVF. With the support of the majority of the population, the IRA was prepared to wage an armed struggle against the British.

The Declaration of Independence and the establishment of the Dail
- Republicans led by Sinn Fein, who did not attend Westminster, met at the Mansion House in Dublin and declared themselves 'Dail Eireann'. De Valera was made the President of Ireland, Arthur Griffith Vice President and Michael Collins Minister of Finance. Most local councils in Ireland, except in Ulster, recognised the rule of this new assembly. By 1921 1,000 Sinn Fein law courts had been set up and Collins raised £350,000 as many people paid their taxes to the Minister of Finance, Collins, rather than the British Government.
- The Dail failed to meet very regularly but worked using couriers carrying communications between those in hiding. Law and order was maintained though, as the Dail relied on 'alternative' courts, presided over by a priest or lawyer and backed up by the IRA. This system won the support of the Irish communities as well as the established Irish legal system.
- The Dail had won the support of masses, the Catholic Church and professional classes in Ireland. The Dail wrested power away from Britain to a considerable extent due to military wing of the Dail.

The position of the Unionists in the North
- Ulster Unionists won an extra 10 seats and now had 26 seats in Westminster, making partition increasingly likely. Additionally, Unionists had made a huge blood sacrifice in the First World War (eg on the Somme) and naturally expected this to be reflected in any post-war settlement in Ireland.

The policies and actions of the British government
- The British aim between 1918 and 1921 was to reduce Ireland to obedience within the United Kingdom and in doing this relied increasingly on military force. The best houses in local areas were taken and used, with the occupants evicted, if the local police station had been burned or destroyed.
- RIC members were instructed to challenge civilians from ambush and shoot them if they did not obey the RIC officers. RIC officers were encouraged to shoot suspicious looking people, sometimes innocent people were killed. RIC officers were protected by their superiors.
- The Black and Tans were responsible for violence, theft, drunken rampages, attacks on villages such as the burning of Balbriggan, village creameries being burnt down and houses destroyed. In March 1919 the Lord Mayor of Cork was shot dead by RIC men. At Croke Park, where there was a Gaelic football match taking place, the Black and Tans fired in to the crowd, killing 12 people and injuring 60.
- The violence led to a drift to extremism, culminating in the sacking of Cork City by the Black and Tans.

Any other relevant factors

15. The candidate evaluates the validity of the view that the role played by de Valera meant that the Irish Civil War was inevitable, using evidence and arguments such as:

The role of De Valera
- De Valera refused to accept the terms of the treaty as they were in 'violent conflict with the wishes of the majority of the nation'.
- De Valera claimed that treaty meant partition of Ireland and abandonment of sovereignty.
- De Valera felt he should have been consulted before the treaty was signed.

- De Valera voted against the treaty and resigned as President, to be replaced by Griffith and Collins became Head of the Irish Free Government.
- The enmity which developed between the two deepened existing political divisions.

Other factors

The Anglo-Irish Treaty

- Ireland was to be the 'Irish Free State', governing itself, making its own laws but remaining in the Empire. A Governor General was to represent the king: Britain was to remove its forces but keep the use of its naval bases. Trade relations were settled. Lloyd George threatened the Irish delegation with war if they did not sign.

Partition

- Government of Ireland Act split Ireland in two, with six counties in the North and 26 in the South. In Northern Ireland, Unionists won 40 of the 52 seats available. A third of the Ulster population was Catholic and wanted to be united to the South.
- The 26 counties in the South had a separate parliament in Dublin. The Council of Ireland was set up. The IRA refused to recognise the new Parliament and kept up its violence. Sectarian violence increased in Ulster; without partition this could have been much worse. Ulster Special Constabulary, Special Powers Act, Local Government Emergency Powers Act.
- In the South, the Government of Ireland Act was ignored. Sinn Fein won 124 seats unopposed. Partition was a highly emotive issue, and it alone would have caused discord.

Dominion status

- Under this agreement Ireland became a Dominion of the British Empire, rather than being completely independent of Britain. Under Dominion status the new Irish State had three important things to adhere to:
  - the elected representatives of the people were to take an oath of allegiance to the British Crown
  - the Crown was to be represented by a Governor General; appeals in certain legal cases could be taken to the Privy Council in London.
  - this aspect of the treaty was repugnant to many Irish people, not just Republicans.

Divisions in the republican movement

- The treaty was hotly debated in the Dail. Collins and much of the IRA supported the treaty, as Ireland now had an elected government. De Valera opposed it and felt it should be resisted even if it meant Civil War. They represented the two wings of the Republican movement.
- Also influential were the widows and other relatives of those who had died; they were vocal in their opposition to the Treaty.
- The Treaty was particularly disappointing to left-wing republicans who had hopes of establishing a socialist republic.
- The treaty was accepted by 64 votes to 57 by the Dail Eireann on the 7th January, 1922.
- Collins and De Valera tried to reach a compromise to avoid war but none was reached. Some of the IRA units supported the treaty, whilst others opposed it. Some of the anti-treaty IRA took over some important buildings in Dublin eg Four Courts.
- This division, crystallised by the murder of Sir Henry Wilson (security adviser for the Northern Ireland Government), forced Michael Collins to call on the official IRA to suppress the 'Irregular IRA'.

The role of Collins

- Collins negotiated the treaty with Churchill, but was pressured to sign it under a threat of escalation of the conflict.
- He recognised that the war was unwinnable, both for the IRA and the UK government.
- Collins claimed Ireland had its own, elected government, so Britain was no longer the enemy.
- Collins defended the treaty as he claimed it gave Ireland 'freedom to achieve freedom'.

Any other relevant factors

HISTORICAL STUDY: EUROPEAN AND THE WORLD

The Crusades, 1071-1204

16. The candidate evaluates the importance of the threat to the Byzantine Empire in the calling of the Crusade, using evidence and arguments such as:

Threat to Byzantium

- The Seljuk Turks had been threatening the Empire for decades. There was fear in Europe that if Byzantium was allowed to fall then the expansion of this new aggressive Islamic group into central Europe would be inevitable.
- Alexius was seen as a bulwark against this eventuality and this letter asking for help was taken very seriously.

Other factors

Fear of Islamic expansion

- Pope Urban used the fear of Islamic expansion in his famous speech at Clermont in 1095. He pointed to the successful Reconquista in Spain. El Cid had only captured Valencia from the Moors in 1094.
- He pointed to the threat of the Turks to Byzantium, a topic that was already talked about across Europe. He claimed that the loss of Anatolia had 'devastated the Kingdom of God'.
- He detailed claims of Turkish activities such as torture, human sacrifice and desecration.

Attempts to assert Papal authority

- The new style of pope, influenced and trained at the monastery of the Cluny, heralded a shift in the emphasis of Christianity. No longer were popes to be subservient to the monarchs or warlords of Europe.
- Popes now actually challenged kings and demanded the right to appoint priests, bishops and cardinals as they saw fit. This led to the development of the Investiture Contest and this power struggle directly affected Urban, possibly influencing his decision.
- The papacy was anxious to re-join the two halves of the Christian church. Since the Great Schism of 1054, where the Pope of Rome and Patriarch of Constantinople excommunicated each other, it had been the goal of every pope to become head of the Greek Orthodox Church. Now the Crusade seemed to offer Pope Urban the opportunity to achieve this.

The Threat to Mediterranean trade

- The development of trade within the Mediterranean Sea had been in the hands of ambitious cities in Italy, notably Venice, but also Pisa and Genoa. By 1095 Venice had bound its future to Byzantium.
- Their preferential trade agreements with Constantinople for silk, spices and other luxury goods meant that they were keen to see Byzantium saved from the expansion of the Turks.

The emergence of a knightly class
- The introduction of Norman feudalism across Western Europe had created the knightly class. Their dedication to learning the arts of war had created a culture based around the skills of fighting. Even the tournaments had come to be seen as an integral part of the culture and as entertainment.

Papal desire to channel the aggressive nature of feudal society
- For knights to use their skills in anger was a sin. Pope Urban had long considered how he could turn the nature of the Western knights to a less aggressive, less damaging activity.
- The Church had already successfully introduced the Peace of God, an agreement that non-combatants would be spared in any conflict. Urban saw the Crusade as a way to channel this aggression in a way that would be of benefit to Christianity.

Any other relevant factors

17. The candidate evaluates the extent to which the success of the First Crusade was due to Muslim misunderstanding of the Crusaders' intentions, using evidence and arguments such as:

Misunderstanding of the Crusaders' intent
- Most Muslims misunderstood the threat of the Western knights. Many saw this as another expedition from Byzantium and thought them soldiers of Alexius. Such raids had occurred before; however this was different. Here the Christians had an ideological motivation not yet encountered by the Islamic leaders and therefore they tended to underestimate what the Crusaders could achieve.

Other factors

Military power of the Crusader knights
- The First Crusade had been unexpected by local Muslim leaders. Those that had witnessed the ineptitude of the People's Crusade expected Christian knights to be as inept in combat. However Christian knights were often ferocious fighters, used to long campaigns in Europe, whereas the knights of the East were seen as gentlemen of culture and education.
- Crusading knights used aggressive combat tactics, and utilised heavier armour and barding for their horses. The constant fighting of the 12th century had well prepared the organized and disciplined knightly classes for warfare. Many, such as Raymond of Toulouse, had combat experience against the Moors in Spain.
- The mounted tactics of the knights were relatively unknown in the east and sight of the largest concentration of knights in history assembled on the field was a truly awesome sight. The full frontal charge of the knights was in contrast to the tactics deployed by the Islamic forces. Their skirmishing horse archers were not prepared for this aggressive style.

Divisions amongst the Islamic states
- The Islamic response to the First Crusade was slow in getting under way. During the crusade Muslim leaders were more willing to fight among themselves than join forces against the common enemy. In fact many did not even realise that this was a common enemy. Kilij Arslan, for example, expected the "Princes' Crusade" to be no more of a concern than Peter the Hermit's followers. Thus he was off raiding his Muslim neighbours when Nicaea came under attack.
- For the Muslims this was not seen as a holy war, at least at the outset. To them, unifying to face the Christians was a more dangerous idea than the Crusaders themselves.

Aid from Byzantium
- The First Crusade was the only Crusade to have significant support from Constantinople. Even though Alexius's army did not participate in the Crusade itself, they did cause problems, diverting a lot of Muslim resources.

- Alexius also provided much needed supplies at the sieges of Antioch and Jerusalem.

The religious zeal of the Crusaders
- The sheer determination of the Crusaders helped them through incredible hardships during their passage through the Taurus Mountains and at the sieges of Antioch and Jerusalem. Because they believed God would help them, they attempted the impossible, where most armies would have surrendered eg Battle of Antioch and the belief in the Holy Lance.

Any other relevant factors

18. The candidate evaluates the validity of the view that the lack of resources of the Christian states explains the fall of Jerusalem, using evidence and arguments such as:

The lack of resources of the Christian states
- The Crusaders had sought to redress their military inferiority by constructing powerful fortifications. Without the army to protect the kingdom even the massive fortifications could not withstand Saladin's forces.
- Even the combined armies of the Crusader States were not strong enough to successfully win a war, especially in the long run. It is arguable that it was inevitable for the Crusader States to fall to a united Islamic state.

Other factors

The death of Baldwin IV
- Baldwin died in March 1185, taking his strategy of non-aggression towards Saladin with him. He was replaced for a short time by his nephew, Baldwin V. However a short power struggle after the boy's death in August let Guy de Lusignan assume the throne, abetted by Sibylla.

Divisions amongst the Crusaders
- Two factions had struggled for power within Baldwin IV's court, those of Guy de Lusignan and Baldwin's close advisor Raymond III of Tripoli. In 1180 Guy married Sibylla, Baldwin's sister. Guy tended to favour an aggressive policy.
- The activities of Reynald of Chatillon helped to destabilise the fragile peace treaty between Baldwin IV and Saladin.
- The Knights Templar, unlike the Hospitallers, were firmly in the camp of the hawks (warmongers). They wanted nothing more than to carry on with the crusading ideal and rid the Holy Lands of Muslims. Treaties and compromise were unacceptable to them.

The Christian defeat at Hattin
- King Guy led the armies of Jerusalem to save Count Tiberius's wife as Saladin's forces had surrounded her castle. Tiberius himself had few worries about the safety of his wife. His fortress could have withstood a siege. Saladin's forces lacked the required siege engines to make a successful attack. Additionally, Saladin could not keep his disparate forces in the field for any length of time. Tiberius' advice to Guy was to hold his forces back to protect Jerusalem.
- However, figures such as Reynald had persuaded Guy that to leave the Countess of Tripoli besieged would be un-chivalric and that Guy would lose support if he did not ride out.
- The army could find little water to sustain them in the desert. Their only option was to make for Hattin and the oasis there. This was an obvious trap; Saladin surrounded them with burning brushwood and dry grass. Trapped on the Horns of Hattin the Christian army suffered badly from the sun and lack of water.
- Eventually they were forced to attack before they lacked the strength to do so. The Christian horses were too weak for a prolonged struggle and their infantry were surrounded by Saladin's horse archers and cut off.

- Saladin ordered the slaughter of all members of the militant orders, but Guy and many of his followers were allowed to surrender and enter captivity.

Unification of Islamic states under Saladin
- Saladin had managed to successfully unite the Muslims of Syria and Egypt behind his leadership. This effectively surrounded Jerusalem and left them with a very weak military position.
- Saladin successfully used the idea of a religious war against the Christians to hold the separate Islamic groups together.
- By way of balance, Saladin himself had his critics within the Muslim ranks, saying he was more interested in maintaining his position than defeating the Christians. It was seen by many that his stance on the Kingdom of Jerusalem was weak. After Guy assumed the throne and Reynald continued his attacks the pressure on Saladin to respond grew. This encouraged him to act aggressively.

Any other relevant factors

The American Revolution, 1763-1787

19. The candidate evaluates the importance of the role of George III in the developing threat to the British position in North America by 1763, using evidence and arguments such as:

Role of George III
- When George III ascended the throne in 1760 he oversaw a re-imposition of British rule over the colonies. This was seen as tantamount to foreign invasion by many colonists who had acted in an independent spirit during the Whig Ascendancy. Colonies had their own militia and did not feel British Army was required in America.
- George III aimed to ensure the security of the colonies by maintaining a British military presence and together with Parliament planned an economic strategy to raise money from the colonists to pay for this.

Other factors

Colonial resentment towards the old colonial system
- Britain treated colonies merely as a source of revenue, and plundered valuables from America. Those in New England and the Middle Colonies objected to being used as a dumping ground for British goods. Wealthy Southern plantation owners objected to members of the British government attempting to control them. Frontiersmen were frustrated at British attempts to prevent them from going beyond the Frontier. However, being part of the Empire meant protection from the British Army against the French and Indians.

The Navigation Acts
- Passed in the 1650s, these stated that colonists could only sell their goods to the British, could only buy goods from the British and could only use British shipping. Royal Navy enforced the Acts by patrolling east coast of colonies for rogue Dutch, French or Spanish ships.
- However, the acts gave colonists a guaranteed market. During the Whig Ascendancy in mid-1700s many colonists were able to ignore the Acts as Royal Navy was unable to enforce them as strictly.

The effects of the Seven Years' War – ending of the French threat
- The war highlighted the status of the colonies as territories to be fought over by imperial powers. Britain, France and Spain all viewed America as a potential possession. The British fought the Seven Years War which prevented the colonies being ruled by France.
- Victory in 1763, and the acquisition of Canada, should have made British rule more secure, but the removal of the French threat meant that many colonists saw less need for British protection.

The frontier issue – the Proclamation of 1763
- Quarrels arose after individual colonists and land companies unwittingly violated treaties agreed between Britain and Indian tribes.
- The British tried to control the situation by issuing the Proclamation of 1763, which attempted to restrict the westward movement of settlers and land speculators. It was only moderately successful, but aroused much ill-feeling.

Grievances of New England, the Middle Colonies, the South
- The colonies were more advanced politically than Britain, each having its own elected Assembly which passed local laws and raised local taxes, and so they resented the lack of representation in the British Parliament which sought to control their lives. However, the British Empire provided an order to the existence of the colonies. Britain acted out the role of Mother Country. Britain appointed a governor for each colony, whose payment by the colony ensured an element of control for the colonists over the governor.
- During the Whig Ascendancy, colonist assemblies had assumed powers which should have been exercised by governors, and they resented Parliament's attempts to reverse this trend.
- The New England Colonies felt most aggrieved about taxation and restrictions on trade.
- The Middle and Southern colonies particularly resented the 1763 Proclamation.

Any other relevant factors

20. The candidate assesses the validity of the statement that the views of the Earl of Chatham represented British people's opinion on the conflict with America, using evidence and arguments such as:

Earl of Chatham
- He had been Prime Minister during the Seven Years War and again in the mid-1760s when he repealed the Stamp Act. He became more aware of the colonists' plight in his final years, and repeatedly warned of the impending situation in America.
- Chatham's warnings fell on deaf ears, as Parliament ignored his pleas for conciliation and his assertion that America could not be beaten if war broke out.

Other factors

Parliament
- In the House of Lords, Lord Sandwich and others disregarded the warnings of impending crisis and seriously underestimated the colonists' forces. However, as well as Burke and Chatham, others such as John Wilkes spoke in favour of radical change in policy towards America.

Thomas Paine
- Paine had been in America since November 1774, making republican speeches and meeting with colonists. He published 'Common Sense' in January 1776 and it sold 100,000 copies in America, and more than that in Britain and Europe.
- Paine was a radical, too radical for many colonists. Some in Britain read his work out of fascination rather than because they agreed with him. In America, many who may have been influenced by 'Common Sense' were already considering independence after the rejection of the Olive Branch Petition.

George III

- George III, popular in Britain, sacked Grenville after the Stamp Act and appointed Pitt (as Chatham) as Prime Minister. He supported Parliament's right to tax the colonies. He asserted his view that the problems in America were 'localised' in New England, and declared the colonies to be in 'rebellion' after 1775.

Edmund Burke

- Burke studied the American situation and took the colonists' demands seriously. He made speeches in the House of Commons, citing the common bond of 'Englishness' which existed between Britain and America, and urging Parliament to 'loosen the reins' on the colonists or lose America for good. However, Burke's views were dismissed as alarmist by many Parliamentarians.

Economic interests

- Mill owners, including some MPs, wanted a speedy resolution to the crisis to ensure continued supply of raw materials from the colonies. Mill workers wanted trade to be maintained in order to preserve jobs.

The press in Scotland and England

- Some Scots and Irish sympathised with the colonists' resentment of 'English' rule and understood their calls for greater autonomy.

Any other relevant factors

21. The candidate assesses the extent to which the American War of Independence was global in nature, using evidence and arguments such as:

The war at sea

- The war at sea meant the long reach of the Royal Navy could carry the war to its enemies and their colonies, either by the traditional blockade of enemy ports (mainly on the continent), or by transporting and supplying expeditionary forces to conquer enemy colonies. This was on a lesser scale than the previous or subsequent wars due to the array of hostile naval forces.
- The battle for control of the sea drew massively on the resources of all countries involved and significantly drained Britain's finances. However, the war at sea continued after the surrender at Yorktown, and the British recognised the Treaty of Versailles despite regaining control of the sea, suggesting the war on land was more significant on the outcome for the colonists.

Dutch and Spanish entry

- When the Dutch and the Spanish entered the war, Britain's navy was stretched even further and it became increasingly difficult to focus on the war in the colonies. European nations now competed for parts of Britain's empire around the world. However, the war between Britain and the colonists on land was not directly affected greatly by the Dutch and Spanish involvement.

Franco-American Alliance

- France entered the war and took the conflict to Europe. Britain was forced to re-assign its military resources to defend itself and the Empire. The French contribution to the colonists' cause took many forms – men, ammunition, training, supplies, and uniforms. However, France was not persuaded until February 1778 to make its alliance with America, by which time the Continental Army was already starting to make progress in the war in the colonies.

The world-wide nature of the war

- French entry turned a war on American soil into a world-wide conflict, although the colonists appealed unsuccessfully for Canadian support, which meant the British were not distracted by concerns about possible rebellion in Canada.
- The war was one of a series (the "Second Hundred Years' War") between Britain and France in the 18th century for European and imperial dominance. War between these powers involved colonial conflicts in other continents, and particularly in India and the West Indies.

Armed League of Neutrality

- This grouping of Russia, Sweden and Denmark gave extra cause for concern to Britain, as they were willing to fire on any Royal Navy ships which interfered with their merchant fleets. However, the League was not actively involved in the war, merely endeavouring to protect its own shipping.

Any other relevant factors

The French Revolution, to 1799

22. The candidate evaluates the extent to which corruption was the main threat to the security of the Ancien Regime before 1789, using evidence and arguments such as:

Corruption

- Absolutist nature of the monarchy – Marie-Antoinette. Decadence of the court.
- Financial Problems – arguably the biggest threat to the Ancien Regime. Created in part by France's involvement in wars – most recently the American War of Independence – brought France to bankruptcy.
- Failure to reform.

Other factors

Taxation

- Unfair nature of the system – privileged orders of the first and second estate. Unfair taxation system – cumbersome administration – tax collected by the Farmers General, who had a vested interest in collecting as much as they could.

The position of the clergy

- The clergy was split into the upper and lower clergy, the latter identifying more closely with the Third Estate. The church hierarchy was resented by the lower clergy; parish priests often sided with the peasants in their locality but the upper clergy viewed peasants with contempt and merely as a source of taxation.
- The Church owned a large amount of land and paid relatively little taxation. The upper clergy were concerned to protect their privileges.

The role of the nobility

- Like the clergy, the upper nobility were concerned to protect their privileged status, particularly access to posts at court and in the army, and their exemptions from taxation. Natural supporters of the monarchy, they saw some threat from the rise of the bourgeoisie.
- There were also tensions between the traditional nobility (of the sword) and the newly ennobled nobility (of the robe) wherein the 'old' sought to hold onto their control of key positions of the State, the Army and the Church, much to the annoyance of the 'new'.

The complaints of the Third Estate:

Grievances of the bourgeoisie

- Rise in the importance of the Bourgeoisie – increased wealth – wish for increased participation.
- Influence of Enlightenment ideas: Voltaire, Montesquieu, Rousseau – questioned tradition – supported freedoms –

press, speech. They attacked the privileges of the Church, its beliefs and the despotic nature of Ancien Regime Government. They were critical of many aspects of the Ancien Regime but not necessarily totally opposed to it. Impact may have been limited, as only certain sections of society would read their works. Some historians argue that Enlightenment ideas were only used to justify the revolution after it happened.

Grievances of the peasantry
- The bulk of French society – range of taxation and feudal rights imposed on them.
- The peasantry was becoming increasingly discontented with the disproportionate burden of taxation which fell on them.
- Pent-up resentment at their lot became clear in the cahiers.

The urban workers
- The urban workers endured exploitation by bourgeois masters and suffered through restrictions on trade.
- They were particularly affected by bad harvests and food shortages.

Any other relevant factors

23. The candidate evaluates the importance of the outbreak of war in 1792 in bringing about the end of the constitutional monarchy in France, using evidence and argument such as:

The outbreak of war
- These events radicalised the Revolution to the point where the position of the monarchy became impossible because of the king's identification with the enemy. Partly, as was said above, this was Louis' own fault but it should be remembered that France declared war on Austria in April 1792 and it suited the radical anti-monarchists who thought that a successful war would bring them increased support at home and prove a decisive blow to the monarchy. The final overthrow of the monarchy in August 1792 had become inevitable under the pressures exerted by the war.

Other factors

Character of Louis XVI
- Even before the outbreak of revolution in July 1789, Louis had shown himself incapable of making the strong decisions necessary to save the monarchy.

His attitudes and actions
- Louis was from the start unsupportive of the principle of constitutional monarchy.
- He dismissed Finance Minister Calonne in the face of opposition from the nobility to the major tax reforms needed to save France from bankruptcy.
- After the Declaration of the Rights of Man in August 1789, Louis failed to openly endorse its principles and in the weeks ahead seemed to be preparing for a counter-revolution through the build-up of troops at Versailles. This aroused considerable suspicion and even at this early stage, made the achievement of a constitutional monarchy unlikely.
- Even before his veto on decrees against 'refractory' clergy and émigrés in December Louis' actions during 1791 had done the monarchy immeasurable harm.
- His lukewarm support for the reforms of the Constituent Assembly had generated popular hostility in Paris from the spring of 1791 onwards.

The Civil Constitution of the Clergy
- This caused great controversy in a traditionally Catholic country and created deep divisions which polarised the Revolution. The monarchy – since it was historically associated with the Church – was irrevocably damaged in the eyes of the radicals who exploited the king's unease over of the Civil Constitution for their own ends.

- Louis' failure to openly endorse this increased the hostility of large sections of the population towards the monarchy. This showed itself most clearly in December 1791 when Louis vetoed decrees against clergy who refused to swear an oath of loyalty to the new French State and émigrés who opposed the revolution. Again, Louis' commitment to the Revolution was called into question and the establishment of a successful constitutional monarchy seemed more remote than ever.

The role of Mirabeau
- Mirabeau was a supporter of a constitutional monarchy and tried to reconcile the reactionary court of Louis XVI with the increasingly radical forces of the Revolution of 1789 and 1790. With the effective overthrow of the absolute monarchy in June – July 1789 and the ending of feudalism in August, French society had changed forever.
- Many of Mirabeau's efforts to achieve a reconciliation between the conflicting aspirations of conservatives and radicals often involved proposals that seemed too extreme to some interests and way too moderate to others. Mirabeau was partly successful in efforts to establish a system of constitutional monarchy by securing for the Crown the right of declaring peace and war, he also fought hard, if largely unsuccessfully, to maintain the absolute royal veto.
- His death in 1791 removed the main figure in the centre ground of politics – though he had been distrusted by both extremes.

The activities of the émigrés
- The émigré nobles (many of whom had left France in the aftermath of the Civil Constitution of the Clergy) were becoming increasingly vocal against the Revolution from the foreign countries to which they had fled.
- They also tried to enlist the aid of other absolutist monarchies.
- The Declaration of Pillnitz (August 1791) in which Austria and Prussia threatened to intervene against the Revolution had been inspired by the king's émigré brothers. This intensified suspicion of the monarchy.

The flight to Varennes
- In June the Royal Family attempted to escape the Revolution by slipping across the border. They were stopped at Varennes and returned to Paris. The mistrust generated by Louis' persistent ambivalence towards the Revolution brought a significant upsurge of support – particularly in Paris – for a Republic. Although not the end of the monarchy, Louis' actions in June 1791 made its demise increasingly certain.

Any other relevant factors

24. The candidate evaluates the validity of the view that Robespierre was the key factor leading to the Terror in France by using evidence and argument such as:

The role of Robespierre
- Robespierre believed that the 'general will' of the sovereign people both created and sanctioned policy-making within the nation. The will of the people could only prevail within a Republic. Any individual who sought to oppose this was, by implication, guilty of treason against the nation itself. In such circumstances death – the ultimate weapon of Terror – was entirely appropriate. Hence Robespierre's belief that 'terror is virtue' – that to create and maintain a 'virtuous' nation which enshrined the revolutionary principles of liberty and equality, it was necessary to violently expunge any counter-revolutionary activity.
- Robespierre became a member of the Committee of Public Safety in July 1793 and came to control its operations. Until his own execution in July 1794, the Committee became the main instrument for the application of terror in defence of

Robespierre's ideal of a 'Republic of Virtue'. During this period Robespierre sanctioned the use of terror against:

- the monarchy and émigré opponents of the Republic eg Marie Antoinette executed
- provincial counter-revolutionaries particularly in the Vendee
- Hebertists, whose anti-Christian stance Robespierre found both distasteful and dangerous
- Dantonists who challenged the authority of Robespierre and who were therefore (since Robespierre's government represented the 'general will') guilty of treason.
- With the imposition of the infamous Law of 22nd Prairial (June 1794), Robespierre was given virtually unlimited powers to eliminate opponents of his Republic of Virtue and during the period of the Great Terror in June and July 1794, over 1500 were executed.
- Had Robespierre lived beyond Thermidor there is no doubt the death toll would have risen even higher. However, while Robespierre must bear responsibility for the intensification of the Terror during 1793-1794, the use of terror as an instrument of state policy was by no means confined to Robespierre.

Other factors

The outbreak of war

- The war put pressure on the Convention to execute the war against the Republic's émigré and foreign opponents as ruthlessly and as effectively as possible. The nation's resources were mobilized to this end. The early reverses raised alarms about sabotage and possible treason in the new armies.

The threat of invasion

- The initial defeats suffered raised the spectre of invasion.
- External dangers France faced radicalised the revolution. It occasioned a witch hunt for enemies within. The war led to the concept of the 'nation in crisis'. This had to be enforced, violently if necessary.
- It was pressure from mass demonstrations in Paris which intimidated the Convention into adopting terror as 'the order of the day' ie a method of government control. This was more to do with the exigencies of the foreign and civil wars which were threatening the Republic at this point than with Robespierre's philosophising over the nature of the Republic and the role of terror within it.

The threat of counter-revolution

- The Convention's other major concern at the start of 1793 was to eliminate counter-revolutionary activity which intensified, particularly in the provinces after Louis' execution. At this point the Convention was still controlled by the relatively moderate Girondins.
- The Convention sanctioned a range of counter-revolutionary legislation such as:
  - the creation of the Committee of Public Safety; The Committee of General Security
  - Revolutionary tribunals to try opponents of the Republic and impose the death penalty if required and Surveillance Committees established in local areas to identify counter-revolutionary activity.
- Thus, most agree that most of the essential institutions of the Terror were actually in place before the Jacobins – and Robespierre – came to power. The moderates in the Convention had set up the structure of the Terror by the spring of 1793.

Political rivalries

- The Jacobins were one of a number of political groupings contending for power. The struggle became more bitter with time. Similarly a number of other prominent individuals had

sought to control the course of the revolution. Some had already died violently. The Terror was a legitimised means of the Jacobins eliminating their political rivals – 'a revolution always consumes its children'.

Religious and regional differences

- The uprising in the Vendee was supported by priests and former nobles. It also secured British support. It was brutally suppressed. Many women and children were drowned in the Loire at Nantes.
- There were also demands in the south for greater autonomy.
- Under the Civil Constitution of the Clergy, priests had to swear an oath of loyalty to the state. Many refused and became leaders of resistance.

Any other relevant factors

Germany 1815-1939

25. The candidate evaluates the importance of the Zollverein in the growth of German nationalism between 1815 and 1850, using evidence and arguments such as:

The Zollverein

- Zollverein – the 'mighty lever' of German unification. By 1836, 25 of the 39 German states had joined this economic free-trade area (Austria was excluded).
- Members of the Union voluntarily restricted their sovereignty [even if only in their own selfish interests] to allow for economic gain through joining the Prussian-led Customs Union.
- German nationalists in the late 1830s saw it as a step towards a wider political union.

Other factors

Economic factors

- Urbanisation and industrialisation of the German states – political fragmentation – can be argued to be the most important obstacle to German economic development. Middle-class businessmen called for a more united market to enable them to compete with foreign countries.
- Prussian economic expansion – drift in power away from Austria and towards Prussia as the latter began to build on the rich resources such as coal and iron deposits.
- Prussia's gain of territory on the River Rhine after 1815 meant it had good reason to reach an agreement with neighbours to ensure relatively free travel of goods and people between its lands in the east and the west.
- Businessmen complained that tax burdens were holding back economic development.
- Prussia created a large free-trade area within Prussia herself – aided needs of businessmen.
- Railway/road development – post-1830s the development of railways/roads ended isolation of German states from each other. This enabled the transport and exploitation of German natural resources. Economic co-operation between German states encouraged those seeking a political solution to the issue of German unity.

Cultural factors

- Main unifying force was language – 25 million Germans spoke the same language and shared the same culture and literature.
- Writers and thinkers (eg Heine, Fichte, Goethe, Brothers Grimm, Schiller, Hegel) encouraged the growth of a German consciousness.
- Post-1815 nationalist feelings first expressed in universities. Growth of Burschenschaften pre-1815 dedicated to driving French from German soil –zealous but lacking a clear idea of how best to accomplish the task.

- The Hambacherfest and student demonstrations – little accomplished by the students.

Military weakness
- French troops had marched across Germany for over 20 years, and had humiliated Prussia, the strongest 'German' state at Jena and Auerstadt. Germany had been carved up by Napoleon, the North Sea coast being incorporated into France itself, and the Confederation of the Rhine set up as a puppet state. Divided, the German states could not defend their territorial integrity.
- Germany had been used as a recruiting ground by Napoleon: Germans had died to protect France. Even the enlarged post-Vienna states would be powerless, with the exception of Prussia, to prevent this happening again.

Effects of French Revolution and Napoleonic Wars
- Ideas of the French Revolution – these appealed to the middle classes in the German states.
- Impact of Napoleonic wars – many Germans argued that Napoleon/France had been able to conquer German states pre-1815 due to their division as separate, autonomous territories. German princes had stirred national feeling to help raise armies to drive out the French, aiding the sense of a common German identity with common goals.

Role of the Liberals
- Many Liberals were middle-class and also receptive to nationalist ideas.
- 1848 Revolutions in Germany raised consciousness greatly even though they failed.

Any other relevant factors

26. The candidate evaluates the validity of the view that the German princes were the most important obstacle to German unification before 1850, using evidence and arguments such as:

Attitude of the German princes
- The leaders of the German states obstructed unification – protective of their individual power and position. They wanted to maintain the status quo which would safeguard this for them.
- Particularism of the various German states – autonomous and parochial in many ways.
- Self-interest among German rulers led to opposition to the actions at Frankfurt.

Other factors

Divisions among the nationalists
- Nationalists were divided over which territory should be included in any united Germany; grossdeutsch and kleindeutsch arguments.
- Failure of the Frankfurt Parliament – lack of clear aims and without an armed force to enforce its decisions. Lack of decisive leadership. Divisions among the 'revolutionaries' regarding aims and objectives.

Austrian strength
- The states within 'Germany' had been part of the moribund Holy Roman Empire, traditionally ruled by the Emperor of Austria.
- Post-1815 the chairmanship of the Bund was given to Austria on a permanent basis, partly as she was considered to be the major German power.
- Metternich's work – to oppose liberalism and nationalism. His use of the weapons of diplomacy and threats of force. Use of the police state, repression and press censorship. Smaller German states were in awe of the power and position of the Austrian Empire. Austrian control over the administration and management of the empire, stamping authority on the Bund. Karlsbad Decrees and the Six Articles.

- Post-1815 Austrian military strength and bureaucracy continued to decline in effectiveness; shift in balance of power between Austria and Prussia, but not apparent till the 1850s.
- Treaty of Olmutz, 1850 – signalled the triumph of Austria and humiliation of Prussia. German nationalism was now a spent force apparently.

Religious differences
- Religion – northern German states were mostly Protestant and southern states mainly Catholic; thus the north looked to Prussia for help and protection while the south looked to Austria.

Economic differences
- The smaller states of the West had more advanced economies than the Prussian heartlands, where political reading was confined largely to the upper class.
- Even within Prussia there were significant social differences between the industrially advanced territories on the Rhine and the largely agricultural areas in the East, which were dominated by the Junkers (although less so than in the 18th century), who were adversely affected by the agricultural depression of the 1820s.

Indifference of the masses
- Popular apathy – most Germans had little desire to see a united Germany; nationalism affected mainly the educated/business classes.
- Lack of coincidence between political boundaries and ethnic/linguistic ones.
- However, politically based literature and propaganda also reached the masses, helping to bond their ideals and strengthen their resolve for both reform and unification.

Resentment towards Prussia
- Smaller states, particularly in the south, resented the economic and political predominance of Prussia.
- There was a reluctance to accept unification within the Prussian state, which had a significant non-German population and which contained a large conservative/reactionary landed class.

Attitudes of other foreign states
- France had been able to dominate central Europe for centuries due to its lack of unity. Although most of Germany had been united by Napoleon into the Confederation of the Rhine, it was not in French interests for Germany to be united, particularly as that would present a barrier to France achieving a frontier on the Rhine.

Any other relevant factors

27. The candidate evaluates the extent to which Prussian military strength was the main reason for German unification being achieved by 1871 using evidence and arguments such as:

Prussian military strength
- Significance of military reforms of Moltke and Roon – creation of modern powerful army which Bismarck used.
- Role of Prussian army in defeating Denmark.
- Role of Prussian army in defeating Austria: contemporaries expected a long war, but it was over in seven weeks. Significant military victory at Koniggratz [Sadowa].
- Role of Prussian army in defeating France: decisive victory at battle of Sedan, a triumph of leadership and military skill.

Other factors

Prussian economic strength
- Growth in Prussian economic power – development of railways, transport links, roads, for example; importance of the Rhineland and the Saarland to Prussian economic development. Able to finance and equip Prussian army. Also able to mobilise Prussian army at speed.

- The Zollverein – the Prussian-dominated free-trade area; the significance to German political unification – the 'mighty lever of German unification'.

The decline of Austria
- The decline in Austrian power and influence – economically and militarily – during the 1850s particularly.
- Distraction to Austria of commitments in Italy.

The role of Bismarck
- Bismarck's aim was to increase the power of Prussia by whatever means necessary.
- Bismarck and his 'realpolitik'/diplomacy in the '3 wars' against Denmark, Austria and France.
- Bismarck took the initiative, as opposed to Austria, in the war against Denmark; his 'solution' to the Schleswig-Holstein question.
- Bismarck's skilful manipulation of events leading up to the war with Austria in 1866 plus his establishment of friendships with potential allies of Austria beforehand.
- Bismarck's wisdom in the Treaty of Prague, 1866.
- Bismarck's manipulation of the Ems Telegram to instigate a war with France in 1870.
- Bismarck's exploitation of the weaknesses of European statesmen/rulers eg Napoleon III; mistakes made by Bismarck's adversaries.
- Bismarck's skill in isolating his intended targets (diplomatically).

The attitude of other states
- Foreign concerns over the idea of a united Germany. None of the Great Powers wanted to see the creation of a strong Germany which might upset the balance of power. Britain, Russia, Austria and France were all happy to see the German states weak and divided.
- Attitudes changed after 1850: Britain was increasingly pre-occupied with her Empire, particularly India (mutiny, 1857).

The actions of Napoleon III
- Napoleon had ambitions to emulate his famous namesake as a major statesman. His successes against Austria may have made him careless in his dealings with Bismarck eg he was seduced by Bismarck's hint that he could have possible territorial gains in the Low Countries.
- He overreacted over the Hohenzollern candidature, giving Bismarck the opportunity to doctor the Ems Telegram and provoke war.
- His military leadership in the Franco-Prussian War was poor. He allowed himself to be surrounded and captured at Sedan, effectively ending the war.

Any other relevant factors

Italy 1815-1939

28. The candidate evaluates the importance of the resentment of Austria in the growth of Italian nationalism before 1850 using evidence and arguments such as:

Resentment of Austria
- After the Vienna settlement in 1815, hatred of foreign control centred on Austria. The Hapsburg Emperor directly controlled Lombardy and Venetia; his relatives controlled Parma, Modena, Tuscany. Austria had strong ties to the Papacy and had alliances with other rulers. Conscription, censorship, the use of spies and the policy of promotion in the police, civil service and army only for German speakers was resented.
- Austrian army presence within towns like Milan and the heavily garrisoned Quadrilateral fortresses ensured that 'Italians' could never forget that they were under foreign control and this inspired growing desire for the creation of a national state.

Other factors

Cultural factors
- The Risorgimento was inspired by Italy's past. Poets such as Leopardi glorified and exaggerated past achievements kindling nationalist desires. Poets and novelists like Pellico inspired anti-Austrian feelings amongst intellectuals as did operas such as Verdi's 'Nabucco' and Rossini's 'William Tell'.
- There was no national 'Italian' language – regional dialects were like separate languages. Alfieri inspired 'Italian' language based on Tuscan. The poet and novelist Manzoni wrote in 'Italian'. Philosophers spread ideas of nationalism in their books and periodicals.
- Moderate nationalists such as Gioberti and Balbo advocated the creation of a federal state with the individual rulers remaining but joining together under a president for foreign affairs and trade. Gioberti's 'On the moral and civil primacy of the Italians' advocated the Pope as president whilst Balbo, in his book 'On the hopes of Italy', saw the King of Piedmont/Sardinia in the role.

Economic factors
- Economic factors were not important directly. Wealth lay in land (landowners were often reactionary) and trade (where the educated bourgeoisie were more receptive to ideas of liberalism and nationalism)
- The election of a new, seemingly reformist Pope, Pius IX, in 1846 inspired feelings of nationalism particularly amongst businessmen and traders as he wished to form a customs union.

Military weakness
- The French Revolution led to a realisation that, individually, the Italian states were weak.
- The fragmentation of Italy in the Vienna Settlement restored Italy's vulnerability to foreign invasion.

Effects of French revolution and Napoleonic wars
- 'Italian' intellectuals had initially been inspired by the French Revolution with its national flag, national song, national language, national holiday and emphasis on citizenship.
- Napoleon Bonaparte's conquest inspired feelings of nationalism – he reduced the number of states to three; revived the name 'Italy'; brought in single system of weights and measures; improved communications; helped trade, inspiring desire for at least a customs union. Napoleon's occupation was hated – conscription, taxes, looting of art.

Role of Mazzini
- Radical nationalist Mazzini not only inspired dreams of a united, democratic Italian republic through his written works, but also formed an activist movement 'Young Italy' whose aim was to make these dreams a reality.

Secret societies
- The growth of secret societies, particularly the Carbonari, led to revolts in 1820, 1821, 1831. Also 'Young Italy' and their revolts in the 1830s.

Any other relevant factors

29. The candidate evaluates the extent to which divisions among nationalists were the main obstacle to Italian unification between 1815 and 1850, using evidence and arguments such as:

Divisions among the nationalists
- Secret societies lacked clear aims, organisation, leadership, resources and operated in regional cells.
- Moderate nationalists feared extremists like Mazzini.

- The 1848/49 revolutions showed that nationalist leaders did not trust one another (Manin and Charles Albert) or would not work together (C. Albert and Mazzini).
- Failure to capitalise on Austrian weakness in 1848.

Other factors

Social, economic and cultural differences
- Geographical difficulties hindered the spread of nationalist ideas.

Political differences
- There was division between those desiring liberal changes within existing states and those desiring the creation of a national state.

Dominant position of Austria and her dependent duchies
- Following Vienna Settlement Austrian Emperor Francis I had direct control of Lombardy and Venetia. Relatives of the Austrian Hapsburg Emperor controlled Parma, Modena and Tuscany (Central Duchies). Austria had agreements with the other states.
- Lombardy and Venetia were strictly controlled – censorship, spies, conscription (8 years), policy to employ German speakers (Austrian) in law, police, army civil service so controlled others (non Austrian).
- Austrian army was a common sight in major cities and in the Quadrilateral fortress towns on Lombard/Venetian border (Verona, Peschiera, Legnano, and Mantua). The Austrian army was sent in by Metternich to restore order following the Carbonari-inspired revolts in 1820, 1821 and 1831.
- Austria had first class commander, Radetsky. In 1848 Charles Albert's army won two skirmishes but Radetsky awaited reinforcements then defeated Albert at Custozza forcing an armistice. Radetsky re-took Milan in August.
- After Albert's renewal of war Radetsky took just three days to defeat him again (Novara). He then besieged Venetia until the Republic of St Mark surrendered on 22 August 1849. Austrians re-established control across north and central Italy.

Attitude of the Papacy
- Pope Pius IX denounced nationalism in 1848.

Italian princes
- Individual rulers were opposed to nationalism. They feared for their position within a united Italy.

Indifference of the masses
- Patriotic literature inspired intellectuals and students but did not reach the vast majority of the population who were illiterate (90% in some areas). The mass of the population were indifferent to nationalist ideas.

Any other relevant factors

30. The candidate evaluates the importance of Cavour in the creation of a united Italy by 1870, using evidence and arguments such as:

Role of Cavour
- He played a vital role – modernisation of Piedmont; diplomacy before War of Liberation.
- Cavour made a secret agreement to help Prussia in the war against Austria 1866. Prussian war against France gave the Italians the chance to take Rome.
- Provocation of Austria; encouragement of National Society especially in Duchies/ Romagna and his handling of the plebiscites.
- The war of 1859 inspired rebellions in Tuscany, Parma, Modena, Romagna and demands for union with Piedmont. Napoleon was not happy, but was persuaded to accept by

British diplomacy and Cavour's renewed offer of Nice and Savoy.
- Cavour's diplomacy and manoeuvring over Garibaldi's expedition; the invasion of Papal States forced unification on Piedmontese terms.

Other factors

Role of Garibaldi
- He was a committed nationalist; he fought in War of Liberation for Victor Emmanuel. His role was crucial in forcing north/south unification – the role of 'thousand'; military success in Sicily and Naples; handing his 'conquests' to Victor Emmanuel at Teano. He tried but failed to take Rome.

Role of Victor Emmanuel II
- The King was supportive of Cavour. Victor Emmanuel of Piedmont/Cavour realised foreign help needed to drive Austrians from Italy.
- The King 'managed' Garibaldi very well in 1866, preventing a diplomatic crisis.

The rise of Piedmont
- Piedmont was the most powerful of the independent Italian states. She was the natural leader of the unification movement.
- Piedmont was also the most economically advanced of the Italian states. Industry developed around Turin and a railway network was built.
- The army of Piedmont was advanced by Italian standards.

Decline of Austria
- Austria's position was in decline in economic and military terms, particularly in regard to Prussia. Italy's relative weakness was redressed by her understanding with Prussia.
- Austria's diplomatic position also declined in the 1850s, and she was increasingly isolated. Partly this was self-inflicted. Russia never forgave Austria for her lack of support during the Crimean War.

Attitudes and actions of Napoleon III
- Crimean War/Paris Peace provided opportunity for Cavour to remind Britain and France of Italy's 'unhappy' state. Following the Orsini Plot, Napoleon III held a secret meeting at Plombieres, July 1858 with Cavour. The result was a formal treaty in January 1859. Napoleon III promised 200,000 men to fight for Piedmont if Austria attacked. This would prove crucial.
- Napoleon did not intervene over Garibaldi's expedition. He made a secret agreement accepting Cavour's proposed invasion of the Papal States to stop Garibaldi reaching Rome. This allowed the Piedmontese to defeat the Papal Army, taking The Marches and Umbria. In 1866 Austria handed Venetia to France who gave it to Italy.
- The Italians took Rome after the defeat of Napoleon in 1870.

The importance of foreign intervention
- War of Liberation of 1859 – the two main victories Magenta and Solferino were French. At Villafranca Austria handed Lombardy to France who gave it to Piedmont. Garibaldi acknowledged the importance of French help.
- Britain was involved in diplomacy over Duchies. British naval presence helped Garibaldi land at Marsala. Britain refused a joint naval blockade with France to stop Garibaldi crossing the Strait of Messina – crucial for Garibaldi's success.
- Britain was the first power to officially recognise Kingdom of Italy.

Any other relevant factors

Russia 1881-1921

31. The candidate assesses whether the validity of the statement that the authority of the Tsarist state was never seriously challenged in the years before 1905, using evidence and arguments such as:

The Church

- Helped to ensure that the people, particularly the peasants, remained loyal to the Tsar. They preached to the peasants that the Tsar had been appointed by God and that they should therefore obey the Tsar. Ensured the peasants were aware of the Fundamental Law.

Opposition Groups

- Opposition and revolutionary groups were fairly weak. There were various revolutionary groups like the Social Revolutionaries (supported by peasants seeking land reform), Social Democrats (supported by industrial workers) and Liberals (who wanted a British style parliament). However these groups on their own were not powerful or popular enough to affect change. Moreover these groups were further weakened by the fact they were divided and disorganized – leaders often in prison or in exile.
- The "Pillars of Autocracy" – the features of the Tsarist state which strengthened it, and made it almost impossible for opposition groups to challenge it.

Fundamental Law

- This stated "To the emperor of all Russia belongs the Supreme and unlimited power. God himself commands that his supreme power be obeyed out of conscience as well as out of fear." This was the basis of the tsarist state.

The Army

- This was controlled by the officers who were mainly upper class, who were therefore conservative and loyal to the Tsar. They ensured that the population and the peasants in particular were loyal to the Tsar. They crushed any insurgence and were used to enforce order in the country and loyalty to the Tsar.

The Secret Police (Okhrana)

- This was set up to ensure loyalty to the Tsar and weed out opposition to the Tsar. They did this by spying on all people of society irrespective of class. Those showing any sign of opposition to the Tsar were imprisoned or sent in to exile. Large numbers were exiled.

Civil Service

- Mainly employed middle class people therefore ensuring the loyalty of that class. The Civil Service was responsible for enforcing laws on censorship and corruption as well as about meetings which made it very difficult for the revolutionaries to communicate.

Censorship

- This controlled what people were able to read, controlling what University lecturers could say, controlled access to schools, limited books available in libraries.

Russification

- This was the policy of restricting the rights of the national minorities in the Russian Empire by insisting that Russian was the first language. As a result, law and government were conducted throughout the Russian Empire in the Russian language. This maintained the dominance of the Russian culture over that of the minorities. State intervention in religion and education. Treated subjects as potential enemies and inferior to Russians.

Zubatov Unions

- Organised by the police, these were used to divert the attention of the workers away from political change by concentrating on wages and conditions in the factories, thus reducing the chances of the workers being influenced by the revolutionary groups. Unions in 1903 became involved in strikes and so were disbanded due to pressure from employers.

Any other relevant factors

32. The candidate assesses how successful the Tsar was in strengthening his authority between 1905 and 1914, using evidence and arguments such as:

Political Reforms – Dumas

- The Duma received legislative powers through the October Manifesto, ie agree to new laws.
- The electorate was widened, and promised freedom of speech, to have meetings and liberty of conscience.
- This split the revolutionary forces with the moderate liberals accepting it.
- Stolypin believed that the Tsarist system would only survive if there were some political and social reforms which would reduce social bitterness and therefore reduce opposition. Stolypin wanted the middle class' support so he showed respect for the Duma and tried to work with it rather than against it. He changed the franchise in 1907 which prevented many national minorities, peasants and workers from voting although they did still have a say in the Zemstvos. This allowed him to obtain a more co-operative 3rd Duma which passed his land reforms.
- Stolypin's work with the Dumas helped to strengthen the Tsarist state as he helped secure the support of the middle class and Liberals for the Tsarist state. However, the majority of Russians still had no political voice in Russia.

Restoring Order

- Stolypin was given the job of restoring order after the rural violence, industrial strikes and terrorism during and after the 1905 Revolution. He used radical measures such as military courts which issued death penalties – 'Stolypin's necktie' – as well as sentences of hard labour in Siberia. He used the Okhrana and censorship to silence the Tsar's opponents.
- Stolypin also enforced Russification and disenfranchisement to suppress the national minorities. Public order was restored as ringleaders were dealt with severely and this acted as a deterrent, thereby strengthening the Tsarist state. However, there was still discontent in some areas.

Economic Reforms: cancellation of Redemption Payments

- Stolypin's main plan for restoring order and preventing another revolution was through economic reform, particularly land reforms. He tried to address some of the economic problems facing Russia like food shortages and rural over-population. Stolypin felt that if the peasants and industrial workers were happy then they would be loyal to the Tsar and therefore any revolutions would fail. Stolypin's land reform details such as cancelling redemption payments, Kulaks, freedom from commune, Peasant Loan Bank and more land available. Peasants were encouraged to leave their overcrowded communes and SQA relocate to Siberia or Central Asia.
- Stolypin also introduced reforms in education which became compulsory and Stolypin hoped this would allow them to get more highly skilled jobs.
- He introduced improvements in industrial working conditions and pay and as more factories came under the control of inspectors, there were signs of improving working conditions. As industrial profits increased, the first signs of a more prosperous workforce could be detected.

- In 1912 a workers' sickness and accident insurance scheme was introduced. Stolypin's economic reforms tried to strengthen the Tsarist state by improving life and work for the vast majority of the population.
- However, the land reforms did not modernise as much as had been hoped and there was an economic slump, which made life difficult for people and affected their loyalty to the Tsarist state.

Role of the Tsar

- Tsar Nicholas II appointed Stolypin to restore order. He used a 'divide and conquer' policy to deal with each of the threats individually. He secured the loyalty and control of the armed forces by promising overdue pay, improved conditions and training.
- The Tsar issued the October Manifesto and the Fundamental Laws which both were crucial in strengthening the Tsarist state. He ruled by divine decree which along with the support of the Russian Orthodox Church, helped the Tsar use religion to secure his power.

Accommodation with the Army

- The Russian Army remained loyal after the failure of the war with Japan

Peace with Japan

- The ending of the disastrous war with Japan allowed the Tsar and his Ministers to concentrate on domestic problems

Any other relevant factors

33. The candidate evaluates how important the impact of the First World War was in bringing about the February Revolution 1917, using evidence and arguments such as:

The impact of the First World War

Military defeat

- The war did not go well for the Russian armed forces and they suffered many defeats. Russia also lost control of Poland in 1915, which was a severe blow to Russian pride.
- The Russian army lacked vital resources, including adequate medical care, and this led to high fatality and casualty rates. There were claims of defeats caused by incompetent officers who refused to cooperate with each other as well as communication difficulties. This led to low morale and desertions; the Tsar began to lose control and support of the armed forces. The generals forced his abdication at Pskov.

Economic problems

- The war was costing 17 million roubles a day and Russia had to get loans from Britain and France. Economic problems such as heavy taxes, high inflation and price rises meant that many were living in poverty.
- The people had expected the war to be won by Christmas 1914 so they were war weary by 1917 and suffering from grief, anxiety and low morale. They wanted the war to end but they knew the Tsar would not agree to that and they became so unhappy and frustrated they protested and went on strike which led to the February Revolution as the army sympathised with them and consequently sided with them against the Tsarist system.

Other factors

Role of Tsar Nicholas II

- The Tsar was seen as a weak ruler as he was so easily influenced by the Tsarina, Rasputin and his Ministers. At times the Tsar appeared to be more interested in his family than in issues facing Russia. He was stubborn as he ignored advice and warnings from Rodzyanko and he failed to understand the severity of events in February 1917.

- In September 1915 the Tsar took personal control of the armed forces, which left him personally responsible for any defeats.
- By February 1917 the Tsar had lost control of the armed forces as well as the support and loyalty of the Russian people, which contributed to the February 1917 revolution.

Role of Tsarina Alexandra

- In September 1915 the Tsar left the Tsarina in charge, which was not welcomed in Russia as she was German.
- Her relationship with Rasputin was viewed with suspicion. His disreputable behaviour tainted the royal family.

Political problems

Discontent among the bourgeoisie

- There had been long-term discontent with the Tsar's autocratic rule as he seemed unwilling to share his power despite promises (October Manifesto and Fundamental Laws). The Dumas had limited power and the Tsar dissolved them and changed the franchise.
- War exacerbated existing problems with the Tsar leaving the Tsarina to run the country in his absence. Frustration grew at the incompetence of the Tsar and his ministers, Rasputin's influence and not having a say in how the country was being run and this led to protests and ultimately to the February Revolution.

Discontent among the working class

- The war put a tremendous strain on the already fragile Russian economy. Long term discontent amongst industrial workers. The inadequate transport system was unable to cope with the supply demands of military as well as the needs of the Russian economy and society. There was a lack of food made worse by the transport problems and the loss of agricultural land to the Germans and as a result in the cities there were long queues and bread riots culminating in International Women's Day protest in Petrograd.

Peasant discontent

- Peasant discontent over the land issue did not abate during the war years. When order began to break down, land seizures by peasants became common.
- The war put extra strains on the peasantry with requisitioning of horses and conscription of men. This hit output. In addition the horror of Russia's huge casualties was felt most among the peasants.

The inherent weaknesses of the autocracy

- The Tsar's taking personal control of the armed forces exposed the frailty of the autocracy and its dependence on the personality and ability of the ruler.
- The Tsar alienated many of his natural supporters among the aristocracy with his tolerance of his wife's association with Rasputin, as well as his poor management of the war effort. Without their support, including those in the High Command, the frailty of the autocracy became apparent.

Any other relevant factors

USA 1918-1968

34. The candidate evaluates the importance of fear of revolution in explaining changing attitudes towards immigration, using evidence and arguments such as:

Fear of revolution

- Russian revolution in 1917 had established the first Communist state committed to spreading revolution and destroying capitalism.
- 'Red Scare' 1919 and it looked as if revolution was imminent.
- Palmer Raids – August 1919.

Other factors

Isolationism

- Change in attitude apparent in the 19th century. 1884 Immigration Restriction League.
- 1882 Federal Immigration Act.
- Chinese Exclusion Act.
- 1913 Alien Land Law.
- At the beginning of the First World War, American public opinion was firmly on the side of neutrality.
- Wanted to keep out of foreign problems and concentrate solely on America.
- President Wilson – America should not become involved in Europe's 'Civil War'.
- When the war ended, most Americans wanted a return to isolationism.
- Would not join the League of Nations; many Senators were concerned that if the USA joined, it might soon get dragged into another European War.

Prejudice and racism

- Changing nature of immigrants. Old Immigrants – WASP's mainly from North and West of Europe. New Immigrants – mainly from Southern and Eastern Europe. New immigrants were Catholic or Jewish – worried WASP America.
- New immigrants unfamiliar with democracy – viewed as a threat to the American constitution.
- New immigrants continued to wear traditional dress and looked out of place.

Social fears

- Immigrants congregated with people from their own culture in ghettos.
- Immigrants blamed for high crime rates in cities – particularly those cities with high levels of immigrants eg Sacco and Vanzetti case.

Economic fears

- Trade unions believed that anything they did to improve conditions or wages was wrecked by Italian or Polish workers who were prepared to work longer hours for lower wages.
- 1919 strikes – new immigrants were used as 'strike breakers'. Caused huge resentment and an increase in the desire to stop immigrants coming into the country.

The effects of the First World War

- Many immigrants during the First World War had sympathies for their mother country.
- Many German immigrants had supported the German side in the war and society was split when the USA joined the war against Germany.
- Irish Americans were suspected of being anti-British.
- Many citizens felt hostile to anything foreign.

Any other relevant factors

35. The candidate evaluates the saturation of the US market as the main contributory factor in causing the economic crisis of 1929-1933, using evidence and arguments such as:

Under consumption – the saturation of the US market

- Throughout the 1920's business had benefited from low tax policies. The result of this was that the bottom 40% of the population received only 12.5% of the nation's wealth.
- In contrast, the top 5% owned 33% of the nation's wealth. Therefore, domestic demand never kept up with production.

Other factors

Republican government policies in the 1920s

- Republican administrations' policy of Laissez-Faire.
- Failure to help farmers who did not benefit from the 1920's boom.

- Low capital gains tax encouraged share speculation which resulted in the Wall Street Crash.
- The depression was also due to the actions – or inactions – of President Hoover.

Overproduction of goods

- New mass-production methods and mechanisation meant that production of consumer goods had expanded enormously.
- Cars, radios and other electrical goods had flooded the market and more was being made than people could buy.
- By 1929 those who could afford consumer goods had already bought them.

Weaknesses of the US banking system

- Major problem was lack of regulation.
- Banking system was made up of hundreds of small, state-based banks.
- When one bank collapsed it often led to a 'run' on other banks, resulting in a banking collapse and national financial crisis.

International economic problems

- Results of the First World War on European economies.
- All European states, except Britain, placed tariffs on imported goods.
- US economy could not expand its foreign markets.
- US Tariff barriers meant that other countries found it difficult to pay back loans, which they had to refinance, becoming increasingly indebted.

The Wall Street Crash

- Atmosphere of uncertainty in October 1929 and shareholders began to sell their stocks.
- 24 October 1929 Black Thursday.
- 29 October 1929 Black Tuesday.
- Share collapse caused panic.
- Stock market crash did play a role in the depression but its significance was as a trigger. Collapse of credit, and of confidence.

Any other relevant factors

36. The candidate assesses how successful the New Deal was in dealing with America's problems in the 1930's, using evidence and arguments such as:

The New Deal – aims

- Context of the victory of Roosevelt in 1932 presidential election after the inadequate response of Hoover and the Republicans to the Great Depression that followed the Wall Street Crash. Roosevelt and the Democrats took a more interventionist approach to dealing with the economy than the Republicans.
- The New Deal aimed to provide relief for the unemployed, aid recovery of the economy and reform to create a fairer society.

Social problems

- The Second New Deal 1935-1937: reforms to improve living and working conditions for many Americans through acts such as the Social Security Act (1935) providing a state pension scheme for the old, widows, as well as help for the disabled and poor children.
- National Labour Relations Act (1935) gave workers the right to join Trade Unions, etc.
- Ending unpopular prohibition to raise revenue and popular morale!
- Debate on the issue of reform of society: 'confidence' in government and its role in running the economy. It changed expectations in America, protected workers and provided social reform.

Economic problems
- Launch of 'Alphabet Agencies' giving relief and recovery in first 100 days of Roosevelt presidency: eg Federal Emergency Relief Administration (FERA), Tennessee Valley Authority (TVA), Public Works Administration (PWA) providing relief and work.
- Confidence building measures such as checking banks in 1933 to ensure they were well run and credit worthy.
- Economic prudence by cutting wages of state employees by 15% and spending savings on relief programmes.
- Debate on the economic effects in terms of relief and recovery: they certainly helped in terms of providing basic relief.
- As to recovery, they made a difference, but its role is open to discussion as unemployment continued to be a problem, never running at less than 14% of the working population.
- The importance of rearmament in reducing unemployment and revitalizing the American economy was considerable, particularly after the mini-slump of 1937.

Any other relevant factors

Appeasement and the Road to War, to 1939

37. The candidate evaluates the extent to which the weakness of the League of Nations encouraged the aggressive nature of fascist foreign policies in the 1930s, using evidence and arguments such as:

Weakness of the League of Nations
- Failure of the League. Divided response of other powers, eg British appeasement, French political divisions, US isolationism, mutual suspicion of Soviet Russia; relative weakness of successor states in East Europe.
- Example of success of Japan in Manchuria in defiance of League.

Other factors

The Peace Settlement of 1919
- Determination to revise/overturn Paris Peace Settlement – German resentment of war guilt, reparations, disarmament, lost territory. Italian resentment of failure to gain control of Adriatic.
- German desire to get revenge for defeat in WW1.

Fascist ideology
- Pathological hatred of communism, anti-Soviet crusade; contempt for democracy.
- Militarism – fascist glorification of war; Prussian/German military traditions.
- Extent to which foreign policies driven by Hitler's and Mussolini's own beliefs, personalities, charismatic leadership.
- Irredentism, eg Hitler's commitment to incorporation of all Germans within Reich.
- Mussolini's 'Roman' ambitions in the Mediterranean and Africa; Hitler's ambitions in Eastern Europe and Russia.

Economic difficulties after 1929
- Legacy of Germany and Italy's post-WW1 economic difficulties – eg labour unrest, unemployment, inflation.
- The impact of the world economic crisis 1929-32 on the German and Italian economies intensified international competition and protectionism.
- Continuing economic problems in the 1930s, eg needs of rearmament and domestic consumption.
- Economic imperatives, eg need for additional resources, leading to aggressive, expansionist foreign policies, eg Italy in Abyssinia, German drive to the east.

The British policy of appeasement
- British appeasement to an extent encouraged both Germany and Italy to increase their demands and do so increasingly forcefully.
- British attempts to bring Mussolini into their camp resulted in the Hoare-Laval Pact, which produced a popular outcry when the terms were leaked. Mussolini saw that Britain and France were not opposed in principle to gains for Italy in East Africa and he was able to defy sanctions and keep Abyssinia.
- Hitler knew of British reservations about some terms of the Versailles Treaty and was able to play on these, increasingly realizing that he would not be stopped eg rearmament, the reoccupation of the Rhineland and then the Anschluss.

Any other relevant factors

38. The candidate evaluates how important were changing attitudes to the Paris Peace Settlement as a reason for the British policy of appeasement between 1936 and 1938, using evidence and arguments such as:

Attitudes to the Paris Peace Settlement
- 1919 Peace Settlement was seen as too harsh on Germany and there was sympathy for what were seen by many as genuine grievances.
- Reluctance to enforce Treaty provisions and preference for policy of making concessions.

Other factors

Economic difficulties
- Economic difficulties – impact of 1929-32 economic crisis and depression.
- Reluctance to further damage international trade and commerce.
- Difficulty of financing any large scale rearmament.

Public opinion
- Fear of another World War – recent memories of losses/horrors of WW1.
- Isolationist feelings, summed up in Chamberlain's pre-Munich speech.

Pacifism
- Public anti-war feeling – Peace Ballot, Oxford 'King and Country' debate.
- Fulham bi-election showed strength of anti-war feeling.

Concern over the Empire
- The Empire was thought to be crucial to British economic well-being and to her status as a Great Power.
- Fears that Britain could not defend the Empire against simultaneous threats in Northern Europe, the Mediterranean and the Far East – review of Chiefs of Staff. Some accommodation with at least one of the unsated powers was thought essential.

Lack of reliable allies
- Failure of the League.
- Divided response of other powers, eg French political divisions.
- US isolationism.
- Mutual suspicion of Soviet Russia.
- Relative weakness of successor states in Eastern Europe.
- Doubts over commitment of Empire and the Dominions in event of war.
- Failure of League of Nations, eg Manchuria, Abyssinia.
- Italy was also appeased in vain attempt to prevent alliance with Germany.

Military weakness
- Run-down state of armed forces following WW1.
- Army: conscription ended post-WW1, scaled right down in size.
- Navy: not so run-down but not fully maintained; many obsolete ships.

- Air Force: lack of adequate air defences and fear of aerial bombing.
- Multiple threats – Japan in the East, Italy in the Mediterranean and North Africa, Germany in Central Europe.
- Warnings of Chiefs-of-Staff.
- Exaggerated assessments of German military strength.

Fear of spread of Communism

- Fear of communism – suspicion of Soviet Russia; Nazi Germany seen as a buffer and destabilising the Nazi regime might lead to questions over communist revolution in Germany.
- Fear of spreading Communism into Western Europe; distrust of French popular Front government; alarm at actions of the Left (more than of the Right) in Spain.

Beliefs of Chamberlain

- Chamberlain's personal control of foreign policy.
- Chamberlain believed that problems could be solved rationally, by negotiation.

Any other relevant factors

39. The candidate assesses how successful Britain was in containing fascist aggression between 1935 and March 1938 using evidence and arguments such as:

The preservation of peace

- This was Britain's foremost aim, and up to March 1938 (and later), this was achieved.
- Conflicts that did occur (Abyssinia, Spain) were on the periphery of Europe/the Mediterranean.

Relations with Germany

- Rearmament: Hitler was successful in reintroducing conscription and rearming but there were significant economic restraints and by the late 1930s Germany's potential enemies were rearming at a faster rate. The growth of the Luftwaffe was a serious reverse for Britain
- The Anglo German Naval Agreement (1935) successfully limited German naval strength to 35% of British, but this was of lesser concern to Germany.
- Rhineland: Hitler was successful in remilitarising Rhineland – more as a result of bluff, clever timing and French/British weakness than German military strength.
- Anschluss: failure of attempted Nazi coup in 1934 due to Italian opposition, but successful annexation of Austria in 1938 – although invasion itself was chaotic and inefficient from military point of view. This was another fait accompli, but Britain could have done little to prevent it.

Relations with Italy

- Mussolini's plans for a new Roman Empire in the Adriatic, the Mediterranean and North Africa were a blow to British foreign policy in hoping to convert Mussolini into an ally.
- Stresa Front (1935) initially seemed successful.
- Hoare-Laval Pact – public revulsion to Franco-British connivance at Italian aggression led to Hoare's resignation.
- Imposition of limited sanctions on Italy alienated Mussolini, thereby driving him closer to Hitler, yet failing to save Abyssinia.

The Spanish Civil War

- Britain's main aim to prevent this becoming an international war, and in this was successful.
- The policy of non-intervention sponsored by Britain; it also guaranteed that Britain would be on good terms with the victors.
- The policy was openly breached by Germany and Italy, and to a lesser extent the Soviet Union. Resolute action did end attacks on British merchant shipping.

Any other relevant factors

The Cold War 1945-1989

40. The candidate evaluates the importance of the crisis in Korea to the emergence of the Cold War up to 1955 using evidence and arguments such as:

The crisis over Korea

- Stalin encouraged Communist North Korea to invade Capitalist South. This led to American-led UN intervention on behalf of the South, and resultant Chinese intervention. Soviet and American pilots fought each other across Korea. Stalemate along 38th parallel.
- Cold war was sealed with a Hot war!

Other factors

Tensions within the wartime alliance

- WW2: suspicion of USSR by allies because of Nazi-Soviet Pact of 1939. Tensions within the wartime alliance as the defeat of Nazism became clear. Soviet Union felt they had done the bulk of the land fighting and wanted security for the USSR.
- Yalta conference: Stalin determined to hang on to land gained and create a series of sympathetic regimes in Eastern Europe. The USA wanted to create a free trade area composed of democratic states. Soviet actions in Poland, Romania, Bulgaria, etc and Allied actions in Western Europe, Greece.

The US decision to use the atom bomb

- One aim of the use of atom bombs on Hiroshima and Nagasaki was impressing the USSR and making them ready to make concessions in Eastern Europe.
- Stalin refused to be intimidated and in fact it made him even more suspicious of the USA.

The arms race

- Stalin was determined to make the Soviet Union a nuclear power as soon as possible; the development of the arms race.
- British and French were also developing their independent nuclear deterrents – which, realistically, were only aimed at the USSR.
- Development of technologies to deliver nuclear weapons.

Ideological differences

- Impact of 1917 Bolshevik revolution in Russia on relations with the western powers: Soviet withdrawal from WW1, involvement of West with anti-Bolshevik Whites: ideological differences between Communism and Capitalism.
- Fears in the West that Communism was on the march led Truman to the policy of containment: British power had been destroyed; decline in their world commitments, specifically in Greece where civil war raged between Communists and Royalists. Fear of similar problems in Italy when allied troops left; activities of Mao in China.
- Truman acknowledged world dividing into two hostile blocs in his speech to support free peoples and oppose totalitarian regimes – exemplified by the Marshall Plan. Fulton speech by Churchill. Creation of competing military alliances: NATO and Warsaw Pact further polarised the world.

Disagreements over the future of Germany

- The Potsdam Conference and policy over Germany whereby the allied sectors remained free as compared to Soviet sector which was stripped of assets as reparations. The economic status of Germany: creation of Bizonia in West. Contrast between the developing capitalist west and centrally controlled east: introduction of Deutsche mark in West led to the Berlin Blockade in 1949.

Any other relevant factors

41. The candidate evaluates the significance of domestic pressures for Kennedy as an explanation for the Cuban Crisis of 1962, using evidence and arguments such as:

Kennedy's domestic context
- US interests and investments in Cuba had been lost in the revolution.
- Cuban exiles in Florida were vocal in their demands for US action against Castro.
- Background of attempts by the CIA to destabilise Cuba. Kennedy inherited a plan to invade Cuba by exiles in order to overthrow Castro's regime. Bay of Pigs incident, 1961, where 1400 exiles landed and were crushed by Castro's army.
- American aggression seemed to be confirmed by the United States practising the invasion of a Caribbean island with a dictator named Ortsac: Operation Mongoose overseen by Robert Kennedy.

Other factors

Castro's victory in Cuba
- Castro had come to power in 1959-60 after overthrowing the corrupt, American-backed Battista regime in a Communist revolution.
- Khrushchev was sympathetic to Castro. Some historians argue that he wanted to use Cuba as a launch pad for revolution in Central America. Missile deployment would provide protection for the revolution.
- Argument that Bay of Pigs incident forced Castro to start preparing to defend himself against another attack and drew him closer to Khrushchev and the Soviet Union. Castro asked for significant conventional military aid.

US foreign policy
- The United States had placed their Jupiter missiles in Turkey and now the USSR felt very threatened. Kennedy had originally placed the Jupiter missiles in Turkey in 1961 because the United States had feared the possible nuclear capabilities of the Soviet Union. These missiles became a major threat to the Soviets because they were capable of striking anywhere in the USSR.
- In order to defend themselves, and let the United States know what it was like to be surrounded by a deadly threat, the Soviets placed missiles in Cuba. Counter view that the missiles were obsolete.

Khrushchev's domestic position
- Criticism of Khrushchev at home over cuts in the armed forces, economic failures and the issues surrounding de-Stalinisation. He believed a foreign policy coup would help improve matters for him at home.
- Foreign policy criticisms: ongoing deadlock over Berlin; shadow of events in Hungary 1956, etc.
- Rise of China as a rival for leadership of the Communist world; pressure on Khrushchev from influential circles within USSR to assert Soviet leadership.

Khrushchev's view of Kennedy
- Khrushchev felt that Kennedy was a weak president after the Bay of Pigs, June 1961 summit in Vienna to discuss Berlin; East Germany's unopposed construction of Berlin Wall. He felt that Kennedy lacked power and support to make concessions over the arms race.

Ideological differences
- America was very sensitive about the presence of Communism so close to Florida. It might be used as a launch-pad for further Communist risings in Latin America, which the US regarded as its own domain (Munro Doctrine). The huge inequalities in many Latin American countries made such risings seem possible.
- Cuba was one of a series of flash-points between Communism and Capitalism around the world, as part of the wider Cold War. This was played out at a number of levels, such as espionage and the arms race, all of which increased international tension.

Mistakes by the leaders
- The Soviets wanted to place nuclear missiles in Cuba because they were trying to balance out the number of nuclear arms between themselves and the United States. Khrushchev underestimated the US reaction.
- Kennedy's use of the media played well in the US, and to an extent in the wider world, but it meant that international diplomacy was being conducted in the full glare of the world. It made it much more difficult for either leader to back down without a major loss of face.

Any other relevant factors

42. The candidate evaluates the validity of the view that changing public opinion in the USA was the main reason why America lost the Vietnam War, using evidence and arguments such as:

Changing public opinion in the USA
- Public opposition supported by the press was probably the main reason for withdrawal. Vietnam a media war, images showed the public the brutality of war eg Mai Lai massacre. Such images damaged American claims to be the 'good guys'.
- Extent of the opposition is debated. Probably a minority in '65, growing by the time of crucial Tet offensive in '68. Oct 1969 largest anti-war protest in US history. Protestors in every major city in America. Opposition of Black Power groups. Protests could be violent: May 1970 protest at Kent State University, Ohio led to four students being shot.

Unpopularity of the draft.
- USA was a democracy: public pressure and perception mattered. Nixon noted extent of opposition: withdrawal of 60,000 troops in 1969, policy of Vietnamisation.
- Economic cost of the war: US deficit of $1.6 billion in 1965 increased to $25.3 billion in 1968. Tax increases unpopular. Congress only got involved in limiting money and action in late 60s and early 70s.
- Divisions within administrations: eg LBJ had Rusk advising to continue the struggle in South-East Asia, compared to Senator Fulbright arguing for de-escalation.

Other factors

Difficulties faced by US military
- Terrain did not suit US military strengths of airpower and firepower.
- Difficulties dealing with the conditions and knowing which Vietnamese were the enemy led to stress and confusion.
- Short commissions for officers and rotation of troops led to loss of expertise in the field.
- Soldiers brave, but a minority did not believe in the war. Many were also reluctant conscripts.

Relative strengths of North and South Vietnam
- North Vietnam: a hard peasant life bred determined soldiers. Viet Cong enlisted for years unlike American troops who signed up for a year. Belief in their cause of Communism also a factor. Great determination: eg the Ho Chi Minh trail was kept open despite American bombers continually bombing it.
- Viet Cong knew the jungle, survived in atrocious conditions, developed effective tactics and were more effective in winning the 'hearts and minds' of civilians than the Americans. Military objectives were realistic: General Giap aimed to break the will of the American Government. Support of Chinese and Soviet aid from 1965 of importance.

- Corruption and decay of South Vietnamese government, especially in Saigon. Lack of political and social cohesion in South Vietnam led to divisions and turmoil which filtered through to their armed forces.
- American accusation that the ARVN sent out 'Search and Avoid' missions rather than confront the NVA/Vietcong

Failure of military methods
- Mass bombing had no real effect according to the Jason Study by MIT in 1966, owing to the agricultural nature of North Vietnam and the widespread jungle cover.
- Tactics on the ground – US technological superiority in heavy weapons negated by the terrain.
- Widespread use of helicopter gunships – inflicted heavy casualties, but were a blunt weapon. Many civilian deaths.
- US (and South Vietnamese) lost the battle for hearts and minds, despite inflicting c2,000,000 casualties for the loss of one tenth of those.

International isolation of the USA
- The media war turned international opinion against the US.
- Major US allies had had misgivings about US military intervention; Harold Wilson's major achievement in keeping UK out of the war, despite dependence on US support for the British economy.
- Feeling that Vietnam was handing huge propaganda bonuses to the enemies and rivals of the US.

Any other relevant factors

HIGHER HISTORY PAPER 2
2014

SPECIAL TOPIC 1: THE WARS OF INDEPENDENCE, 1286-1329

1. The candidate makes a judgement on how far Source A illustrates Edward's resolution of the Great Cause in Scotland, in terms of:

Points from the source which show the candidate has interpreted the significant views:
- (Scottish nobles) John Balliol, Robert Bruce, John Comyn of Buchan and Alexander de Balliol were summoned to meet Edward I at Norham
- The Scots initially refused to cross the border into Norham…in an attempt to prove to Edward that they would not accept his authority
- Edward's threat that if denied, he would direct the English Army at Norham against the Scots
- The claimants eventually accepted the English King as overlord, out of fear of war
- Judicial process leading up to the Great Cause

Points from recall which support and develop those in the source:
- Edward saw this as an opportunity to take advantage of Scotland under its Guardians. He had a consistent policy aimed at extending his rule over the Kingdom of Scotland
- Edward refused to make a judgement on who would be King of Scotland until he was accepted as overlord. The Chief Justice Roger Brabazon asked the Scots to accept this in May 1291
- Edward I brought a huge army to Norham, 67 Northern magnates and their feudal quota of men at arms, its meaning was clear to Scotland
- The competitors to the throne finally agreed overlordship of Edward, although they may have believed in it being temporary

Points from recall which offer a wider contextualisation such as:
- Death of Alexander III, left no male heir
- The threat of Civil War in Scotland
- Edward I was experienced in European legal matters in Gascony, the Low countries, Italy and Spain
- The Treaty of Birgham, arranged marriage of Margaret, Maid of Norway to Edward of Caernarfon, Prince of Wales, 18th July 1290
- Margaret's death changed the situation completely for Edward, who was now forced to press his claim for overlordship
- Edward I announced that he intended to bring Scotland under his control, just as he had subjugated Wales
- Edward gathered his Nobles and councillors together in 1291
- The agreement of the claimants is generally known as the award of Norham, 12th June 1291
- Royal castles handed over to Edward in his capacity as overlord
- 1291-92 Edward had little time for his own political matters, due to the affairs of the Scottish Succession crisis
- Edward was Feudal Lord of Scotland and was exercising his rights to resolve the cause. In his opinion he had legal authority
- The first stages of hearings were dominated by arguments over Edward's rights of jurisdiction
- Edward established a court of 104 Auditors to hear the Competitors claims
- There was a long adjournment between August 1291 and June 1292 to assist in the claim of Florence, Court of Holland

- Descendants of David I of Scotland likely claimants
- 13 claimants to the Great Cause, only John Balliol, Robert Bruce and John Hastings rightful claims
- Summer 1292 Edward sought legal advice overseas, the issue was whether 'Proximity' (Bruce) or 'Primogeniture' (Balliol) should be preferred. Local custom was to be applied by the Feudal custom of Primogeniture
- Bruce and Hastings claim to have the Kingdom divided, was that they had no case, by then the rest of the competitors had either withdrawn, or been told their claims were invalid
- Edward's councillors unanimously agreed that the candidate descended from the younger sister, even if closer male to the throne (Bruce) should not be preferred to one descended from the elder sister (Balliol), 3rd November 1292
- Edward's decision on 17th November, 1292 after much political debate, decided John Balliol had the better legal claim
- The judgement in Balliol's favour was immediately followed by a warning that if he did not govern justly, Edward would intervene
- Edward's demand for homage for Balliol on 26th December 1292 recognised the English King's sovereign lordship
- John Balliol was possibly seen as weak enough, for Edward to put pressure on him. The English King always intended to exercise his right and authority
- John Balliol, had probably been trained for the church and not for politics and war
- The Great cause was only part of a wider story of Edward's involvement in Scottish affairs
- Guardians (Wishart) to help resolve the succession crisis
- Any other relevant points

2. The candidate makes a judgement on how useful **Source B** is as evidence of John Balliol's difficulties in ruling Scotland, 1292–1296 in terms of:

Points from the source which show the candidate has interpreted the significant views:

Origin
- It was written then adapted at the Augustinian Lanercost Priory. It covers history in both England and Scotland

Possible purpose
- To provide a possible insight into Anglo – Scottish relations in the 13th century, in particular, it is sympathetic to King Edward I

Content
- The Scots were unsuccessful in making John defy Edward, so they chose instead to replace his authority as King with a council of twelve peers
- Commanded the King of Scotland to attend his (King Edward) parliament in accordance with his legal obligation both for the Kingdom of Scotland and for lands owned by him within the English realm
- The King of England sent an expedition against the Scottish King, invading at Berwick

Points from recall which support and develop those in the source:
- In 1295, twelve new Guardians were elected by the community of the realm to defy Edward I, and decreed that King John could not act by himself
- King John had been frequently humiliated by King Edward, in his demands to make the Scottish King answer in an English court
- Edward I at the head of an impressive English army invaded Scotland on 12th March 1296. Marching first on Berwick, sacking the town, then on to Dunbar

Points from recall which offer a wider contextualisation such as:
- John Balliol was elected King of Scotland in November 1292, perhaps he was easier to manipulate, despite his better legal claim
- King John had limited political and military experience
- King John paid homage to Edward I in front of English officials in December 1292
- King Edward overruled King John's legal verdict over the Burgess of Berwick. This humiliated King John as he was seen as inferior to King Edward
- Edward threatened King John over the terms of Birgham, they were no longer enforceable
- The Bruce Dynasty did not offer support to the Balliol Kingship
- Balliol's inexperience as King meant that the Comyn's remained the dominant partner in the Scottish Royal Court
- The Burgess of Berwick took his legal complaint against the Guardians to the English King. King John had upheld the Guardians decision. Edward ordered King John to change his decision
- The Macduff case – Macduff had been disinherited from his lands and appealed to King Edward. King John was summoned to Westminster to explain his decision in 1293
- Edward's preparations for war with France in late 1294, summoned Balliol to give him military service
- Franco – Scottish treaty negotiated in October 1295 and ratified in February 1296 was directed against the King of England
- Anglo-Scottish relations rapidly turned to war after 1295
- The defeat and surrender of the Scottish Army at Battle of Dunbar, 28th April, 1296
- Edward's march north and John's humiliating surrender ceremony at Montrose on 10th July 1296
- Any other relevant points

3. The candidate makes a judgement on how fully Source C illustrates Scottish resistance to Edward I, 1296–1305, in terms of:

Points from the source which show the candidate has interpreted the significant views:
- Andrew Murray and William Wallace, leaders of the resistance army in the Kingdom of Scotland
- By your own goodwill are giving advice, help and favour, in our struggle with England, in all causes and business concerning trade with Scotland
- The Kingdom of Scotland, has been recovered from the power of the English by force of arms
- The letter is written in the name of Lord John, illustrious King of Scotland, by agreement of the community of the realm, in whom we fight for

Points from recall which support and develop those in the source:
- William Wallace first to rebel in South West of Scotland and Andrew Murray started his rebellion in the North East of Scotland
- The importance in re-establishing trading links between Germany and Scotland
- The Scottish victory at the Battle of Stirling Bridge, 11th September, 1297
- Wallace and Murray fought on as Guardians in the name of King John

Points from recall which offer a wider contextualisation such as:
- Wallace started his rebellion by the murder of Heselrig, the Sheriff of Lanark

- Wallace's military actions against the English started in May 1297, based in the Forest of Selkirk
- Murray's rebellion from May to August posed an insuperable problem to the English in the North eg castles at Urquhart, Inverness, Elgin and Banff
- Bruce and Steward raised an armed revolt at Irvine in July 1297
- The joining of Wallace and Murray, possibly around 8th September 1297
- Wallace and Murray were at the head of the Scots Army at Stirling
- The battle of the Stirling Bridge proved that the Scots could defeat a superior English Army in a pitched battle
- Andrew Murray and William Wallace appointed Guardians of Scotland
- Despite the death of Murray in November 1297, Wallace became more ambitious
- Support of the Scottish nobles in the resistance
- Despite the defeat at the Battle of Falkirk, July 1298, Wallace survived
- Wallace resigned as Guardian, but he was replaced by representatives of both the Balliol and Bruce factions, John Comyn and Robert Bruce
- Use of Guerrilla warfare
- The changing military balance between 1298 – 1303 eg castles
- Wallace's travels to France and Rome to generate support
- Wallace returned to Scotland around 1303 and rejoined the resistance
- Continued Scottish resistance and success eg Roslin 1303
- By 1304 majority of Scottish nobles had accepted Edward's authority
- Wallace fought for his King, until his betrayal, 3rd August 1305, by Sir John Menteith
- The execution of Wallace on 23rd August 1305 did not end the struggle. The importance of Wallace's reputation could be found in the subsequent actions of Bruce once he became King
- Battle of Dunbar
- Siege of Berwick
- Any other relevant points

4. The candidate makes a judgement on how far **Sources D** and **E** agree about the ambitions of Robert the Bruce:

Overall: **Source D** and **E** agree about the ambitions of Robert the Bruce because.
Developed through detail:
- Both sources agree about Bruce's ambitions. After Bannockburn, Bruce accepted that this was not an end to the Wars of Independence. The military conflict had produced a decisive victory for Scotland and Bruce. His political authority could be asserted with his increased confidence. Bruce set about removing his enemies, amongst the Scots, by holding a Parliament and asserting his legal authority by passing new legislation, forcing the Scottish nobles to choose their loyalty. There is a slight overall disagreement between Source D, which sees a move towards peace (a political option), although Source E recognises the need for continuance of the war (the military option).

Source D
- Robert Bruce had no wish to prolong the war. He saw his victory, above all, as an opportunity for reconciliation and peace: with the Scottish nobles who had fought against him, with the English whom he had defeated.
- In November 1314 Bruce with increased confidence, convened a Parliament at Cambuskenneth.
- Scottish landowners who had failed to offer allegiance by that date should be disinherited.
- They (Scottish landowners) could no longer be feudatories in two countries and serve two kings. They must choose their nationality once and for all.

Source E
- Few battles in history are truly decisive, and Bannockburn was no exception. The war was nowhere near an end, the military campaign would continue, despite his hopes for peace.
- In the November, after the battle, Bruce was ready to take the next step, the Scots Parliament met at Cambuskenneth Abbey.
- The new class of the 'disinherited' were men on the English side…men…who…held estates in Scotland.
- Landowners could no longer have divided political loyalties: they had to choose one side or the other.

SPECIAL TOPIC 2: THE AGE OF REFORMATION, 1542-1603

1. The candidate makes a judgement on how far Source A explains the weakness of the Catholic Church in Scotland between 1542 and 1560 in terms of:

Points from the source which show the candidate has interpreted the significant views:
- The wellbeing of religious orders varied from one order to another and from one religious house to another.
- Monasteries were criticised as being out of touch with the needs of sixteenth century society.
- Economic pressures on monasteries – such as huge tax demands – meant that they were forced to rent out property to help them survive.
- To supplement their income, parish priests resorted to pluralism or imposed unpopular charges on their parishioners.

Points from recall which support and develop those in the source:
- For some time the Catholic Church had suffered from a decline of monasticism and corruption in nunneries.
- Over the years the Catholic Church had accrued money and land and was far wealthier than the king. During the reign of James V, the Church had an income of approximately £300,000 a year, while the king had less than £20,000 to pay for governing the country. This led to resentment and Scottish monarchs sought ways in which to get money from the Church which caused weakness.
- The Church in Scotland had to pay taxes to the king. To raise the money, the Church rented out its land to local nobles.
- Some clergy were given several positions/parishes. These 'pluralists' collected several salaries but could not do all of the work properly. Some parish priests worked hard for the people in their parish, others did little.

Points from recall which offer a wider contextualisation such as:

- Monarchs gave jobs to minors, relatives and other nobles who wanted the income but not the religious duties.
- Some good clergymen were reluctant to become parish priests because the work was so poorly paid and the quality of parish priests declined. Parishes suffered.
- Many clergy lacked knowledge of scripture and the Catholic faith.
- Clergy were supposed to be celibate but many kept a 'wife' and many had children.
- Illegitimate sons of clergy often inherited parishes from their father.
- Leaders of the Church in Scotland were disliked: Cardinal Beaton persecuted Protestants, executing the poplar preacher, George Wishart in 1546. Anger and resentment towards the church increased.
- In May 1546, some Scottish Protestants – seeking revenge for Wishart's death – broke into St Andrews Castle and murdered Cardinal Beaton. As a clever and powerful leader his loss was a blow to the Catholic Church.
- In 1557, some Protestant Lords organised themselves as 'Lords of the Congregation' to promote the Protestant religion in Scotland.
- During the winter of 1558-59 the 'Beggars' Summons' demanded that the friars leave their friaries claiming they were rich and ungodly and that the needs of the poor were greater.
- Mary of Guise, following the advice of the French and the Pope began to prosecute the reformers. The reformers began to seek secret help from England. In the spring of 1559, the towns of Dundee and Perth announced that they were Protestant.
- John Knox landed at Leith on 2 May, 1559. He made his way to Perth, where on 11 May he preached at St John's Church. His sermon was followed by a riot. Many religious houses in and around Perth were attacked and their religious statues, shrines and other decorations were smashed. Disenchantment with the Catholic Church was spreading.
- None of the bishops actively opposed reformation in 1560. Three joined the Protestants.
- Any other relevant points.

2. The candidate makes a judgement on how useful Source B is in explaining the contribution Mary, Queen of Scots made to the loss of her throne in terms of:

Points from the source which show the candidate has interpreted the significant views:

Origin

- The source was written by the Earl of Bothwell, Mary's husband, reflecting on events at Carberry Hill. Bothwell's account is clearly biased and seeks to gain sympathy for the Queen and demonstrate how the Lords betrayed her.

Possible Purpose

- To explain how Mary was deceived by the Protestant Lords who had promised her safe passage to Edinburgh, when in fact they intended to imprison her.

Content

- Bothwell had repeatedly denied involvement in the death of King Henry, and had many enemies.
- At Carberry Hill his enemies, the Lords made out that they had been sent to offer the Queen genuine loyalty and safe-conduct which she foolishly believed.
- Mary trusted that this promise would be honoured by the two armies and asked Bothwell to return to Dunbar where she would shortly meet him.

Points from recall which support and develop those in the source:

- Mary and Bothwell married in a Protestant Service. Her reputation was ruined: she had married her husband's murderer and appeared to have abandoned the Catholic Church.
- Mary and Bothwell fled from Borthwick to gather an army in the Borders. On 15 June 1566, the Protestant nobles faced Mary and Bothwell at Carberry Hill. Talks lasted throughout the day ending with Protestant Lords agreeing to obey Mary if she sent Bothwell away.
- During the talks Mary waited until Bothwell had a chance to escape before agreeing to accompany the lords.
- As soon as Mary reached the Protestant Lords she discovered that the troops opposed her. They cried 'Burn the whore!' She had the same reception in Edinburgh before being sent to Lochleven Castle.

Points from recall which offer a wider contextualisation:

- Following Darnley's murder, posters appeared in Edinburgh accusing Bothwell of the crime. They also showed Mary as a mermaid – the symbol for a prostitute. Stories about Mary re-marrying spread across Scotland, England and Europe.
- After Mary was imprisoned in Lochleven Castle some nobles seized power for themselves. On the 24th July 1567, Mary was forced to abdicate in favour of her son James and Moray was declared regent.
- Any other relevant points

3. The candidate makes a judgement on how fully **Source C** explains the relationship between monarch and Kirk in the reign of James VI in terms of:

Points from the source which show the candidate has interpreted the significant views:

- Although James had a Protestant education, the Kirk remained suspicious of the king.
- James's belief that kings should have control over the church led to a powerful struggle which was present throughout his reign.
- James favouring of Catholic noblemen further increased the suspicion of the Kirk.
- From 1588 – 1590 harmony between the Kirk and the king increased.

Points from recall which support and develop those in the source:

- James was viewed with suspicion because of friendships with people like the Catholic Earl of Huntly.
- James's friendship with Catholics may have been a means of avoiding papal excommunication.
- In 1589 the king took action against the Catholic nobles who rebelled in March of that year, gaining support from the Kirk.
- James marriage to a Protestant princess, Anna, daughter of the Danish king in the same year also gained greater approval, although even Lutherans were viewed with suspicion by some.

Points from recall which offer a wider contextualisation such as:

- The Second Book of Discipline (1578) had proposed a Presbyterian Kirk which could make the church independent of the King and his nobility.
- By 1581 plans to establish 13 Presbyteries appeared to challenge royal authority.
- In 1582, a group of Presbyterians sought to take control of the government by kidnapping the king. The 'Ruthven Raid', as it is known, was designed to increase their hold on power by controlling the king.

- In 1584, all ministers were required to accept the 'Black Acts' abolishing Presbyteries and asserting royal authority over the Kirk forcing some into exile.
- In 1592 the 'Golden Act' accepted the recovery of Presbyterian influence within the Kirk, but did not reduce the power of the king.
- Relations with the Kirk deteriorated after 1592, leading to conflict in 1596.
- James' belief in the divine right of monarchs clashed with the Melvillians' view that the Monarch should be accountable to the authority of the Kirk.
- Extreme Presbyterians/Melvillians were marginalised on account of James' views.
- James sought to extend the power of the monarch and bishops over the Kirk by: having bishops recognised as moderators of Presbyteries; allowing them to hear cases of excommunication and deposition of ministers.
- Elders were excluded from Presbyteries and the monarch had the power to determine the time and place of the General Assembly.
- James would ensure that the General Assembly would meet in towns like Perth or Aberdeen where he could expect more ministers to support him.
- As a result of rebellion in December 1596, James fled from Edinburgh and made him more determined to control the Kirk.
- 1597 riot in Edinburgh after a sermon preached against the king. James VI had the ministers of Edinburgh briefly imprisoned. The king ordered that no minister was to be appointed without his consent.
- In 1597, Andrew Melville was deposed as rector of St Andrews.
- James attended every General Assembly from 1597 to 1603, by which time assemblies were becoming more agreeable to the King's aims.
- In his writings, James asserted that no human institution could limit the powers of a monarch.
- James preferred form of Church government was by bishops and in 1600 he appointed three bishops to Parliament.
- Further detail of Trew Law and Basilikon Doron.
- Any other relevant points.

4. The candidate makes a judgement on how far **Sources D** and **E** agree about the impact of the Reformation in terms of:

Overall both sources agree that the Reformation brought changes in the practice and ministering of faith in Scotland. The sources agree on the importance of the influence and role of the minister on the lives of his congregation and the strong sense of discipline instilled by the Kirk.

Source D	Source E
• In Fife, Protestant ministers appointed to parishes were well educated.	• In the Reformed church, ministers must be educated and godly and appointed following election, examination and admission.
• By the seventeenth century ministers and elders were imposing a strict programme of discipline for minor offences such as drunkenness	• For faults such as drunkenness, fighting and common swearing, the offender must be called before the minister, elders and deacons and admit to his sin.

Source D (continued)

- Evidence suggests that people accepted the need for this disciplinary system even though they were not always so content when they were the ones to have offended.
- The role of psalm, prayer and in some cases poetry and song were important in spreading Protestant doctrines and values.

Source E (continued)

- Individuals accept discipline and must appear before the whole church to repent, before being received again into the society of the church.
- All persons should be encouraged to learn the Psalms and when the Psalms are sung, they may be the more able with common heart and voice to praise God.

SPECIAL TOPIC 3: THE TREATY OF UNION, 1689-1740

1. The candidate makes a judgement on how far Source A explains the relationship between the Scottish Parliament and England in terms of:

Points from the source which show the candidate has interpreted the significant views:
- English parliament passed Act of Settlement, ensuring the Hanoverian succession.
- Scottish parliament passed Act anent Peace and War giving the Scottish Parliament the right to consultation before Scotland became involved in a war.
- Scottish parliament passed Act of Security stated that they would name Queen Anne's successor.
- English parliament passed Alien Act threatening Scots would be treated as aliens unless Scotland accepted the Hanoverian succession.

Points from recall which support and develop those in the source:
- Series of laws passed in Scotland and England created climate of distrust.
- Act of Security asserted Scottish independence.

Points from recall which offer a wider contextualisation such as:
- Opposition to King William in the Highlands due to Scottish parliament's judgement that the Glencoe Massacre was an act of murder.
- Scots parliament disagreed with England over status of the monarchy: in England there remained a notion of monarchical rights whereas in Scotland the Claim of Right and Articles of Grievance of 1689 suggested a notion of a monarch bound by contract.
- Scottish parliament objected to King William and English ministers seeking to gain advantage over Scottish interests, eg England's role in failure of Darien Scheme.
- Successive appointments to posts in Scottish government were awarded to those who were subservient to English command.
- Some Scottish members of parliament felt England had ruined Scotland by giving land and pensions as bribes to Scottish government officers.
- Members, eg Lord Belhaven, felt Scotland was a conquered province of England.
- Scottish MPs felt King William in England did not do enough to support them through the "ill" Years of famine and poor harvests in the 1690s.
- Scottish parliament was aggrieved by the English Navigation Acts and the effect of English wars or military intervention on Scottish trade.
- Many Scottish MPs had been hit badly by the cost of the Darien Scheme and held England responsible for this.

- Scottish parliament passed the Wool Act and Wine Act in 1703; Scotland would continue to trade when England was at war.
- Scottish parliamentary opposition to the Anglican church. [Episcopalian Church in Scotland?]
- Some Scottish MPs still upheld the Covenanters' objections to monarchical interference in church affairs
- English parliament through King William discouraged Dutch investment in the Darien Scheme.

2. The candidate makes a judgement on how useful **Source B** is as evidence of attitudes towards union in Scotland in terms of:

Points from the source which show the candidate has interpreted the significant views:

Origin
- Address sent by Dunbar Town Council, read to parliament during the debates.

Possible purpose
- To give reasons for opposing union with England.

Content
- the treaty will damage trade with Holland or other overseas markets.
- the treaty will badly affect the salt industry in Scotland.
- the treaty will badly affect Scotland and its fishing trade.

Points from recall which support and develop those in the source:
- Over 90 addresses/petitions were sent to Parliament by burghs, royal burghs and town councils during the debates, warning against passing the treaty in its proposed form.
- Many councils did wish for a closer relationship with England but did not wish it to take the form of the treaty as negotiated during 1706.
- Fishing districts objected greatly to the increase in salt duty 7 years after the treaty.

Points from recall which offer a wider contextualisation such as:

- **Attitudes against union:**
  - Increased taxation.
  - Scottish manufactures would be ruined.
  - Royal burghs would be deprived of rights.
  - Fear of loss of European trade.
  - British parliament would favour English trade over Scottish.
  - English currency, weights and measures to be introduced.
  - Public opinion against union.
  - Scotland would be suppressed as a nation.
  - Scotland would lose its heritage as an independent sovereign state.
  - Reduction in status of Scottish nobility in British parliament.
  - Scots Episcopalians opposed union and Hanoverian succession – only Stuart dynasty might restore episcopacy to Scottish church.
  - Protestants feared a British parliament dominated by Anglican Episcopalian church with bishops' seats in the House of Lords.
  - Scots liberties at risk.

- **Attitudes for union:**
  - Advantages in commerce and trade
  - Economy would improve – national produce would increase
  - Scotland's trade would catch up with other European nations'.
  - Free trade with English colonies.
  - Protection of being in Great Britain.
  - Common interests already with England.

- Advantages of Scottish politicians being part of the court of the king in London.
- Hanoverian succession offered security to Protestantism.
- Threat from "Popery" reduced.
- Property preserved.

3. The candidate makes a judgement on how fully **Source C** explains the reasons for the passing of the Treaty of Union in terms of:

Points from the source which show the candidate has interpreted the significant views:
- Protestantism confirmed as the true religion of Scotland.
- Monarchy not to alter religion in Scotland from now on.
- Presbyterianism established as the method for church governance.
- University, college and school appointees to be members of the Church of Scotland.

Points from recall which support and develop those in the source:
- Act of Security for the Kirk made many Scottish MPs less hostile to union, if not in favour of it, and turned some Scottish MPs in favour of it.
- English spies, including Daniel Defoe, advised government of proceedings in Scottish Parliament and suggested that securing the Kirk would bode well for the eventual votes on the articles of the treaty.

Points from recall which offer a wider contextualisation such as:
- The Equivalent payment persuaded some Scottish MPs to vote for union.
- The Equivalent: £398,085.10s to cover the taking in of English debt.
- Equivalent effectively compensated for Darien, so took edge off opposition to union.
- Squadrone Volante, whose hold on the balance of power was crucial, were persuaded to vote for the Union by the Equivalent.
- Bribery of Scottish ministers/politicians through £20,000 issued to Earl of Glasgow by English government to distribute as "arrears in pay".
- Promise of favours, pensions, military patronage high-ranking positions and cash ensured government majorities; threats of loss of civil list pension.
- Political management of Court party better than Country party.
- Court members consistently voted through all Articles of the Treaty.
- Role of Hamilton as an erratic and divisive leader of Country party.
- Hamilton may have been bribed by the Court party.
- Hamilton refused to participate in planned walkout of parliament.
- Failed armed rising proved opponents of union were unwilling to engage in violence.
- Economic assurances, incentive of free trade with England and English colonies.
- Payment made to wool industry.
- Payment of Scottish public debt.
- Last minute concessions by Godolphin on tax issues, eg salt, liquor.
- Incentives for Scottish nobles regarding retained privileges, seats in House of Lords.
- Rights of burghs and Royal Burghs to remain.
- Legal protection, Scottish law and courts to remain.
- Future stability within one kingdom secured; peace secure by being in Great Britain.
- Military argument; threat of English invasion as forces moved north in late 1706.

- English and Scottish parliaments in agreement over union for the first time.
- Security of liberty and stability under one parliament.
- Any other relevant points.

4. Overall **Source D** and **Source E** agree that tax increased for Scots but there were military and trade advantages; **Source D** refers to the attempt to repeal union in 1713, **Source E** emphasises the migration of Scots to the Empire.

Source D	*Source E*
• Increased duties, eg malt tax	• Increased tax burden, eg salt and linen
• Golden opportunity for landowners and merchants	• Scottish landed elites presented with a golden opportunity
• Association with England's military force allowed prosperity	• Obvious benefit of English naval protection for the trade
• Scots involved in overseas trade through colonies	• Employment of Scots in colonial trade

SPECIAL TOPIC 4: MIGRATION AND EMPIRE, 1830–1939

1. The candidate makes a judgement on how far Source A shows the reasons for internal migration within Scotland in terms of:

Points from the source which show the candidate has interpreted the significant views:
- Fears of committing to long distance migration – those who would have gone to America, had the prospects been favourable, have preferred a home migration.
- Migration to the southern parts of Scotland particularly Glasgow and Paisley where the textile mills cry out for more workers.
- Seasonal migration – a constant pressure to move through lack of land and money, a pressure made less by the employment given in lowland farms during the harvest.
- From other parts, the homeless made by the arrival of sheep.

Points from recall which support and develop those in the source:
- Employment opportunities in central belt.
- Effects of the Agricultural Revolution on farming and employment.
- Easier transport links to urban centres with development of railways and coastal traffic.
- Agricultural improvement in Lowlands caused move to cities.
- Technological change reduced jobs in rural areas.
- Attractions of the "big city" – employment, better wages, easier work.
- Dangers and difficulties of migration overseas leading to significant return rate.
- The Highland Problem – absentee landlords, rising rents, falling income, overpopulation, subdivision of land into crofts, 'Balmoralism and the romance of the empty glens'.
- The Highland Clearances – the attempt to increase income from Highland estates by 'industrialising' it and optimising income by creating profitable sheep farms that need grazing land but do not need local people living there.

Points from recall which offer a wider contextualisation such as:
- Domineering landlords and lack of real opportunities encouraged emigration from the Highlands of Scotland.
- Development of tourism in Highlands – deer stalking and grouse shooting reducing.
- Failure of the kelp and herring industries.
- Effects of Industrial Revolution on craftsmen.
- Potato famine in Highlands and Islands.

- Harsh employment conditions on the land.
- Easy to find factory and labouring jobs eg navvying, building reservoirs etc.
- Growing demand for domestic help in cities
- Any other relevant points.

2. The candidate makes a judgement on how useful **Source B** is as evidence of the experience of relations between immigrants and native Scots in terms of:

Origin
- Memories of a first generation Jewish Scot.
- Primary source evidence of a Jewish boy growing up in Scotland.
- Evidence from the early 20th century therefore relevant to the period of investigation.

Possible purpose
- As an archive to record the experiences of his family arriving in Glasgow in the part of an archive organised to collect and retain information about Jewish immigrants to Scotland and their assimilation into Scottish society.

Content
- When I went to school I was the only Jewish kid in class, in fact I was the only Jewish kid in school.
- I was knocked around a lot. The kids used to crowd around me, pinch my lunch from me and shout 'You German Jew, You German Jew'.
- Jews created their own businesses that tended to employ other Jews – "I went to work in a warehouse and the Jewish manager there....."

Points from recall which support and develop those in the source:
- Jewish migration limited in size and focussed in Glasgow are in late 19th century so Alec would not be among an extended Jewish community in Ayr.
- Anti-German propaganda around time of Great War created poisonous atmosphere against anyone sounding foreign.
- Lack of local knowledge about Jews and their experiences before arrival in Scotland.
- Stereotypical Jewish jobs especially around Glasgow eg tailoring.
- Assimilation by name changing.

Points from recall which offer a wider contextualisation such as:

Jews
- Anti-Semitism never that widespread, possibly owing to low numbers of Jewish immigrants in relation to other groups.
- Prejudice and discrimination affected the Jews in Scotland – The Daily Record – Aug 1905 'Alien Danger: Immigrants infected with loathsome disease'.
- Very few Jews received any help from local poor relief. It was members of the Jewish community that helped each other eg The Glasgow Jewish Board of Guardians and the Hebrew Ladies Benevolent Society in 1901 were dealing with 500 cases of needy Jews.

Lithuanians
- Between 1860s and 1914 about 7000 Lithuanians decided to settle in Scotland.
- Scots complained about the Lithuanians being dirty and immoral but soon most were accepted.
- At first Lithuanians used as strike breakers but soon Lithuanians joined with the local workers and joined the strikes.

Italians
- Assimilation of Italians helped by popularity of ice cream parlours and fish and chip shops

- Young Italians soon adopted local speech patterns due to frequency of contact in catering trade.
- Some tension between Catholic Italians and Presbyterian Scots.
- Italian cafés criticised by Scottish Presbyterian church leaders for opening on the Sabbath.
- Italian café owners also met with criticism from local people who claimed the cafés were sometimes the scenes of unruly behaviour.
- There was a greater degree of acceptance of Italian cafés from the Temperance Movement as the cafés chose not to sell alcohol.

Catholic Irish
- Often resented as competition for jobs.
- Blamed for spread of diseases and poverty.
- Catholic Irish workers were also accused of being strike-breakers and being willing to work for less money than Scottish workers.
- Often blamed for being 'benefit scroungers' claiming poor relief after 3 years residence.
- The Catholic Irish had a shared experience with the Scottish worker in that they were affected by industrialisation, urbanisation, as well as fighting together during the First World War.
- Even into the 1930s Catholic Irish faced persecution, sometimes organised by Church of Scotland.

Protestant Irish
- Irish Protestants had a lot in common with the average Scot – long term and deeply embedded cultural interaction between Ulster and lowland Scotland.
- Much easier assimilation because of religion.
- The first Scottish Orange Lodge opened in 1800 in the weaving centre of Maybole in Ayrshire. The growth of the lodge system in Scotland shows the spread of Irish Protestantism.

3. The candidate makes a judgement on how fully **Source C** illustrates the impact of Scots emigrants upon the Empire in terms of:

Points from the source which show the candidate has interpreted the significant views:
- Sir John MacDonald, Glasgow born, was the father of the Canadian Confederation and the first Prime Minister.
- Toronto Globe, founded and ruled by Scotsman George Brown.
- The names of Sir Alexander Mackenzie and Simon Fraser are remembered in the Mackenzie and Fraser rivers.
- Donald Smith was one of the founders of the Canadian Pacific Railway which linked Canada. The completion point was named Craigellachie, in memory of where Smith was born in Scotland.

Points from recall which support and develop those in the source:
- Scots gave a thorough and honest character to Canadian business and financial life.
- George Stephen organising finance and creation of Canadian Pacific Railroad.
- Scots' control of the fur trade.
- Religious development through Church of Scotland.
- Contribution to laws and learning/education (eg McGill University).

Points from recall which offer a wider contextualisation such as:

Australia
- farming/sheep grazing and the wool trade.

- Scots also invested heavily in mining/the Gold Rush of the 1850s brought to Australia a considerable number if Scottish miners and many gold camps were recognisably "Scottish".
- Shipping and trade were other areas of enterprise in which Scots excelled. An example is McIllwrath McEachen and Burns Phillips.
- Scots played large part in creating the sugar boom of the 1880s in Northern Queensland.
- Role of Church of Scotland in developing education in Australia, eg Australia College, Scots College in Melbourne, and influence of development of Melbourne and Sydney universities.
- Negative impact on indigenous people: Warrigal Creek massacre

New Zealand
- Scots founded banks and financial institutions as well as having a political impact.
- Scottish influence on NZ education.
- Negative impact on indigenous people.

India
- Scot's impact on education, the development of the banking system.
- Many Indian institutions such as elite schools, universities and press owed much to Scottish emigrants.
- Scots' contribution to development of tea plantations and the jute industry.
- Role of Scots in suppression of First Indian War of Independence/Indian mutiny
- Role of Scots as Viceroys: Dalhousie
- Any other relevant points.

4. The candidate makes a judgement as to how far **Sources D** and **E** agree about the impact of the Empire on Scotland in terms of:

Overall: Both sources agree that Dundee was the centre of the Jute industry in Scotland and some families made fortunes out of the trade. Some of the profits were used to build large mansions in the suburbs and also to reinvest and develop landed estates. They also agree that once Bengal developed its own Jute production factories then hard times fell on Dundee.

In detail:

Source D	Source E
• For a time Dundee could boast the title Juteopolis, the jute capital of the world, exporting to the world and especially the Empire.	• Dundee developed a way of turning jute fibre from Bengal into a useable cloth….that supplied the Empire with cloth sacking.
• Jute and linen barons such as the Baxter Brothers and the Gilroys who were amassing great fortunes from the growing trade, some of which were devoted to the construction of palatial mansions on the outskirts of the city in West Ferry and Broughty Ferry.	• The display of their wealth and confidence can be seen in the growth of elegant suburbs such as Broughty Ferry near Dundee.
• Their money was also used to purchase great country estates further away from Dundee.	• Money from the Indian textile trade was used by Alisdair Forbes to purchase and improve country estates in the Strathdon area.

Source D (continued)

- Competition was growing from Indian jute mills…but after the war the advantages of Empire trade that had made Dundee boom now deserted the town.

Source E (continued)

- Empire…became serious competitors for Scottish producers…by 1914 Bengal jute mills were making huge profits…employment levels in the Jute industry in Scotland fell between 1929 and 1939.

SPECIAL TOPIC 5: THE IMPACT OF THE GREAT WAR, 1914-1928

1. The candidate makes a judgement on how far Source A on the Western Front explains the contribution of Scots to the military effort in terms of:

Points from the source which show the candidate has interpreted the significant views:

- Haig mentions the huge contribution made by Scots in the war.
- Haig mentions his sympathy for those mourning the countless thousands of Scotsmen who died.
- Haig mentions the thanks he owes to McCrae's battalion giving tribute to them for serving their country so well on 1st July at the Somme.
- Haig states that Scotsmen served their country well which offers some consolation.

Points from recall which support and develop those in the source:

- Details specific to McCrae's battalion - the 16th was raised in Edinburgh in less than a fortnight by Sir George McCrae, many Hearts players enlisted. Four years later, there was barely a player left who had survived unscathed.
- Involvement of Scottish divisions – 9th, 15th and 51st (Highland).
- Involvement of McCrae's battalion and Cranston's battalion in the initial assault at La Boiselle.
- Scottish losses on first day – 16th (McCrae's Battalion) Royal Scots lost 12 officers and 573 soldiers; 15th lost 18 officers and 610 soldiers; 51st Highland Division suffered 3,500 casualties.
- Somme success – the 51st (Highland) Division launched a successful attack at Beaumont Hamel with relatively few casualties in November 1918.
- Role of Haig at the Somme.
- Details of the attacks on Munich and Frankfurt trenches by 16th Highland Light Infantry (Glasgow Boys Brigade).

Points from recall which offer a wider contextualisation such as:

- Scale of contribution – the huge number of Scots volunteering across the country as 'war fever' took hold.
- Contribution of the kilted regiments on the Western Front – Black Watch, Queen's Own Cameron Highlanders, Gordon Highlanders, Argyll and Sutherland Highlanders…
- Reputation of Scots – the 'ladies from hell'.
- Scots bravery – important contribution as 'shock troops'.
- Contribution of the pipers.
- Individual heroism - VC winners such as Laidlaw.
- Detail of Scots contribution at the battle of Loos.
- Role of Haig at Loos – 'unfavourable ground', use of gas, problem with reserves.
- Loos casualties – 20,598 names of the dead on the memorial at Loos – one third are Scottish.
- Detail of Scots regiments at the battle of Arras.
- Details of casualty rates.
- Overall losses of Scots – estimated deaths well over 100,000 (148,000 is accepted as possible total number of deaths).

- Contribution of Haig overall.
- Contribution of Scottish doctors and nurses such as Elsie Inglis
- Any other relevant points

2. The candidate makes a judgement on how useful **Source B** is as evidence of the impact of the war on Scottish women in terms of:

Points from the source which show the candidate has interpreted the significant views:

Origin
- Contemporary source from a journalist who had visited the Gretna Munitions Work in 1916

Possible purpose
- To inform people of the vital work done by 'munitionettes'. (West, a feminist, was keen to demonstrate the importance of women).

Content
- The girls work 12 hour shifts and stay on site in barracks.
- They have to be prepared for emergencies like explosions facing more danger than men on home defence.
- It is due to their efforts that the amount of cordite produced is so great and for which the country owes them a great debt.

Points from recall which support and develop those in the source:

- By the end of the war 31,500 women were working in the munitions industry.
- Detail on the Gretna works – 9000 women and 5000 men worked there living in a purpose-built village that connected with the works via a light railway. They worked twelve-hour shifts and the work was dangerous. Order was maintained by the Women's Police Service.
- Dangers from TNT poisoning – sickness, yellow skin (canaries) and orange hair but medical problems in the future such as being sterile.

Points from recall which offer a wider contextualisation such as:

- Other work done by women such as VAD nurses.
- Scottish Women's Hospitals and Dr. Elsie Inglis.
- Women taking on jobs previously done by men, doing the same job but not getting the same wage.
- Many women now 'head of the house' as their men were away at war. Looking after families as well as working.
- Had to cope with worry/grief as well as getting on with things.
- Women worked on the trams, the railways, the shipyards and in the rubber industry.
- Continuation of work in the Jute industry.
- Dilution of labour allowed women into previously skilled engineering jobs.
- Women were becoming more involved in politics – Helen Crawfurd, Mary Barbour, Agnes Dollan and Jessie Stephens.
- Role of women in the rent strikes.
- Role of women in the Peace Crusade.
- Any other relevant points.

3. The candidate makes a judgement on how fully **Source C** describes the impact of the war on the Scottish economy between 1914 and 1928 in terms of:

Points from the source which show the candidate has interpreted the significant views:

- Scottish economy was ruined by war with overseas trade disrupted and slow to recover.
- Those returning from war faced poor prospects of getting jobs in agriculture, fishing and heavy industries and unemployment grew in the 1920s.

- Shortage of land in the Highlands and Islands caused problems and land raids continued.
- Thousands decided to emigrate helped by the free passage scheme for ex-servicemen and women.

Points from recall which support and develop those in the source:
- Post-war Scotland suffered badly from the slump in the world economy.
- Industries like shipbuilding, mining and engineering were badly hit and because these were the main industries in Scotland, the economy suffered more than in the rest of Britain.
- The 1920s also saw significant emigration from Scotland by people seeking a better life elsewhere. Push factors such as overcrowding and poor housing, poverty at home.
- Many of the people who emigrated came from rural Scotland, where the on-going land issue and land raids continued to be problems.

Points from recall which offer a wider contextualisation such as:
- Problems in agriculture continued as competition came after the war from cheap foreign imports of food like refrigerated meat from Argentina, frozen lamb and tinned fruit from Australia and New Zealand.
- The collapse of foreign markets for herring greatly affected the fishing industry - European countries started to compete strongly with Scottish fleets and in 1920 the government removed the guaranteed price for the herring. The price of herring dropped dramatically; it was no longer profitable; and for twenty years the industry went into a steep decline.
- Post-war decline of the jute industry – During the war Dundee's jute industry boomed as demand for sack cloth rose but after the war the industry faced direct competition from Calcutta in world markets. Price of goods collapsed resulting in mass unemployment, deep social misery and discontent especially in Dundee and several firms went into liquidation.
- Problems in heavy industries like coal, iron and steel: demand for iron decreased during the war years. Demand for steel increased during the war as it was needed for the shipbuilding industry but other countries increased their steel making during the war years and Scots manufacturers could not compete. As a result the iron and steel industries were severely affected by the downturn in demand from 1921 onwards.
- The decline of shipbuilding – the immediate impact of war on Clydeside shipyards was very positive and profits were good. However, after the war a return to competitive tendering along with the decline in the demand for steel and for ships, foreign competition, labour disputes and a shortage of manpower and materials all led to problems and shipbuilding went into decline.
- Attractions of Canada and the other Dominions, pull factors such as the availability of land, better employment opportunities caused many economically active Scots to emigrate.
- War time was positive for many of the staple Scottish industries. Jute saw an increase in demand for sandbags, etc.
- Shipbuilding saw a boom to replace lost shipping.
- Diversification of firms like Beardmores from shipbuilding to tanks to airships.
- Scottish agriculture benefited through government purchase of wool clip for uniforms and oats for horse feed.
- Any other relevant points.

4. The candidate makes a judgement on how far Sources D and E agree about the events on 'Red Clydeside' 1919 in terms of:

Overall: **Source D** and **Source E** agree that the police attacked using batons and that the strike leaders tried to disperse the crowd peacefully, but the police did not listen. Both sources agree that David Kirkwood was attacked, but they disagree over whether the attack on the strikers was planned by the Government or whether the situation was simply misread by them.

Developed through detail:

Source D	*Source E*
• Police were ordered to draw their batons and forcibly disperse the crowd.	• The outnumbered and nervous police charged with batons raised to try to clear the tramlines.
• Willie Gallacher of the CWC urged the crowd to disperse.	• Gallacher's horrified reaction was to try to get the crowd to disperse.
• Davie Kirkwood was thrown to the ground in attack.	• Kirkwood was trying to pacify the crowd when he was beaten to the ground by police truncheons.
• The attack on the strikers was a prearranged affair with the attack on the strikers being deliberately planned and ordered.	• The 'riot' was not planned, that the situation was misread and violence erupted not because of a revolutionary plot but because the government, seems to have taken the possibility of revolution seriously.

Acknowledgements

Permission has been sought from all relevant copyright holders and Hodder Gibson is grateful for the use of the following:

An extract from 'Robert Bruce' by G.W.S. Barrow, published by Edinburgh University Press 1988 (2012 page 2);

An extract from 'Sir William Wallace' by A.F. Murison, published by Waverley Books Ltd, 2000 (2012 page 3);

An extract from 'Kings and Queens of Scotland' by Richard Oram, published by The History Press Ltd 2006 (2012 page 3);

An extract from 'John Knox' by Rosalind K. Marshall, published by Birlinn Ltd 2000 (2012 page 4);

An extract from 'Scotland: A History' by Jenny Wormald, published by Oxford University Press 2005 (2012 page 4);

An extract from 'The Scottish Reformation' by Ian B. Cowan, published by St Martin's Press 1982 © Macmillan Education (2012 page 5);

An extract from 'The Scots and the Union' by Christopher A. Whatley, published by Edinburgh University Press 2006 (2012 page 6);

An extract from 'The History Of The Union Of Great Britain' by Daniel Defoe, published by The Heirs Of Anderson 1709 (public domain) (2012 page 6);

An extract from 'The Price of Scotland: Darien, Union and the Wealth of Nations' by Douglas Watt, published by Luath Press Ltd 2007 (2012 page 6);

An extract from 'The Union of 1707' by Paul Henderson Scott, published by The Saltire Society 2006 (2012 page 7);

An extract from the Scotsman, 20 February 1923, 'Emigration boom in the Hebrides' © The Scotsman Publications Ltd. (2012 page 8);

An extract from 'New Arrivals' by Tony Jaconelli taken from www.ourglasgowstory.com (2012 page 8);

An extract from 'Irish Immigrants and Scottish Society in the Nineteenth and Twentieth Centuries', edited by T.M. Devine, published by John Donald 1991. Reproduced by permission of Birlinn Ltd. www.birlinn.co.uk (2012 page 9);

An extract from 'Private 12768: Memoir of a Tommy' by John Jackson, published by The History Press Ltd 2004 (2012 page 10);

An extract from The Glasgow Herald, 29th October 1915 © Herald & Times Group (2012 page 10);

An extract from 'The Scottish Economy and the First World War' from Clive H. Lee, taken from 'Scotland and the Great War' edited by C.M.M. MacDonald and E.W. McFarland, published by Tuckwell Press 1999. Reproduced by permission of Birlinn Ltd. www.birlinn.co.uk (2012 page 10);

An extract from 'Scottish Popular Politics: From Radicalism to Labour' by W. Hamish Fraser, published by Edinburgh University Press 2000 (2012 page 11);

An extract from 'Robert the Bruce's Rivals: The Comyns, 1212–1314' by Alan Young, published by Tuckwell Press Ltd, 1997 (2013 page 2);

An extract from 'The Scottish Civil War: The Bruces and Balliols and the War for Control of Scotland 1286–1356' by Michael Penman, published by The History Press Ltd 2002 (2013 page 2);

An extract from 'The Age of Reformation: The Tudor and Stewart Realms 1485–1603 (Religion, Politics and Society in Britain)' by Alec Ryrie, published by Longman 2009 © Pearson Education (2013 page 4);

An extract from 'Mary, Queen of Scots, and the Murder of Lord Darnley' by Alison Weir, published by Vintage, 2008 © The Random House Group Ltd (2013 page 4);

An extract from 'Court, Kirk and Community: Scotland 1470–1625' by Jenny Wormald, published by Edinburgh University Press 1981 (2013 page 5);

An extract from 'The Union of 1707' by Paul Henderson Scott, published by The Saltire Society 2006 (2013 page 6);

An extract from 'The Scots and the Union' by Christopher A. Whately, published by Edinburgh University Press 2007 (2013 page 6);

An extract from 'Jacobitism (British History in Perspective)' by Murray G.H. Pittock, published by Palgrave Macmillan 1998 (2013 page 7);

An extract from 'Glencoe and the Indians' by James Hunter, published by Mainstream 1996 © The Random House Group Ltd (2013 page 8);

An extract from The Ayr Advertiser, 1849 © Clyde and Forth Press Ltd (2013 page 8);

An extract from 'The Scottish Nation 1700–2000' by T.M. Devine (Allen Lane and the Penguin Press 1999, Penguin Books 2000). Copyright © T.M. Devine, 1999 (2013 page 9);

An extract from 'Red Scotland!: The Rise and Fall of the Radical Left, c. 1872 to 1932' by William Kenefick, published by Edinburgh University Press 1999 (2013 page 10);

An extract from 'The Flowers of the Forest: Scotland and the First World War' by Trevor Royle, published by Birlinn 2006 (2013 page 10);